"The title, epigraphs, and style o
ute to Jack Kerouac, a surprisin
man's Mormon conversion and
Latter-day Saint missionary. . . . Memoir readers as well as Mormons
looking for a somewhat edgy affirmation of their faith will appreciate the lusty, brawling but tenacious missionaries and the tender
love story in this sprawling coming-of-age tale."

— Publishers Weekly

"I have never read such a gripping story of conversion and missionary labor. It held me fast partly because of the winsome romance
mixed into the story of a mountain hippie who finds life's meaning
in Mormonism. But the gritty descriptions of friendship and adventure in the Colorado wilderness and of missionaries working the
mean streets of Colombia are enthralling in themselves. The candid
view of the vicissitudes of a spiritual life will startle readers accustomed to more staid narratives."

—Richard Bushman, author of *Joseph
Smith: Rough Stone Rolling* (Knopf)

"Converts of the world, who came to the church from colorful and
outrageous pasts, rejoice! Here is somebody who tells it like it was,
without apology and without regrets. *On the Road to Heaven* is a tale
of spiritual adventure, sacrifice, and change-the-world energy to rival any turned out by the born-in-the-covenant crowd."

—Patricia Karamesines, author of *The
Pictograph Murders* (Signature)

"Poetic and enchanting, Coke Newell's *On the Road to Heaven* is a
romance odyssey of love and religion driven by the consumptive
gravity of yearning and discovery. Honest and fearless, Newell has
crafted for us the real power of gospel Mormonism."

—Ronald O. Barney, author of *One Side
by Himself: The Life and Times of Lewis
Barney, 1808–1894* (Utah State University),
winner of the Evans Biography Award

"This is the book Jack Kerouac might have written had he met Moroni instead of Allen Ginsberg. A wonderful romp to faith!"

—Rodney Stark, Ph.D., author of *The Rise
of Christianity* (Princeton) and *The Victory
of Reason* (Random House)

"An utterly original spiritual tale—lively, quirky, and profoundly moving. Think of it as St. Augustine for the Woodstock generation. Newell's writing is an exuberant ride."
—Terryl Givens, Ph.D., author of
The Viper on the Hearth (Oxford) and
By the Hand of Mormon (Oxford)

"A rollicking, satisfying conversion story."
—Tania Lyon, Ph.D.

"Newell tells a good tale, but he also furthers Mormon discourse, beautifully illustrating how powerful and fragile this whole idea of finding God is, of figuring out how this time-bound, messy, mortal existence all works—what it means and what to do when you are fairly certain that you have some answers that make sense. And that he does it by linking the revelatory discourse of the mountain hippies with that of Mormons makes it all the sweeter. And fun."
—William Morris, founder of *A Motley Vision* (www.motleyvision.org)

"*On the Road to Heaven* is perhaps the most unique book its particular audience will ever read. Often entertaining, occasionally hilarious, and sometimes even startling, this is a book that will leave its readers feeling as if they have just gotten to know a very real, very unconventional, and very interesting human being."
—Mike Smith, author of *Towns of the Sandia Mountains* (Arcadia)

On the Road to Heaven

An autobiographical novel by Coke Newell

ZARAHEMLA BOOKS
Provo, Utah

ISBN-13 978-0-9787971-3-3
ISBN-10 0-9787971-3-2

Cover design by Bryce Newell

Published by
Zarahemla Books
869 East 2680 North
Provo, UT 84604
info@zarahemlabooks.com
ZarahemlaBooks.com

To "Annie" –
For Then
For Now
For Ever

Remember back in seventy-four
When love was in the air? (People, can you feel it?)
That bus rolled down (Love is in the air)
To Summertown
And we almost rode it there.

We tried to stop a war
We tried to change the world
But the world was nuts
And so we skipped the bus
And kept looking for Forever More.

And somehow
We ended up being here now.

– Coke Newell, from "Being Here Now"

I would not tell this if it were only my story. What is one man that he should make much of his winters? Hear me not for myself, but for my people.

—Black Elk, Oglala Sioux Holy Man

Preface

THE TRADITIONAL STORY OF MORMONISM, the one in which an estimated seven thousand men, women, and children lost their lives to mobs and on the long Mormon Trail west, is an incredible story, a valuable story, an indelible drama seemingly without parallel or precedent in American history or literature. Yet a parallel exists. It is the contiguous story of the Mormon convert experience, another journey to the same Zion.

Different trails, same reasons.

I've been down only one of them, after all. This is the story of the trail I walked.

Part One:
From Zero to Zion

Music, Mountains, and Subliminal Mayhem

Beauty before me
Beauty behind me
Beauty all around me
With it I wander
On the beautiful trail am I.

—Mountain Chant of the Navajo

1

"Start at the beginning and let the truth
seep out, that's what I'll do."
—Jack Kerouac, *The Subterraneans*

YEARS LATER I WOULD STILL REMEMBER the whole setup yet have no clue just why it went that particular way. I think it had something to do with the way Cris cooked the beans.

We were on the ridge leading to Mount Kolob about a thousand feet below timberline when we first saw the cabin, and we saw it then only because its logs lay perpendicular to the entire surrounding forest. It was that oddly geometric break in the more fluid pattern of the woods that stopped me and made me stare as my mind pieced the puzzle.

We approached almost reverently, knowing with little doubt that the structure must be unoccupied—and thus available—because the two of us were one third of the entire human population in the surrounding thirty square miles, and the others were back home watching television or chopping wood.

The cabin was slightly smaller than Jack Kerouac's Hozomeen Mountain–framing hideaway on Desolation Peak, but so much more portentous—only I didn't know that at the time. Unlike Kerouac's window-bedecked fire lookout, it consisted entirely of a single one-windowed room, with the standard steeply pitched roof of Colorado log cabins built by anyone with at least a smattering of brains. In this case, the builder had evidently been contracted by the United States Department of Agriculture, which—if the paperwork we found stuffed into the cracks between the logs was accurate—had built this cabin as a high-altitude beekeeping research facility in 1948. It looked to be not long after that year that the cabin had seen its last conscientious occupant.

Although we already squatted in two other abandoned cabins,

neither one was ideal, so this new cabin was a most welcome discovery. The afternoon we stumbled upon it, we were combing the
woods for anything that could be jerked, jimmied, or jammed into
the basic shape and application of a wood stove for our Christopher
Drive cabin, about four miles away and a thousand feet below this
new cabin. That cabin had seen much better days and, if the gradu-
ally increasing tilt of its walls was any augury, would very likely
never see such again.

The Christopher Drive cabin was bigger than this new one,
probably twelve-by-twenty or so, and it had a loft with actual stairs
leading up to it. Nearby, a tiny brook emanated from the perpetual
spring about a hundred and fifty feet uphill, where it bubbled forth
from a microcosmic paradise of mountain bluebells and Colorado
columbine, nestled into the shaded ecotone of a small forest of the
grandest and most sacred of all trees: the quaking aspen, *Populus
tremuloides*. A much better choice for the Colorado state tree, by the
way, than the blue spruce, but I wasn't around when they voted.

While the Christopher Drive cabin already had a stove, an actual wood cook stove with an oven and an ash-cleanout tray and everything, it was so old, rusted, and busted when we got it out of the
creek bank—pronounced *crick* bank—that there was a certain unanimous and ever-present apprehension that we would soon burn the
joint down if we used it for anything more than the occasional pot of
Red Zinger tea, which at that altitude took a good twenty minutes
to boil.

In addition to needing a replacement stove, however, the cabin
on Christopher Drive suffered from an even greater threat and severe incapacitation as an abode for We People of the Peaceful Mountain: Christopher Drive was an actual road that occasionally hosted
actual cars driven by actual people. Not acceptable.

We kept the other cabin in our collection, the one on the front of
the mountain, toasty and pleasant with a stove fashioned from the
box of an old coal furnace, pulled from the residue of a residence
that once stood on the fringes of the old town of Paradise. That particular cabin never had a name as I recall, as it was near no roads or
evident landmarks. It was just the cabin on the eastern front of the
mountain. That's all you had to tell any of the five of us who knew
about it: "I'll be in the cabin down the front of the mountain."

"Far out. See ya there."

The problem was getting there. There were no trails, no rock
outcroppings, no prominent here-I-am trees. An old logging road

from below led to it from the east, but from above, the direction from which we approached, we just took our bearings when we emerged from Happy Gap going east and headed down into the steep lodgepole-pine wilderness, hoping for the best. And we never tried it at night.

There was another problem with the cabin on the front of the mountain. After the property owner had discovered us there one day and asked us to leave, we'd never gone back.

So when we leveled out that afternoon on the old logging road on the narrow ridge to Mount Kolob and saw this new cabin perched right at the fulcrum at 10,060 feet, with an unobstructed view of the sunrise horizon far out on the eastern plains and a sunset panorama framed by Mount Rosalie on the right, Windy Peak on the left, and Pikes Peak far off to the south, the other cabins became an instant memory.

Over the next few weeks, we found another stove for the new cabin, an old oil-burning water heater that turned out to glow so red when you really got it stoked that you could see through it. We mucked out thirty years' worth of chipmunk and deer mouse droppings and nesting, backpacked in twelve bags of mortar mix and a hundred gallons of water, and rechinked the logs. We tacked on a whole new roof's worth of tarpaper shingles, stretched sheets of four-millimeter plastic over the window opening, built a loft and a gear box for our backpacks, hung a handmade door, and sat down to eat the raspberries festooning the east wall of our new digs.

It was the tarpaper that would eventually drive me from the place.

2

"Me in my shack in the middle of the woods."
—Kerouac, *The Subterraneans*

MY PARENTS' HOUSE SAT at 9,860 feet, pretty much the high point of a road that led back down the west side of Paradise Mountain, just past the mailbox. I know it was 9,860 feet because we had it pegged on a seven-and-a-half-minute topographic map, one of about a hundred USGS quadrangles my dad had joined at the edges with tape and set up on a roller system in the family room, the entire Colorado Front Range.

A broad plank of ponderosa pine suspended by chains from two aspen log poles spanned the entrance to our "driveway," a quarter mile of rough, rutted trail ascending at nearly a fourteen-percent grade. We never got a lot of visitors, but those who came this far could at least be comforted—and perhaps satisfied—when they found the big plank that my dad had chainsaw-carved and then hand-painted with the name of our spread: WEST'S WORLD.

My dad was William Kittredge West, and I was named after him, kind of.

We were eighth-generation Westerners, and I was a fifth-generation Coloradoan. My ancestors had come to America from England, Ireland, and Scotland beginning in 1620 and not taking too long about it. Then they moved quickly across New York into Wisconsin, Iowa, Nebraska, and then Colorado, where they panned gold in Clear Creek and Cripple Creek and helped build the first wooden structures along both of them.

Which is how I got my name: the West part was inherited, of course, but that perpetual looking toward the far horizon, the next adventure, the continuance of the journey was something my father was genetically constrained to pass on, not to mention his absolute adoration for the land of his heritage and nativity. And so with the birth of their second and final child, a son, there I was: Everon West.

Trouble was, once they'd signed the form, my folks could never get clear on whether they wanted to call me "Everon," which kids at school teased into "Chevron," or "Ev," which was quickly turned into "Evy," clearly short for "Evelyn." So before I was eight they legally added my father's middle name, Kittredge, to my records and I became "Kit," a good western name to boot. (They hadn't used it at birth because it interfered with the message they were trying to project with my first and last names.) My sister, on the other hand, just ended up Michelle because they thought it went with West.

Anyway, Paradise Mountain was the southernmost summit in a ridge that climbed ever higher to the north over Mount Kolob, then west over Mount Meridian, up Rosalie, and finally up onto Mount Evans, Colorado's thirteenth-highest summit at 14,264 feet. My dad walked the entire length of that ridge one time, just a man and his pack and five days of solace. He could have done it quicker, technically, but what was the rush? He was in the woods. The rest of us sat at home — my mom, my sister Michelle, and I — and worried about bears a little bit, but not enough to deny a man his time in the woods. Sacred time.

My dad, an AT&Ter since the age of seventeen, was supervisor of the Mountain Bell garage that serviced about six hundred square miles of phone line running hither and yon over three counties. He'd strung most of it himself, and he knew the knot and splinter topography of ten thousand poles. (And exactly what it felt like to come off one onto his back from thirty-five feet up when lightning struck the line four miles away.)

My room was on the third floor of the house, where a single window welcomed the sun in the full expanse of its arc across the southern half of the sky. When it got too cold to go outside and play, say about twenty-five degrees below zero, when my spit would freeze in midair and crackle when it hit the ground, I could just sit and look and enjoy the view. It was a nice room; my dad even let me paint it. Steve Ferretti showed me how a roller dipped in bright red paint could make some amazing designs on the white undercoat when you just kind of twirled it around while moving across the gypsum canvas. Enhanced at discriminating intervals with black-light posters, my finished walls looked kind of like a Spirograph playground. Within a year or so, my discrimination maturing, the velvet posters would be replaced by wildlife posters and Ansel Adams prints. Steve had asked if I wanted to add some blue to the red-and-white mayhem, and I said, "Don't be crazy." This was the early seventies, after all, and I was a blooming flower child.

It was in this house that I spent winter nights, partook of most meals, and indulged in the occasional comforts of modern American housing: toilets, hot water, a good stereo. By some definitions I suppose you could say I lived here, but I do believe I spent quite a bit more time out on the mountain, or out on the road, or in one of the cabins than I did in my folks' house. My folks and I were doing okay; I simply preferred the woods and the open highway.

I could get from my bedroom door to the cabin on the front of the mountain in about nine minutes at full run: down the driveway, straight across the aspen and lupine meadow, up and over Happy Gap—our own twist on The Who's *Happy Jack*—and into the lodgepole-pine maze, a dense, dark forest of impenetrable poles. The perfect hiding place.

Outside of the maze, however, as a youth I could move through the woods with more than the grace, and nearly the speed, of an elk—mule deer give way to elk at about 8,500 feet in the southern Rockies—barely touching down on the ball of one foot before springing over the next log, bush, or boulder; twisting, zigging, zagging, and bounding with a reverent familiarity and bold competence so sweet they made me giddy with exhilaration.

I'd like to say I twice outran a bear on that mountain, but in fact the first time I just stood there and wet my pants.

My dog, Uriah, was a beautiful golden rough collie, a perfect stand-in for any episode of Lassie ever filmed, except for the fact that he was completely blind by the time he was three. When we ran the road as it wound up toward Eagle's Nest or west toward Lion's Head, he would softly grip my extended thumb in his mouth so as to follow along. In the woods, we either walked or he just understood it was an afternoon to stay behind with the Fat Dog—Freckles, a prototypical Clumber spaniel—as she nibbled ripe wild raspberries from bush to bush or lay in the sun and belly-grazed on the tiny summer strawberries.

One spring night Uriah wouldn't stop barking, and his tone bespoke unfamiliar tension. I headed downstairs and grabbed a flashlight on my way outside. He was about twenty yards from the house, his nose aiming north and his ruff full and bristled. Settled only modestly by my approaching presence, he moved forward a couple of feet and continued staring—unseeing, of course—at the box of the old camping trailer where we stored the weekly household garbage between bimonthly trips to the county landfill. And he continued to bark, a little more boldly now.

Then the bear stood up. Your typical Rocky Mountain black, about five feet high and, perhaps atypically, shaking a box of Cheerios off his left forepaw. Uriah barked, I warmed my leg, and the bear just looked at us in turn: dog, boy, dog, boy. Boy clearly alarmed. I may have been wrong, but the bear didn't appear frightened at all.

So I ran, turning to call for Uriah only after reaching and opening the front door of the house. Knowing now he was surely in over his head, and probably smelling something of a change in the balance of power, he turned and moved toward the house as fast as he dared. (He had once risen up in a rush to answer the call of a squirrel who wanted to play and, nose skimming the ground as he ran, hit a tree face first, knocking him flat out. Once.)

I called for my folks, and we yelled at the bear from the doorway until he decided to go look for a quieter place to eat.

When it happened again two weeks later, I was ready. I went out with the flashlight and a big stick, yelling as I moved toward him, the door propped open behind me. Uriah looked like a bristle brush, and he remained a good twenty yards from the trailer, while I didn't get much closer. When the bear stood up, it was the same look, the same balance of power. Unbalanced. Or was it?

He came up and over the side of the trailer, slowly, clumsily, giving me time to get my thumb in Uriah's mouth and move us both toward the house. Out of the trailer, the bear just stood on his hind legs and looked at us for a half-minute. Then, when he dropped to all fours, it was as if I could hear him mutter, "Ah, forget it," as he trotted off into the woods.

Last time he ever came to our house for dinner.

Even without Uriah, the new cabin, the one on the ridge to Mount Kolob, could not be reached in fewer than thirty minutes at a steady trot. It was all uphill, much of it was northern slope—always denser, more demanding forest—and the way was strewn with boulders and blown-over trees.

One evening in late September I arrived at the cabin to find Cris just putting the finishing touches on a pot of beans. The old water-heater-stove was glowing red enough to see through, and Cris had the feeder door open to let out a little bit of torque and not launch the thing through the roof. But a good pot of beans took a good spot of time, and you had to just let 'er bubble and burp for well over an hour to get out the crunch. (Our beans came from a bag, of course, not a can.) Toward the end of the run, the lid off, you could start dropping in the carrots and potatoes and onions and such. This is about the time the sparks and clinkers popping off the lodgepole-pine fuel supply began dropping into the pot as well, and a good pot of beans typically had a pretty good garnish of charcoal by the time one ladled out the goods. (In contrast, I have heard that the city-bred human has a hard time getting enough charcoal in the diet.)

Little was said—half the reason for living in the woods in the first place: quiet—and Cris and I enjoyed a private meal, once again thrilled at our teenage self-sufficiency. Being somewhat more self-sufficient than I, Cris had a job as a night dishwasher, and soon he left me for the forty-minute run to his house, the key to his mom's van, and the seven-mile drive down to the paved highway where the Highlander Inn served the only sit-down-and-use-a-fork food for thirty miles in any direction.

I fired up the single-mantle coal-oil lantern, hung it on a nail, and sat to ponder. That was the usual business of a cabin evening and one of the best uses of time ever conceived or expended. I had found two of the lanterns in a vacated campsite in Lost Park several summers before. It was an odd place, the camp: a tarpaulin roof stretched between four trees, city-slicker aluminum cots tossed into one corner, emptied canned goods, beer bottles, and trash strewn about the woods—the look of a perennial roosting place. And the remains of two deer hides rotting into the ground.

Hunters. The enemy. The only thing I could think of to appropriately reimburse the Trashy Ones for their wanton ways with the woods and the deer was to take their lanterns.

And pee in their fire pit.

Take that, you Bambi-blasting slobs.

I don't recall that these were the thoughts on my mind that evening in the cabin, but just about the time the final remains of the day disappeared behind Windy Peak, the roof started coming apart. I grabbed the lantern and ran outside to see what was happening. Nothing was on the roof. I stared at the tarpaper long enough to make it think twice and then went back inside. No sooner had I retaken my tractor seat nailed to a log than the noise flared up again.

It was a scraping, a scratching, and a violent mess of it at that, right above where I sat. Again, the lantern and out, but this time I grabbed my bear-warning stick, a stout sucker of worm-whittled lodgepole. Again, nothing. And no noise at all each time I was outside.

I stood and stared at the roof, then walked around the cabin slowly and methodically, my stick lofted to the ready, and saw nothing.

By now I was jumpy, and an elk or a bear in the night woods could have driven me right out of my hide, but I went back in, my ears straining for a tip, for a clue, and resumed my seat. Twice more it happened, violent, vicious ripping at the roof. Twice I smacked the ceiling with my stout stick, disrupting the chaos only for a moment. As the roof shredded to bits the third time, I was heading out the door, the stick held high. I pivoted immediately toward the roof, the place of madness falling clearly within the purview of my lantern's domain, and saw nothing. Nothing at all. No wind stirred the night. Not another sound was heard. The roof was silent.

I spun on my heel and headed home, the lit lantern in one hand, my rascal beater in the other, never looking back.

It took me twenty-five minutes. My mother would ask why I was home, knowing I had gone for the weekend. I would mumble something about a stomach ache and disappear to the comfort of my room, my Koss headphones and the silk-and-sledge, layered-crunch cosmos-cruising melodies of Uriah Heep.

Demons and Wizards wove its magic through my soul in those days and, with the thematic paradox posited by its title tracks — "Rainbow Demon" and "The Wizard" — the album offered alternative trajectories for the rest of my life. Of Ken Hensley's kindly, beneficent wizard I had no knowledge — nor of anyone else's — but the demon appeared to be seeking a place to shack up on the ridge to Mount Kolob.

In the morning I stood and looked at myself critically in the bathroom mirror. Was I a man or a mouse? Five-foot-ten, the firm jaw and prominent cheekbones I liked to claim from my three Native American ancestors, thick brown hair parted down the middle and falling straight to just mid-back, and an above-average lean and muscular build from years of weight lifting, gymnastics, and rock climbing. A beard good enough for most men ten years my senior — definitely not from the Indian ancestors.

Yet inside? Walking turmoil.

I ate some breakfast and headed back up to the cabin, sworn to renew my commitment and regather my wits in the bright light of a new day. But no branches from adjacent trees came anywhere near the roof. No debris cluttered its surface. And not a single scratch assaulted that fresh tarpaper in its happy midmorning repose.

The high lonesome cabin on the ridge to Mount Kolob began to trouble even my daylight dreams. Something was about to change.

3

THE FIRST NIGHT I EVER SPENT above Lost Park, in early May at ten thousand feet on the northeastern edge of Windy Peak, I was exactly that: lost. No sleeping bag, no dinner, not even a long-sleeved shirt.

Oh, and I was twelve years old.

But I was not alone. No, I was up there showing my buddy John Dunham what a woodsman I was. As it turned out, I did *not* get us killed. Directional dysfunction aside, I did know what I was doing. Kind of.

By the time I was twelve, I had been on most of the two-lane highways and dirt roads in twenty-seven states. And in exactly two cities: Denver, where one set of grandparents was stuck by economics; and San Diego, where an aunt and uncle lived near the ocean, which is really why we went at all. My dad avoided big highways like the plague and thought interstates were the bane of existence.

"They put them in the ugliest places," he would say, "and everybody just speeds along, not knowing what they're missing." But then my mother would coax him, and he'd add, "Which is just perfect for me. Keep 'em off the good roads, the back roads; let me drive at my own pace."

If I learned anything as a kid, it's that the doctrine of Dirt-Road Redemption is much more than a travel preference; it's a philosophical covenant with life. It's a covenant that I learned early on was shared by such luminaries as Henry David Thoreau, Black Elk, and Edward Abbey. But Ed Abbey—born and reared in Pennsylvania—did not introduce me to slick rock, red dirt, and a land ethic. My daddy did.

To be frank, my dad was a hippie born thirty years too early, and his primary drugs of choice were two-lane highways and wilderness.

I was born addicted.

The sound of a rushing river, the scent of pine, and the expectation of a jagged horizon against a blue sky thirty degrees above level were natural and innate benchmarks of my earliest cognition.

All components of the Covenant. Here's how it goes as I learned it: I am a visitor on the earth, one of many creatures given some role and some serious responsibility to see that it survives my sojourn. Living upon it carries an inherent and unalterable obligation to live lightly, to honor the collateral cohabitants, to do no harm and leave a small wake.

I can honestly say that as a child I never shot a bird — I owned no gun until my fourteenth birthday, and I privately bequeathed it to my sister before the day was out. Nor did I pelt a squirrel with a rock. Nor did I want to. Simply unacceptable behavior.

We didn't four-wheel or snowmobile or race motorcycles up and down the hillsides, carving the land into scraps and blowing noxious fumes and *ob*noxious noise into the air. My daddy taught me that you didn't throw your refuse out the car window or leave it planted in the woods, long before the slowly awakening contiguous culture called it *litter* in the late sixties.

We just called it wrong.

As a kid playing cowboys and Indians — kids don't do that anymore, do they — I was always the Indian. The Indians — yeah, I know we don't call them that anymore either, but since we were fourteenth-generation and fifteenth-generation Americans with at least two full-blooded Iroquois ancestors, my father always figured we were about as "native" American as one can get — were the ones who loved the land, respected the life forms, and left a small wake.

Which was kiddie stuff, really, a philosophical framework just kind of smoldering around the edges until I was fourteen.

But I'm getting ahead of myself. At twelve I was still trying to stay alive on Windy Peak. I had heard my dad's stories of summer excursions to Lost Park with his pals for years: how the four of them, thirteen and fourteen years old, would ride the trolley from Knox Court clear out to Kipling, then thumb rides out to the Turkey Creek Highway and up into the mountains, through the Hogback above Morrison, then into the canyon, through the Colorado Front Range to the inner ranges above Paradise and into Redtail. I remember clearly

On the Road to Heaven   17

the lesson learned and passed down about how Howard Perrin had
tried splitting a log into kindling by holding it on the ground with
his foot—he had bounced the axe off the log and right through his
shinbone. Cleanly split, but not real useful for firewood. It did keep
them warm in a way, however, as my dad and his pals carried him
out seven miles to the remote highway, his leg held together with a
flannel shirt tourniquet. (He lived; he walked again.).

As a twelve-year-old, I couldn't wait to do the same kind of
thing, sort of.

My hitchhiking era was still a couple years distant, so my dad
drove John and me up to the trailhead, handed me a seven-and-a-
half-minute topo, and said, "See ya next week, kid." I wasn't exactly
a compass sort of guy, and, as it would turn out, I wasn't real handy
with a map either. Or maybe even a trail.

Somewhere up the mountain, two paths diverged in the dense
lodgepole woods, and I took the one less traveled by. And that made
all the difference. Along about mile four, I finally admitted that I
must have taken us up the wrong trail, because for a good half-mile
now it hadn't been a trail at all but rather a quarter-mile-wide jungle
gym of fallen trees.

Turning around, I could find no trail to show that we had just
come this way. It was jumble upon jumble. To the left: trees. To the
right: trees. Behind, trees; all around, trees.

Trees.

Up ahead, however, through the trees, I could see a rock outcropping that appeared to lift above the blanket of forest. If we
could get to those rocks and climb up out of the blinding myopia of
solid forest, perhaps we could get our bearings.

That decided, we relieved ourselves of our backpacks, leaning
them against a blown-down tree, and bounded unburdened up the
hill another eighth of a mile and onto the rocks, where we scrambled
to the top and took a peek. Sure enough, there was the trail, topping
a nice gentle saddle in the mountain about three miles away. At its
terminus lay the broad, open meadow of Lost Park.

We eased back down off the rock outcropping and descended
through the forest the eighth-mile to our packs. Or to where our
packs should have been.

Or were they over here?

Nope.

There?

Nope.

We zigzagged the hill for thirty minutes, then ascended once again to the rock outcropping to get our bearings. Those gotten, we descended and proceeded to zigzag the hill for another hour. Just before it got dark, I decided we better make shelter for the night. Making dinner was out of the question. So was putting on a jacket. (Both were in our packs.)

In hindsight, perhaps a bivouac in the woods would have offered better shelter from the wind, but I chose the solidity of rock wall and directed us back to the rock outcropping for the night: generally exposed, but solid. In fact, a good nook-and-cranny campsite in the bowels of solid pink granite is pretty good shelter. I've done it a number of times since, even in winter, and found it quite to my liking. Solid walls, a good roof, even if the elbow room is a bit restrictive.

So I picked a good cranny, custom-fit to my width if not my height, swept the floor free of marmot droppings — *thanks for the bed; I'll leave you a tip if I ever find my pack again* — and then emerged to gather some fresh branches of lodgepole and limber pine with which to feather my bed.

That's when I noticed John lying flat on his back, hugging himself, on a slab of rock with ample roof but no walls. It was a veritable wind tunnel, and as the sun set over Kenosha Pass, that wind was getting cold and brisk. I told him to pick a better spot, something like unto actual shelter, then went back to my den.

About a half-hour after dark, he stuck his head in my hole, on the verge of tears, and said, "What do I do next? I'm going to die." Well, not on my watch, so I let him in, and we attempted to lay side by side, spoons or otherwise, for what seemed like fifteen hours. Then, about halfway through the world's longest night, we could find no position more comfortable or reminiscent of actual warmth than one on top of the other. So we lay like that for the next fifteen hours, shivering, moaning, occasionally switching layers like musical-chairs lasagna. Really cold lasagna.

Sometime before switching into a prepubescent coma, I saw what appeared to be a lightening of the sky. I lay and watched it, unconvinced, for what seemed another whole night's worth of hours. Finally, I could see detail, color — the pinkness of the feldspar that filled the walls of our crypt, the blue-green needles of the limber pine bough I had draped over John's back for a blanket.

I told John to get off me, morning had come, and I scooched past him and out of the hole.

It was definitely dawn, but the sun was still below the horizon. The top of our rocky mount was shaped like a dishpan or a flat, sandy-bottomed skillet, roughly circular in dimension, the salmon-pink granite pillars forming a ring-like defense around the edges and then dripping down in jumbles over the sides like too much stew. The small pockets of captured spring runoff scattered across the hard pack wore a firm skin of ice.

I chose a spot in the middle of the pan and sat down to await the warming fire of sunrise. The place and its construct reminded me of what I had seen in photographs taken from inside the ring at Stonehenge, the land, and possibly the religion, of my ancestors. (Back when my ancestors might have practiced one.) Yet this was not a manmade monument. And as far as I knew, I was the first human to ever occupy this summit.

As I sat, shivering, I determined to greet the day as if I had planned to be right here all along. But hurry the day I would not. This was the sun's moment, and my moment was to be merely a witness, a recipient, a humble observer who had waited patiently and would be offered his reward.

I closed my eyes, reliving the torments of the night, the long, long hours thinking I might freeze to death and never wake. And I waited. I opened my eyes and scanned the horizon as it melted from gray to purple to pink, then to luminescent scarlet with golden threads. John was still in the little crevice. I got up and moved a couple of times when my senses told me that the first ray of sun would in fact break across the sacred ground of my mountain cathedral at a point farther left, or right, or forward.

And then it came.

A tiny pinpoint of brilliant gold light raced its way west along the summit ridges of the Kenosha Range, bounced off the snow-capped summit of Windy Peak, then raced quickly toward me down the western ridge, across the sand to my right, and directly onto my forehead. It was like a pulse of energy, and I couldn't help but breathe it in, first in gulps, then in deep, purposeful inspirations. It moved down my nose, over my throat, and then took up residence in my chest. I could feel the night burning away, the power of light and warmth swimming into me.

I raised my arms high, exhilarated as I had never been before. I had lived. I had survived. I had possibly even saved a life other than my own.

My thoughts raced back through a novel I had completed just

before the trip, Jack Schaefer's *The Canyon*. In that little book, a young, self-despising, club-footed Indian boy had gone out to pursue his Vision Quest, a rite of passage to manhood, and had accidentally fallen into a deep box canyon, barely surviving the fall. But survive he did, against all odds, emerging many months later a hero to his tribe.

I was twelve, and I was a warrior.

I stood and faced the sun as it spread its welcome warmth across the basin. It had come for me.

I had found religion.

That was the summer I also found my first completely nude woman, standing right there in the river, her arms and hands lifted high to hold her long hair out of the water as if she didn't even know her big plump breasts, pregnant tummy, and densely carpeted private area were staring me in the face.

Warrior that I was and all, I just stood there and stared back, trying to neither gulp nor giggle.

We were down on the South Fork of the South Platte, where my dad spent the best times of his life fishing. His wasn't some citified sit-in-a-lawn-chair-and watch-your-bobber-till-it-dips loafing like my Uncle Ben did, but some real fishing: fly fishing, in a river, with flies of his own tying and a nine-foot rod. Hip waders. A stinky creel with a million stream miles on the odometer.

It was getting harder and harder to find solitude on the river anytime of the year, but in summer the hippies moved in, lining the dirt road and stuffing the woods with their vans and Beetles and VW busses. And their trash. Especially beer cans.

They came by the thousands, it seemed. Something drove them to live in herds. My dad didn't have a lot of nice things to say about hippies; we'd had our Coleman cooler cleaned out during the night by a small herd of them near Aspen earlier that spring. Our loaf of bread, jug of milk, and package of cold cuts could clearly be seen on their picnic table the next morning. They left us the mustard and one half-leaf of lettuce.

Something intrigued me about the hippies—their apparent freedom to roam; their communal society, however itinerant; and their women, nude or otherwise. I especially loved their women: their long flowing hair, their long flowing dresses, and their happy light-as-the-wind laughter. Yet these were my mountains, my backyard, and a bunch of city-slicker tramps were treating it like the city dump.

My father was hoping to drive quickly past the spot where the pregnant lady and her fellow hippies were swimming beneath the chutes where the river cut a chasm through solid granite, but traffic along that narrow section of dirt road was moving *very* slowly. Finally we got past, my mother telling me — and my father — to avert our eyes. We continued on, finding a quiet, unpeopled spot down the road a piece. Dad pulled off to the side, parked the car, put on his waders, and wandered into the river. I found an empty grocery sack in the trunk and wandered into the trash, filling my bag with aluminum that could be turned in for money.

Then my father headed downstream, away from the hippies. I was heading right toward them.

4

"The mountains are a kind of poultice
for a man's abstract pain. Among them he
laughs, oh, far more than he cries."
—John Steinbeck, *Cup of Gold*

THE FIRST TIME I MET Cristopher Cassady Wilde the Second was in the midst of a May snowstorm. He was jogging in silk shorts that barely covered his fanny. He looked so out of place, just rounding the bend going north below Eagle's Nest, that my dad stopped the Ramcharger to see if we could be of assistance. Six feet tall, skinny, and freckled — all over — with strawberry-blond hair falling midway down his back, Cris told us he was new on the mountain.

"No kidding," my dad said straight-faced, as Michelle and I chuckled in the back seat.

From Connecticut.

A *serious* flatlander.

Anyway, within weeks Cris and I were close friends; within a year, on that wild and wonderful mountain of my childhood, we were almost as close, I suppose, as friends ever get. Close enough that we decided to change the world.

We looked out over our new domain, a domain for which we could not help but feel a deep, even reverent concern, and we each said: "I quit."

We quit eating meat. We quit wearing leather. We quit using things that came in wrappers (trash) or that were intended for a single use (really *stupid* trash). We lived free of electricity as much as we could. We even turned off other people's lights for them.

Which was just fine with my folks, but my paternal grandfather, may he rest in peace, once told me to turn the light back on in an un-occupied room — he could afford to pay the bill. (I've heard the same sort of claim my entire life from other otherwise-intelligent adults.)

I explained to him patiently — he was old, after all — that money had nothing to do with it. Never had, never would. Electricity meant an ugly hole carved into a mountainside, or a river-plugging dam, or plutonium waste scattered across the feral hills of Nevada.

I told my grandpa that, and he told me to turn the light back on. So I went and unscrewed two of the light bulbs in his bathroom fixture.

Take that, you coal-burning brute!

And then I got serious. Having pushed for two years and now using Cris as the example — my folks liked him, after all — I finally prevailed upon my parents to let me quit cutting my hair. Life was for making statements, and I had one to make, a firm one born of my Vision Quest: the earth was sacred, living, and powerful; she was our home, the mother of our being; and I was her newest Guardian.

My childhood Indian fantasies began to take on a new depth and meaning. I reread *The Canyon*, then moved on to more serious works like *Cheyenne Autumn*, *Black Elk Speaks*, and *Bury My Heart at Wounded Knee*. Cris read them when I was finished. Our blood boiled over the way our race had treated the Indigenous Ones, driving them, cheating them, slaughtering them like rodents. Typically holding the gun, like at the Sand Creek Massacre in eastern Colorado, was a preacher or an officer of the United States Army.

Colonel John M. Chivington of the Colorado First Cavalry was both. Known as "the fighting parson" since he was the presiding Elder of the Methodist Church in the Rocky Mountain district, by 1864 Chivington had already made public his intent to "kill Cheyennes whenever and wherever found. I have come to kill Indians," he told a group of recalcitrant fellow officers, "and believe it is right and honorable to use any means under God's heaven to kill Indians."

So, in the name of God, kill he did.

On November 28, 1864, Chivington rode at the head of seven hundred armed soldiers and four twelve-pound mountain howitzers toward a winter encampment of Cheyenne and Arapahoe Indians on a bend of Sand Creek in northeastern Colorado. The warriors were off hunting for food, which the parson knew, so he just massacred more than a hundred and thirty women, children, and old men.

In his official report, Chivington would claim between four and five hundred dead "warriors." At the same time, he would feel compelled to justify the killing of children and babies — which several nonmilitary witnesses reported—with the statement that "nits make lice."

I began to despise uniforms and the men within them, including clergy and the Boy Scouts, that modern equivalent of the U.S. Cavalry, with its badges and handbooks, its outfits and oaths. Wilderness wasn't a program, and you didn't learn to love it from a book or from the side of a forest-devouring bonfire. My budding view of America, the United States, and its flag, its politics and its purposes, began to be influenced infinitely more by Chief Joseph, Black Elk, and Cochise than by George Washington or Patrick Henry. George Washington was the guy on the quarter. Chief Joseph was the man who got trampled, tricked, and deceived his whole life.

No one in American history, except perhaps the Africans, had been treated as inhumanely as the Indians.

In 1973, the Vietnam War in full stride, my disparate and unpracticed perceptions of American honor were coalescing into a distinct shade of red—white and blue not being involved. I recall watching with growing passion the TV protests of those ready to flee to Canada and feeling increasing willingness to join them, river trashers or not. They could always be taught something new.

Cris and I began to retreat entirely from the white man way of living. We discovered Henry David Thoreau when I sought out a copy of *Walden* after reading a single quote in *National Geographic*: "I went to the woods because I wished to live deliberately, to front only the essential facts of life, and see if I could not learn what it had to teach, and not, when I came to die, to discover that I had not lived."

We began watching the weather and the sun, and we would test ourselves on the time and temperature, getting to where we could each tell the temperature within five degrees and the time within fifteen minutes. And then we moved beyond that effort completely, white man thermometers and clocks be damned.

We started learning about edible and medicinal herbs, a course of study instantly field-testable outside our front doors. I learned that the tiny white blossoms of candytuft were the first welcoming word that spring would actually come again to my mountain perch; that wild raspberries and great mullein and orchid beardtongue preferred disturbed soil, like roadcuts; nodding onion liked sandy soil and full sun; lodgepole pine favored south slopes, Engelmann spruce—and its companion old man's beard—north.

I assembled necklaces and headbands from juniper berries, dried squaw currants, and pinecone scales. I hand-sewed a denim shoulder bag with a long strap, so that I could wander the woods like Johnny Appleseed, the quintessential antidisestablishmentarianist.

On Paradise Mountain I stopped walking the road completely and turned to the woods for both my trail and my training. Cris and I started traversing the mountain by walking only on fallen logs or by hopping from boulder to boulder as much as possible. In the first place, such passage left no tracks; in the second, it burdened no foliage, destroyed no habitat. When we had to leave tracks—through winter snow, for instance—the one following would step perfectly into the tracks already made by the trailbreaker. On the road, if such passage was absolutely necessary, we would avoid soft areas—dust, silt, wet spots—that would leave a track and disturb the already overdisturbed planet. And in the forest we would never step on fragile ground: moss, ground lichens, new growth.

Never, never would we intentionally break a stick, snap a living branch, step on a flowering plant. Never would we disturb the burrow of a fellow creature, or chase one down, or throw something at it.

Never be seen. Never be heard. Practice until perfect approaching within fifteen feet of your mother hanging laundry on the south slope before quietly saying "hi" and scaring her out of her wits.

I learned to find wildlife paths and burrows and dens. I studied tracks and scat, the shapes of nests and the songs of birds. I started memorizing the mountain in random radii: where a seam of brilliant white quartz lit up the dense forest between Eagle's Nest and Happy Gap, good for nighttime runs to the cabin on the front of the mountain; where perennial freshwater springs broke the surface; where mountain strawberries flourished and elk bedded for the night; at what altitude the Clark's nutcracker first appeared (10,000 feet and up—and it would have been a much better choice than the lark bunting for the Colorado state bird, by the way; but again, I wasn't around when they voted.)

I knew where the ponderosa forests ended, the lodgepole-aspen forests began, and the names and traditional uses of most of the plants that grew within each. I cherished a copy of Michael Weiner's classic *Earth Medicine, Earth Foods*, with its brown-paper-bag paper and hand-drawn illustrations. I chewed pine needles for vitamin C and used the pollen on the trunks of aspens for hand lotion and the dried leaves of Rocky Mountain beeplant—an oregano mint—for stomachaches.

I read books on snow chemistry, avalanches, survival, and first ascents, then tested myself further by doing solo campouts in summer, then winter, and then summer campouts without food and winter campouts without a tent. I climbed things no one should have climbed without a rope or a parachute. I ate things no one should have eaten without a field guide, a stove, or a clinic nearby. Cris and I firmly believed with Thoreau—the Master—that in wildness was the preservation of the world, our earth mother. My communion with it, my oneness with it, my ability to see, interpret, and withstand all it handed me, even on its own terms, was the prime focus of my life.

And then one summer day some guy hauled a bulldozer up the mountain and started carving a slash across the land. I spoke to him once, and he referred to the damaged domain as a "driveway" on "his" property, but of course it was mine before his and no one's at all ultimately. So read the Covenant.

Thereafter, as Guardians now empowered with both knowledge and politics, Cris and I regularly plucked up property stakes along with beer cans and Twinkie wrappers—they all went into my ample Appleseed bag—and sabotaged the occasional tractor as we harvested king bolete mushrooms and carried away signage to use as plywood sheeting in the loft of another log cabin.

And in between missions I often sat alone on the top of Eagle's Nest, surveying minutely the extensive domain of my uncommon delight and memorizing the horizon to the south and west, a green-then-purple panorama of successive mountain ridges extending as far as the eye could see, from Pikes Peak, standing watch over the southern Great Plains, to its perfect silhouette in Long Scraggy, and west up the Kenosha Range toward Mount Rosalie. The high point on the southern rim of the world, and the most prominent and memorable jut in the broken robin-blue-eggshell of the sky, was Windy Peak.

There my soul had felt its first awakening. But like Black Elk and Spotted Eagle and Sitting Bull and all the other Native Americans I had read about—I was one-eighth of them, after all—what I really wanted to discover was the Great God of nature, the Great Spirit, the Designer, the One.

My unplanned Vision Quest beneath Windy Peak was still underway and still unfulfilled.

5

"Here is a woman, a soul in my rain,
she looks at me, she is frightened."
—Kerouac, *The Subterraneans*

CRICKET URBANI CALLED from the city: "Got this friend, see, and we're looking to escape to the woods for a few days. I figured you'd know a place."

Cricket was the genuine article, a frizzy-haired flower child with a penchant for opinions and a lust for independence. She signed her name over a peace sign. Living forty-five miles apart, she in the flats and me on the mountain, we nevertheless attended the same high school and had been close friends for a couple of years.

"You want a cabin or wilderness?" I asked her. Stray, abandoned, middle-of-the-woods-so-I-moved-in cabins, I was up to three. Wilderness, I was stocked even better.

"Woods," she said. "Middle of nowhere."

"No problem."

"Oh," she added, "ya got a tent we could borrow?"

They also needed a ride. For that I commissioned another mutual friend, Jim Mason, a moon-faced kid who looked half his age but dug physics and chemistry and Pink Floyd and happened to own a beautiful lemon-yellow '54 Chevy pickup. I hitched to the city one afternoon to notify him of his employment. That midnight, we picked up Cricket at her house — she walked right out the front door carrying a satchel of clothing — and then drove over to the other girl's neighborhood, coasting silently up to the corner three houses away from where she lived. Dressed in dark clothing, she emerged quickly from some bushes, threw her gear in back with Cricket's, and jumped up front with the rest of us.

Jim and Cricket, seated next to each other, kept up an incessant chatter for the next hour and a half. They loved to argue. Actually, Jim loved to prod, to provoke, to question, and Cricket loved to volley them all. I was hugging the opposite door, seated next to the New Girl. She said not a word and offered not a wiggle.

Annie Hawk was as quiet a thing as I'd ever met: polite, but shy as the sun on the north side of midnight. A fragile-looking creature in the pale dashboard lights, with beautiful blond hair that fell in thick waves clear to her waist, she seemed almost wounded, as well as scared. I didn't know why, nor did I know why she was sneaking out at midnight.

Off we went up Turkey Creek Canyon, climbing away from the Great Plains and into the front ranges of the Colorado mountains, past Indian Hills and then Sky Village and into the long green valley of Pine Dell. Straight ahead, eyes rising, stood the ridge between Paradise Mountain and Mount Kolob, Eagle's Nest glowing blueish-pink in the just-risen full moon.

Jim turned off the highway and onto my dirt road just past the town of Paradise, where he asked me to start navigating. I didn't take the wheel because, although I did know how to drive, I had neither license nor inclination—cars were for riding in, not driving. But I conducted him up the mountain, taking the right fork toward Christopher Drive, where we installed the girls for the night in the cabin and returned to my folks' house. "Decided not to stay down in the city tonight, Mom. Got any hot rolls?" Kids drove up to the mountain every Saturday for my mom's fresh, hot rolls.

In the morning we waved good-bye to my folks as they pulled out for a week on the road to simply follow their noses through New Mexico and Arizona, then Jim and I grabbed my tent and headed back to the cabin on Christopher Drive. We snagged the girls and made for the cliffs, a 170-foot chasm cut into the pink granite of Mount Kolob's southeast flank that marked the top of the trail leading down a thousand feet into a lush and remote mountain valley. That's where I was sending them: a sheltered valley at a lower altitude, miles from any road, with a stream. Upstream there was even an old abandoned sawmill, for entertainment.

Jim let us out, waved good-bye, and headed back to do whatever kids did in the city. The new girl was still silent—coy and retreating, which somehow attracted me almost as much as her red-kerchief halter top and blue-jean shorts. Wonderful legs, with absolutely impeccable knees.

Me and Cricket alone, I would have said: "Looky here, walk

south and don't get lost." But this new girl had me all puffy in the head, so I played mountain-man tour guide, pointing out a few essential landmarks and tips: Windy Peak to the southwest, overlooking the Lost Creek Wilderness Area; the seven-hundred-foot sheer granite face of Lion's Head straight west, the nape of the sphinx flowing smoothly into the trailing flank of Mount Rosalie, a mere mention in the endless ranks of Colorado thirteeners. Directly behind that, Mount Evans carried the world's highest paved road to 14,200 feet, nearly a hundred feet short of the mountain's summit.

I led Cricket and Annie down into the shadows of the rock canyon, where I located the remains of the old logging rail bed. The tiny stream was flowing, promising water in the valley. I cautioned them to boil first, however, as this and the larger water course down below channeled the runoff from a hundred square miles of elk and bear domain—Coors' famous mountain spring water). I tied my three-man Nesco tent onto Cricket's pack and bid them adieu.

That night—June eighth—it snowed twenty-eight inches on Paradise Mountain.

At five thirty in the morning the phone rang at my house. Guy down the backside of the mountain says sorry, but two girls stumbled into his door thirty minutes ago, pretty well frozen and quite lost. Now that they're finally talking, they say that they know me; can I come down and fetch them? He has to try to get to work.

When Tim Baxter opened his door another thirty minutes later—it took me a while to break through the half-mile of twenty-eight inches of powder in our 1966 Scout—I saw the two girls sitting on the fireplace hearth in just their panties and bras, blankets over their blue shoulders, frost-nipped hands and feet soaking in basins of lukewarm water, the fire roaring.

When she can finally speak, Cricket tells me the roof of their tent—correction: *my* tent, as if I had anything to do with it—ripped wide open under the weight of the snow, and the whole world came in. Unable to see in the dark, with wind-driven snow burying them where they sat, they just scrambled for footgear, wrapped their Slumberjack sleeping bags around their heads and bodies, and started to walk. Cricket's pet rabbit got a ride on her head.

They found what appeared to be a road around 4:30 A.M. and Baxter's place thirty minutes later.

Lucky, I tell them.

It was love at first sight.

6

"Goodhearted kids in pain of soul
doing wild things out of desperation."
—Kerouac, *Letters*

ANNIE AND CRICKET WEREN'T going out on the road for a few days —
they were going out for a couple of months. They had purchased
a pair of those go-see-America bus passes with money earned at a
weight-loss telemarketing firm, where they mostly just pretended to
call actual phone numbers. The tickets expired in eight weeks.

Paradise Mountain wasn't on the bus route. Rather, it served
them as a sort of outlaws' hole in the wall, the place where no one
would ever find them, where any early trail would quickly go cold,
literally if not just figuratively.

They were running away.

More accurately, Annie was running away. Cricket was just
along for the ride; she would likely even read the descriptive entries
in the Rand McNally road atlas she was packing. For all Cricket
knew, they might just stay on the road for ever — Annie was certainly game. Somewhere along the way, when they ran out of cash,
they could just stop and take jobs for a while.

In the five days we were all stranded on the mountain before
the plows made it through, I decided that Annie would likely spend
most of her journey staring out the bus window, her mind and heart
searching for somewhere and something far beyond the confines of
the atlas. Quiet as she was, it didn't take long to find out that we were
both focused on rebellion, a common complaint exploring divergent
themes. Hers was against religion. Mine was against the trumpet.

By age fifteen I had played the trumpet, pretty well, for seven
years. I'd traveled the western United States, marched in parades
in Mexico, and cut a couple of albums with my high school band.
But at fifteen and a half I was so sick of the instrument, the sound

it made, and the music written for it that I almost threw it out a bus window somewhere north of Santa Fe. In fact, I would end up keeping it another fifteen years or so, selling it for five bucks in a garage sale in the late eighties. But I never played it again, and at sixteen I wasn't at all sure what I wanted to play next, although music drove me like a fork through soft cheesecake.

It was inherent: my dad played the acoustic guitar, having once played the lap steel professionally with a guy named Pete Moss; my mother sang; and I had been joining in songs around the campfire since I was two. I grew up knowing a good chunk of the American folk catalogue, with a distinct leaning toward the South and the West: "Long Black Rifle," "Old Black Joe," "Tom Dooley," "Darlin' Corey," "Oh Susanna." (Years later I would hear the Mormon Tabernacle Choir tackle a couple of these, in the most incongruous coupling of intent and attempt in the history of sound. But more on that later.) We sang everywhere, my mother taking a strong and clear alto lead. I could sing along with every song the Kingston Trio had ever recorded, play most of the Herb Alpert catalogue, and name more backwater blues artists than most of my friends could name models of Hot Wheels cars.

But now Deep Purple's John Lord and Uriah Heep's Ken Hensley had me thinking keyboards were my next gig. I drew pictures of myself on stage with three Moogs and a Leslie, hair clear to my knees. But organs and pianos weren't cheap, and neither were they portable. Stranded at my grandparents' in Torrington, Wyoming, during my fifteenth summer, I picked up my sister's Kmart guitar, learned three chords, and got hooked. The poetry I'd been writing for a couple of years started finding its way into musical verse.

"Appalachian Sweat" was my first song:

Swingin' on a windmill
Down on the farm,
Rompin' through the sagebrush
With a flower in my arms.
Well, life, as I see it,
Could never be so fun
If I lived like everybody
And I looked like everyone.

There was no chorus—I hadn't studied lyrical song structure yet, but it was a fairly radical rag about the living earth getting fed up with getting dug up and causing an earthquake to close down the local coal mine — with a few human casualties, unfortunately. Meanwhile, uptown:

The people they were laughing
Sippin' on their booze
Thinkin' crazy thoughts on life
Until they heard the news.
Some trees sparked up a happy song,
The animals gathered 'round,
To turn and face the maddened crowd,
To stand and hold their ground.

I played and sang it for Cricket and Annie. Cricket said, "Was that an actual chord structure?" But Annie said, "Far out. What's it mean?"

I took Annie's cue and explained the Way of the Woods with the passion of a preacher — the animals killed only when they needed to eat; they never carved up hillsides and meadows with tractors or motorcycles; they didn't belch smoke and fumes into the air or diesel fuel and feedlot manure into the rivers. They didn't mass-produce and then mass-murder cows or chickens as if they were carnations in a greenhouse.

Nor did the Indians, I went on. They killed only to eat or for shelter, and they thanked the buffalo and asked his forgiveness before they let the string go *thwang*. They honored the planet, their earth mother, the father sky and his life-giving sun, the one that had come to me on Windy Peak.

I was sitting cross-legged on the floor of my living room, a position I associated with Indianness, a position I had become entirely comfortable with since my initial empowerment in the sunrise four years before, a position wholly and intimately connected to the earth. Annie came over and sat down that way too, leaning her back against my back. I had held hands a few times with a girl that spring, a half-blooded Cherokee on the school tennis team, and I had stolen a couple of tequila-tinged kisses from a member of the drill team a year and a half earlier, during one of our Mexico band trips. But I had never felt the fire inside that I was feeling for this girl. I leaned back into her.

Cricket said, "So what happened to your trumpet?"

I told her that the trumpet and I were history, the trumpet and all it stood for: conventional music, conventional thinking, conventional life. My trumpet had become the unfortunate symbol of convention. Herb Alpert had been sacrificed on the altar of revolution. What I really didn't like, I told them, was people and their ways. People were the problem. They were destroying the earth, and the earth was my best friend, my confidant, my shelter, and my inspiration. I bore the dual burden of both a genetic and a geographic predisposition to enjoy the company of trees more than the company of humans.

Annie finally spoke up and said that people were her problem too, but in a different way. Her parents were zealous converts to Mormonism, and she'd been baptized at eight and had it shoved down her throat ever since. Her skirts were longer than the other girls', the rims of her glasses more pointed, her curfews tighter. They sang hymns on Monday nights and bottled peaches on Saturday mornings.

But then she started noticing Mormon boys at school smoking pot behind the temps and then blessing the holy sacrament on Sunday. She learned that a good friend and her mom were being beaten up at home by a stepdad who helped run meetings on Sunday. The meaningless restrictions and the outright hypocrisy had finally plugged her air vents; it clearly didn't work, so she was getting out.

"Where're you going?" I asked.

Annie said anywhere.

Cricket said, "My aunt's. In Minnesota."

7

"He who is attached to
things will suffer much."
— Tao Te Ching

As a peace offering for my ruined tent, which I hiked to and hauled out a week later, Cricket gave me a book: the *Tao Te Ching*. But she took what I really wanted. She took the Girl.

Suddenly I was heartsick, lonely, and in love. Drawn together like a shade tree and its shadow, almost without words spoken between us, Annie and I had found in each other deep and instant companionship. For five days she just wanted to sit and be held, and I just wanted to hold her. Then she asked me to lie down with her on night number four, and she never let go of me all night long.

I had known the exhilaration of cheating death, of greeting the earth at sunrise; I had blazed silent and sacred trails on a masterpiece mountain, sipped cold water from a thousand mountain springs, surveyed alone the backside of nowhere. But I had never known the touch, the warmth, the stirring reality of a soft girl in my arms.

Cris was a friend, as true and good as they get, but *this*—this was a companion, and I did not think I could live without her.

But the plows came, the road opened, and the Girl went.

Being mid-June by now, the snow melted quickly, all twenty-eight inches of it. I soon took my new book, a loaded backpack, a bag of twelve-penny nails, and a hammer and headed toward the cabin on Christopher Drive for a few days. Cris joined me, and we installed a shelf for our dried beans, aluminum cook pot, and Celestial Seasonings Red Zinger, the shelf plank salvaged from the pile of old scrap that always accompanied abandoned cabins in the woods. The same pile produced a box spring—no mattress, of course, but a fine and fortunate foundation for Ensolite pads and our sleeping bags.

One night Cris slept in the loft, but in the morning he could have sworn that he felt the cabin tilting farther toward the west during the night, which may well have been true. Years of weather and neglect had drawn the cabin far from plumb, and it was certifiably going to California. Box spring or not, we slept outside under the sky for at least half the nights, bedded comfortably into the thick carpet of golden lupine that was Paradise Mountain's signature June blossom.

On the second morning we succeeded in extracting from the sand an actual iron cook stove that had settled deep into the tiny stream's bed over the decades. We cleaned it up, slid it to the cabin door on a sheet of old tin, and lifted it into the cabin, where it would surely outlive the building by a hundred years. We found sections of stovepipe scattered about in the woods—you always do—and completed the job, bubbling beans over lodgepole and not butane by night three.

During the days we read and hiked, exploring the periphery and extent of the old logging road that led past the cabin, uphill and down. It was on one journey down, at a distance of about seven miles—I later looked it up on my dad's roll of maps—we first discovered the cabin on the front of the mountain.

This was a jewel, remote and beautiful. Measuring only about eight feet by twelve, it was in solid condition except for the uphill wall to the north, where a four-foot boulder had smashed halfway through, probably dislodged and sent rolling when the bulldozers carved the modern road into the mountainside a quarter mile above us. It had a plank floor, the welcome and obligatory single window—meaning a nice rectangular hole, no glass—and a solid roof. It was in much better shape, although much smaller, than the cabin on Christopher Drive, and probably closer to my folks' house. (That would be tested, in the affirmative, later.)

But mostly we just tinkered around the cabin and read. Mine was the *Tao Te Ching*. It spoke to me, like Native American literature, with what seemed a familiar spirit, a voice low and out of the earth, an earthy heavenness.

The valley spirit never dies;
It is the woman, primal mother.
Her gateway is the root of heaven and earth.
It is like a veil barely seen.

.

Cris often closed his own book while I read out loud. He too
was hearing the voice. The language and the message were remark-
ably similar to what we had been reading in Native American literature. But while much of the latter was translated oral history,
most frequently wistful remembrances of the way things were or
indignant responses to the way things were ended, the *Tao Te Ching*
looked forward with hope, permeated with peace.

Man follows the earth.
Earth follows heaven.
Heaven follows the Tao.
Tao follows what is natural.

The best of humanity is like water,
Which benefits all things
And does not contend against them,
Which runs in places others disdain,
Abiding within flow.
So the gentle live within nature . . .
They do not contend,
And none contend against them.

Much of it I didn't understand, but the message was gentle and
kind, speaking often of virtue, courtesy, patience, kindness; counseling he who would be "sage" to seek the peaceful way, the gentle
path, and the low road. My associates down in the big city, freed
from the high school prison for three months, were racing cars,
draining kegs, bashing heads, and looking for love in all the wrong
chicks.
The rock group Kiss ranted.
Vietnam raged.

In dwelling, be close to the land.
In meditation, go deep in the heart.
In dealing with others, be gentle and kind.
In speech, be true.

With the snow off the ground and summer finally a reliable
reality—it never snowed after June tenth, but it never *quit* snow-
ing before June eighth—I had a job: scooping dog poop and then
grooming the lawns (a strictly urban herb) at the fancy-schmancy

new strip mall down on the highway that had sent Hoppy's Grocery into the archives of local history.

Cris's mom, who worked as the receptionist at the real estate office that developed the place, got it for me. Six or seven hours a week at two bucks an hour, if I worked really slowly, three or four hours if I really got after it, still two bucks an hour. One way or the other, Cliff, the real estate broker, had an opinion about how scooping poop should be done correctly. Amazing. He was retired military, so that probably had something to do with it.

Anyway, I was worried sick about Annie out on the road, so on day five Cris and I loaded up our gear and headed for home. I couldn't get her off my mind. I had never, not since that long night keeping my soul in my body on Windy Peak, been so consumed with a single thought in my life.

There is no greater sin than desire.
No greater curse than discontent.
No greater misfortune than wanting something for oneself.
Therefore he who knows that enough is enough
Will always have enough.

There was a postcard waiting when I arrived home. Cris smiled sheepishly and continued on to his place with a wave. Over the next several weeks I received two phone calls, numerous postcards, and one long letter from the aunt's place in Minnesota, where they'd eventually landed.

And then they came home, four weeks early.

Once again, I got a call from Cricket, who put Annie on as soon as she confirmed it was me and not an adult.

The first thing she said, so quietly I could hardly hear her, was "Hi. I love you."

In reality, Cricket was home and Annie was looking for one. She had contacted her parents once or twice during the trip, letting them know she was safe but never where she was. Now they did not know that she was back in Colorado. Could she come up and stay at the cabin on Christopher Drive for a while?

As I've mentioned before, the cabin on Christopher Drive had a fatal flaw as a refuge for outlaws, and it wasn't the roofline—it was the road. But did I have good news!

"I've got a new cabin," I said. "It'll be perfect."

Jim brought her up in his pickup. There was no way I could

have directed them straight to the new cabin, and besides, the only road that approached it hadn't been used by a wheeled vehicle in about fifty years. I sat on top of Eagle's Nest and watched the road far below me until I saw the lemon-yellow dot climbing the mountain. Then I hoofed it on down through Happy Gap and over the front, reaching the graded red-dirt road straight west of the cabin about five minutes before Jim did.

On seeing them approach, I slid out of the woods—one never emerged sooner than was necessary—and down the roadcut with Uriah on my thumb, coming to a perfect landing thirty feet in front of the slowing vehicle. Jim pulled right up and nudged me with the bumper, a sly grin on his mug. He was wearing his floppy suede hat, and his straight, black hair matched its lazy demeanor perfectly. Jim's whole being matched that hat, except that leather was possibly too bold a cloth.

Annie sat still on the passenger side of the bench seat and smiled shyly. She'd eventually become courageous on the phone, but once again she was in the presence of a person before whom her stature as a human being was still in question. I moved quickly to her door, opened it, took her hand, and pulled her out, confirming my welcome with a caressing embrace. Then I pushed her back to remember what she looked like. Her hair was beautifully long and wavy, thicker than I remembered it. It was still damp with the smell of an exquisite herbal shampoo. Her skin was ruddy and clear, her smile demure and cautious. She wore the most awesome pair of denim overalls I had ever seen, faded in factory glory but resurrected in dozens of patches of sunflowers, daisies, and Coats and Clark forget-me-nots.

She was a flower child incarnate, and I found her the most desirable thing I had ever seen. I moved into her and found her mouth, and we stayed that way for what seemed like about three days.

Especially to Jim.

"Can you guys breathe? Geez, Kit, I thought you hugged only aspen trees."

I couldn't wait to show Annie what I had found for her, so I told Jim to just pull over to the side and park the truck. While Annie pored over Uriah—my kind of girl—I took her backpack from the bed of the pickup and then over the side we went, downhill through the steep lodgepole labyrinth. Approaching from above, you couldn't see the cabin until you were practically upon it, and I had to maneuver the woods a bit every time before I found it.

When I did, it was usually the roof that first came into view. So I led us around in a wider arc, coming back from the south to a full side view. Annie saw it and inhaled sharply.

"Oh, Kit, it's beautiful!"

Definitely my kind of girl.

Over the next couple of days, Cris and Annie and I hauled in wood, nails, assorted decorating materials, and a big water cooler, one of those real-live galvanized Farmer Brown milk pails. While Cris and I rigged up a door that actually closed and opened, Annie decorated. The half-boulder that burdened the northern wall became a macramé mantle piece for a big patchouli-scented candle that Cricket had given to Annie. We hung a couple of shelves—for books, of course—and built a corner box to serve as a pantry, cupboard, and table. Then we framed out a platform for a bed, just a nine-inch riser that would get her off the floor, so to speak.

And Annie moved in.

In between stints doing dog poop or chores around my folks' house, I spent most of my days with Annie and many evenings far past dark, telling my mom that Cris and I had been out on the hill somewhere. Cris would often join us—he and Annie adored each other immediately—and Jim and Cricket and one or two other people would often come from the city and spend long days or evenings with us.

I had soon carried down one of the coal-oil lanterns discovered in Lost Park years before and a jug of fuel, and we would just sit around talking by lantern light and the glow of Panama Red embers late into the night. Sometimes, particularly after a number of numbers, it was pure malarkey, Cris entertaining all with his unique ability to speak in whole sentences with the words articulated entirely backward, word by word in almost-flawless reverse:

"Os, taw lass ew klat tuoba no tis riaf th-gin ni et senredliw? A tib fo shadredlab? Ro, on, spahrep et nips fo et esrevinu ni kitoak noizlover." *So, what shall we talk about on this fair night in the wilderness? A bit of balderdash? Or, no, perhaps the spin of the universe in chaotic revulsion.*

Or with equal skill in talking pure nonsense, like Kerouac's Henry Morley, although I was the only one who knew Kerouac or Henry Morley: "Run a tile up that mizzenmast, matey, and we'll sell a pot of coppers to the dog bath."

Or: "I don't know. I think the fuzz from marmots chins should be put to better use; say, hawk it to hawkers in Bangladeshi markets for use in stirring the fires of upper Mongolian barbecues with ample room for mother-in-law sitting parlors. I had one of those, you know. As a kid."

Some of which he had probably learned from reading things like Pink Floyd song titles, although he also knew world geography like I knew the play list on Lynyrd Skynyrd's first. Really well.

We'd all sit around and wonder privately if we were the only one who hadn't understood what the heck Cris was talking about. It usually sounded very serious.

But most times those night conversations actually were serious: ponderous and crucial. I was often the lead voice here, this being my domain and all, and Cris would join me, expounding the ways of the woods, of the Indian, of the Gentle Path. As the conversation would catch fire and carry on, I would frequently just pull back into a corner and stare at each face, one by one. This was my new family, of one mind and purpose. We were going to change the world.

One lazy afternoon in late August, exactly two weeks after she moved in, Annie and I were lying together half-asleep when I felt her grab for the quilt as she whispered, "Kit, there's someone at the door!"

Sure enough, a human male, a grownup, an old guy of at least fifty years or so. Holding a long-handled shovel at his side. My heart was beating wildly, drawn so abruptly away from other attentions. I could only sit up and say hi.

"You living here?" he asked calmly, almost gently.

Annie pulled herself back into the corner.

I thought of saying something bold or sassy, but he seemed patient and reasonable. And I hadn't yet realized it was only a shovel in his hands.

"She is," I said cautiously. "I live up the hill."

"I'm gonna have to ask you to leave," he responded, just as patiently. "Not really your property, and I'm not so sure I ought to be harboring a runaway."

I looked at Annie with nothing to say. As far as I could see it, we were without valid options, excuses, or retorts.

Then Annie asked, "Right away?"

He said, "Soon as you can."

So the next day Jim came up, Cris came down, and we packed her up and moved her out, leaving our boulder unadorned. You may think us a pack of pusillanimous pups to up and run so instantly, lily-livered squatters, but in fact we simply could not abide the oppression of knowing we had been found — our world had been discovered, the wall breached, our privacy violated. It was intolerable.

As the boys hauled a load up to the road and into Jim's pickup, Annie and I just stood, arms around each other, and stared through the open doorway of our little cabin. We stood and stared at everything it could have meant, would have meant, should have meant. We looked at us, and wondered, and wept a little Rocky Mountain requiem.

The only current vacancy in the area was the utility room in Cris's basement, so she moved in there until we could think of something better, sleeping next to the water heater. Almost immediately I remembered something that Cris had brought to my attention nearly a month before, but I just sat on it for a few days, thinking *Oh my goodness, how crazy are we?* It was a three-day music festival happening one week and a thousand miles away in Missouri. He and I had talked about it. Jim and I had talked about it. I'd talked with people right and left, saying, "Wow, wow, wow, a real rock festival, Joe Walsh and Aerosmith!" But so far no one was going.

So that's where we went.

On the Road with Jack and Don

"For me there is only the traveling on paths that have heart . . . And there I travel looking, looking breathlessly."

—*The Teachings of Don Juan:*
A Yaqui Way of Knowledge

8

"Our world is so full of beautiful things: fruit
and ideas and women and banjo music and
onions with purple skins. A virtual paradise."
—Edward Abbey, *Down the River*

To help us out, Cricket asked her mom if she could go backpacking with Annie, just backpacking in the woods. Cricket's mom had no clue where Annie was, figured she was home as well, so she said, "Yeah, sure."

Cricket and her new boyfriend, Conner Stearns, met us in the mountains north of Silver Creek in the dirt-and-gravel parking lot of The Colorow Inn, a knotty pine-log restaurant that was somewhat of a landmark on the highway, named for an old Arapahoe Indian chief.

Cricket, real sentimental and tender and all, had at first said, "Wouldn't it be more reasonable for you guys to come down to the city and we do the little bye-bye thing from here?" But Conner had said, "You and me, baby, we're going west anyway, so this just saves some time."

So we did the little bye-bye thing at The Colorow Inn. Conner and Cricket waved and headed west. They'd find a trail or a hideaway somewhere, stay out of sight and off the roads, and see us again in eight days at Cricket's house.

Cricket's last words: "Don't get busted somewhere."

Annie and I looked at each other for several moments, trying to size up the adventure ahead of us. It was huge. I had put maybe two thousand miles on my thumb in the last couple of summers; I'd crossed the state, crashed out in backseats, in pickup beds, next to trickling streams and four-lane highways. But I'd never crossed the state line on my own, and I'd never traveled with a girl. I was suddenly scared for both of us. I was sixteen years old and walking to Woodstock.

Actually, it was the Ozark Music Festival: three days and thirty-six bands, including Marshall Tucker, the Eagles, and Aerosmith. Seven hundred and fifty miles, three state lines, just me and the girl. We stood there with our backpacks on, staring at each other.

"Are we ready for this?" Annie asked.

"Hah!"

Which comment could, I suppose, be taken either way. She knew exactly how I meant it.

And then, mellowing to the task at hand, I said, "What could go wrong?" I pulled from my pack a previously prepared cardboard sign reading MISSOURI, and we headed on over to Highway 74 and wandered along it as it approached its terminal merge with Interstate 70. To the north of us, across the highway, lay the butterscotch-scented hideaway of Stapleton Park, perhaps the largest contiguous stand of ponderosa pine between there and Woodland Park, seventy miles south. To the west stood the Continental Divide, here punctuated by James Peak, Mount Eva, and Mount Bancroft, their summits and couloirs still hosting snow. And to our east were the rapidly descending ridges of the Front Range, dropping like a stairway out of heaven to Denver and the Great Plains, which we would cross all the way to Missouri.

While we were still walking, my sign held aloft, heading for a spot visible to and accessible by both highways—it was illegal to hitchhike on the Interstate—a yellow Jeep Wagoneer pickup heading the other direction slowed and then pulled to the side of the road. Three authentic mountain hippies were sharing the front seat, and the one driving asked us across two lanes where we were heading.

"Missouri."

"Where in Missouri?"

I said Sedalia, for the Ozark Music Festival, and the guy said, "We're going there tomorrow."

Annie and I were somewhat speechless.

A car whizzed between us.

"Tell ya what," he said. "We got a lot of preparing and all to do today, but if you show up at our place later this afternoon, you can just bed down there and we'll pull out in the morning. Take ya all the way."

• • •

Bob and Larry and Peanut and a half-dozen other adults of both sexes — and three little kids — shared a beautiful log cabin overlooking Bear Creek just down the canyon from Silver Creek. And by *beautiful* I don't mean some Lincoln-Log machine-spit thing out of *Log Home* magazine: I mean fifty years old, a sagging porch, chinking made with clay and grass and maybe horse hair.

When Annie and I got dropped off at the address at about 4:00 P.M., the fellas were inside packing boxes of beads and macramé twine for the trip. Ceramic beads, some handmade right there in the cabin, some imported from places like Santa Fe and Vancouver and Littleton. This was their seventh year selling jewelry at rock festivals around the country. Annie and I mostly just stayed out of the way, spending a good hour just rocking on the front porch swing.

Around eight o'clock, the packing completed, Peanut came outside with his guitar and started to pick. The others joined us, and Annie and I quickly relinquished the throne of honor to Bob and his lady. Like my dad, Peanut had a hands-free neck brace for a harmonica, and he proceeded to entertain us for well over an hour. I spent most of my time watching him, trying to memorize movements and fingerings, but from time to time I'd wander off to find Annie, who had joined the other ladies in domestic tasks and conversation in the tiny, rustic kitchen. Their topics included the leaky pipe above the water heater, fennel versus caraway in sourdough bread, and the take from last year's festival circuit.

I went to Annie, who was not adding much to the conversation, and pulled her into a snuggle, and the lady called Diane asked, "How long you guys been together?"

Annie said, "All summer," and Diane and Misty both said, "Cool," and that was that. From then on we were a couple in the eyes of all, including ourselves, the last ones of all to look in the mental mirror and ponder what that meant and say, "Yeah, that's right — it's you and me, baby."

We all fell asleep while Peanut played on and on outside on the porch, and then we woke up to a gentle nudging from Bob at about 3:00 A.M. Time to roll.

We took the Ford pickup, Annie and I all alone with the beads in the back, a camper topper protecting us from a Great Plains thundershower just east of the Kansas state line. Up front, Bob drove, then Larry, then Bob again. The ladies back in Colorado had made us a cooler full of sandwiches, and we passed it around every few hours. Peanut took the wheel between Salina and Topeka, then Annie and I fell asleep. At about 11:00 P.M. Annie told me to wake up, she thought we were there.

I looked out the side windows and saw car headlights straddling a narrow road for at least a mile in both directions. Larry was easing forward into position on the side of the road, where we joined all the others in a one-lane single-file parking lot for the night. Peanut came around, opened the back window, and told us we were just outside the gates of the Sedalia fairgrounds. We'd crash out here for the night, and they'd open the gates in the morning. Did we want the ground or the back of the truck?

I was sick of the inside of the truck, so we took ground, along with a thousand other campers. The air was thick with humidity and just losing its edge as far as temperature went.

I awoke in the morning to two sensations: one was the feeling that I was burning up, and the other was that I was being eaten alive. From the first opening of my eyes, it was apparent that other campers were having the same dream. Half a dozen neighbors, including Peanut, were jumping around like wild men at a rain dance. The Missouri sun was blazing down on us, and big, brown ticks were crawling all over our faces and arms.

There was a road-kill deer about twelve feet into the weeds, smothered with the critters. It still makes my head itch to remember it. I woke Annie up, and we both jumped up and joined the rain dance. No one had occupants, just visitors. And it never rained.

At 9:00 A.M. they opened the gates to the fairground park, letting those with vendor passes — like us — into the treed, lusciously lawned compound. At ten they opened the gates to the fairground itself, a big, flat, sun-baked plain with nary a tree in sight, unless you looked in our direction over in the park. Nevertheless, I could see the gates being swarmed with people, more hippies — probably more people — than I'd ever seen in one place at one time. The gate-keepers were trying to take tickets, but hundreds of people were going up and over the fifteen-foot chain-link fence or just pushing past the legitimizers and swarming the field. It was total chaos.

Bob told us how it worked. Annie and I would probably want to go stake out a claim on the fairgrounds, maybe take one of our sleeping bags or a blanket and lay it out flat and stay long enough to establish the grubstake. That way we'd have a place whenever we wanted to be close to the music. But we'd probably want to come back to the vendors' park at night to crash out in the grass. According to Bob, the fairgrounds sleeping bag would probably not get stolen; everybody would be too stoned to think that analytically.

So by 11:00 A.M. we were staking out our six-by-six at a point about a hundred and fifty feet from the two huge side-by-side stages. It would have been about the fortieth row on the floor at the Denver Coliseum. Here it was about 260,000 people from the back of the "hall."

Good seats.

But this was a veritable zoo. A madhouse. The estimated 330,000 people were soon engaged in a massive party. The booze came out, the bongs roared, hundreds of women's boobs burst forth into the freedom of rock and roll abandon.

Annie and I practically huddled in fear.

Before the first band—no one I'd ever remember—was announced at about five thirty, we had watched two guys shooting up, another guy carried off on a stretcher with his head bleeding, some cowboy puking out his guts, and a couple not twenty feet away having sex in the dirt, probably not even contemplating what Kerouac's Japhy Ryder would posit in *The Dharma Bums* as a transcendental exercise in *yabyum*, the sacred nature of the act. Completely nude and stoned, they were just doing it.

And then there was the music.

The bands got better as the night roared on, each successive evening bringing forth acts like the Eagles, Aerosmith, Ted Nugent, Joe Walsh—long before his Eagles era—and Bob Seger.

Each night we'd return to the park and each morning to our plot on the concert floor, still intact but burdened with trash that we hadn't left—if we packed it in, we packed it out; that was the way of the woods. In the morning or when bands that didn't interest me were playing—quite a few of them—we'd wander the periphery of the fairgrounds or hang out in the shade of the park listening to civilian jam sessions, reading, or taking naps. The Sedalia fire department had set up several tanker trucks, and people stood in line to pull the chain, allowing the water to flow out by the hundreds of gallons. I wanted to yell at everybody, *Don't you know how much water you're wasting?* It seemed no one cared for anything sacred.

A hundred port-a-potties ringed the fairgrounds, and most were putrid by the second day. That same day I discovered a sight much to my amusement: a beautifully bronzed girl with flaxen hair standing completely nude and smiling while an artist painted baby-blue morning glories from her kneecaps to her collarbones. And Annie found one to hers: a makeshift Mormon chapel, one of six or seven temporary churches trucked in for the benefit of parishioners. Annie laughed out loud and said, "Can you believe it? I can't get away from it anywhere!"

The whole gig ended the third evening at about 7:00 P.M. with a very anticlimactic performance from America—"A Horse with No Name" and a band with no flame. We gathered our goods, having seen six of everything and too much of most, and moved with the crowd off the fairgrounds. In all honesty, I was sick of the fairgrounds and its sun-drenched, dust-and-sweat-stained orgy of excess and hedonism. But the campground I would miss, with its camaraderie and communality, its beads and banjos and beatnik reverie. That night the vendor-park jam session went on until midnight. A hundred or more people sat in a circle, passing around guitars and jugs of water and wine and hand-carved onyx pipes and hand-rolled joints. But Annie and I sat back against a tree, she in my arms, both wondering: Is this where we fit?

When we awoke in the morning, everybody in the campground was sad and hugging everybody else, even the two kids from Colorado. Larry told Annie and me that they could take us out to the highway, but from there they'd be heading east to points unknown. Maybe Chicago. Peanut was going down to Oklahoma to visit family.

We dropped Peanut at the exit ramp to U.S. 50 westbound and waved good-bye. By the time we were 180 degrees opposite on the cloverleaf, he already had out his guitar and one foot up on his open case. I burned his image, or that which he represented, into my mind for future reference: *Give me a ride or not, I'm just playin' a tune and crossing America.*

Bob and Larry dropped us off at I-70, shook our hands, and waved good-bye. They went east, and we went west, getting to Kansas City and clear across the Big Muddy in a single ride with a college geology professor returning home to Lawrence, Kansas, after giving a presentation on sedimentary disconformities at the U of Mo in Columbia.

After we got out on the exit ramp in Lawrence, Annie and I laughed about the ridiculousness of making a career teaching geology in Kansas. Then we dropped down the far-side embankment to dig in my pack for a package of Hostess donuts, the little powdered-sugar ones that never let you lie about what you've just done.

I was taking my first bite when the Kansas state patrolman pulled over and stopped on the shoulder above us, not eight feet away.

9

"What's in store for me in
the direction I don't take?"
—Kerouac, *The Subterraneans*

THE JAIL CELL IN LAWRENCE was six slabs of concrete, its floor about the dimensions of a sheet of plywood. In fact, that's probably how they'd laid them out. The cast-iron door had a six-inch plexiglass and chicken-wire window at the top and a ten-by-three-inch slot at the bottom for my food. The two bunk beds were just cast-iron shelves bolted into the wall, each hosting a thin foam pad with a single, folded wool blanket. The toilet was right there on the wall, no privacy door or anything. Of course, I didn't really need one; I had no bunkmate to worry about.

We had held hands until the last minute, and then we were led to separate desks and processed.

Where ya from? Colorado.
Whaddaya doin'? Traveling.
How old are you? Sixteen.
Say what?

I had no ID to prove anything one way or the other. I didn't own a driver's license, after all, but I did have a reasonably good beard for my age. So why on earth would I tell him I was *younger* than legal age? If there was such a thing for hitchhiking across state lines.

"Who's she?"
"My girlfriend."
"Your parents know where you are?"
Pause. "They think we're in Colorado, with friends."

I didn't even get to make my one telephone call; the cop did it for me. He laughed when my dad told him I was supposed to be in Colorado with friends camping—*boy* friends.

"Nah, she's a long-legged blonde in a halter top and shorts. Name's *Aaaa-neee*," he said real cutesy.

I knew what my dad was doing then: he was laughing, chuckling with a peer about the mindless ways of kids. But when I got home, he was gonna fry my butt in bear grease.

They never really busted me, just held me there for three days for my "safety." The nights were longer and lonelier than any I've ever spent. What made it worse was that some girl down the corridor moaned and sobbed her way through two of the nights. I couldn't tell if it was Annie or not, but the fear of that possibility tormented my own interminable hours. I tried asking a passing guard, but he didn't give me the time of day or night. I was just a crook.

The first time some guy slid a tray of food through my slot, I asked him if he could tell me whether the girl down the hall was a seventeen-year-old blonde with a really good tan. He said, "I'll see what I can find out."

Then I saw what he had handed me and spoke again. "Ya got anything besides white bread?" He said, "Yer in jail, bucko." Then I peeled it open, saw bologna with mustard, and said, "I'm a vegetarian!" And the guy—I learned later he was a black guy; I'd never met a black guy before—said, kinda sympathetic, "Look, I don't cook the food. I just serve what they hand me." Then he said, "I'll see if they got anything else."

I never saw him again until next morning, when he slid one of those tin bread-baking pans under the door full of milk and cornflakes. I asked him about the girl; I was near insane from worry and lack of sleep. Once again, he said he'd find out.

Then it was white bread and bologna for lunch and dinner for two more days. I got him to kill the mustard. I never touched the bologna, except to pull it out, roll it up real polite like an hors d'oeuvre, and hand it back to him on the metal plate. And I never got an answer about the girl until day three.

"Nah, the little blonde, she went home after the first night in here. Her daddy sent a plane ticket."

My daddy let me sit and stare at green walls for three days.

He met my plane in Denver. It cost a hundred and sixty bucks for my first airplane ride, and I'd never been so scared. On the way home, about an hour and a half from Stapleton up to Paradise Mountain, he said nothing beyond "So you made it; that all ya carrying?" and "You look like hell" until about Morrison. At that point, we were entering the mountains, and I suppose the scent and semblance of home got him thinking along lines other than *Should I kill him?*

Half a mile into Turkey Creek Canyon, he says, "If you've never thought about losing your mother, you might think about it now."

And I was speechless.

They had rushed her into the hospital two days before, thinking it was a burst appendix or a gall bladder attack or worse. It was appearing to be something less, possibly just a strangulated hernia, but it was touchy time around my house. The call from the Kansas State Patrol hadn't helped.

But I lived. Mom lived—minus a gall bladder—and Dad would later tell me, chuckling, how dumb I was to get caught.

"You never travel on an interstate, stupid!"

What Annie's dad said to her on the phone was "Are you okay? How can we help?"

Annie said, "I think my summer's over. Okay if I come home?" And her folks said, "We'd like that—we'd like that very much." In fact, they were missing her and looking forward to seeing her. Annie told me later that she could hear her mother crying. She hung up the phone there in the Kansas cop shop, fuzz all around, with tears streaming down her face.

She snuck a phone call to me a few days after I got home, and after we hung up I remember thinking: *My little family's coming apart.* I went out to the knob of rock just south of our back door and sat looking at Pikes Peak and the valley of the South Platte River, wondering how a mom and dad could possibly deal with a child—especially a daughter—openly running away. I'd plain and simple just lied about it. She'd left a note eight weeks before, *I'm outta here,* snuck out her bedroom window at 1:00 A.M. and joined Jim and Cricket and me rolling down the street in Jim's pickup. I wondered what nightmares her folks had suffered about her being on the road—young, pretty, and vulnerable. I wondered what I would do in their shoes.

I loved this girl, but I wondered what, really, had driven her out of a home that by all indications seemed to love her, first enough to let her go and then enough to let her return, few questions asked, a smothering hug offered, and reciprocated, at the airport.

Or so she told me later—at that particular point in time, I was still rolling up the baloney in a Kansas clink. I couldn't stay away for long, of course. Within a few days of my return, I hitchhiked down to the city wearing my mountain best—a pair of faded and fine-looking Farmer Brown overalls, no shirt, my logging boots, and a juniper-berry-and-rainbow-trout vertebrae choker—and hiked right through suburb and side street to the address she gave me. I wanted them to know that Annie had been in the responsible care of someone who loved her.

Her mother answered the door.

It was later reported secondhand that I was the oddest-looking thing Mrs. Hawk had ever let into her house, Cricket notwithstanding. She was surprisingly cordial, but she felt it was her duty to explain that we had but a few minutes to say hi, because Annie was grounded.

We went out back to the patio swing and sat down, Annie taking my hand without the slightest pause. Mrs. Hawk hung out in the kitchen, and a cute little three-year-old girl with blonde hair as long as Annie's played in a corner sandbox with a Fisher-Price farm set. I knew nothing about Mormons, but the home seemed normal and the people in it looked normal. No buggy in the garage. No black cloaks or top hats suspended from the coat rack. I was nervous. Annie was smiling.

I asked her how things were; she looked happy. She said she was okay and not fighting the incarceration; it was tolerable. She was quite amazed that they had taken her back so readily.

All in all, she told me, she had gotten something out of her system. Or into it. She had proven that she could stay alive on her own, that she was capable, that she was brave.

And she had proven to herself that she was worthy of love, even the kind of love in which a boy would build her a cabin, braid her hair, and trust her with his dream of saving the world. She said she missed me miserably. I said I missed her worse.

She squeezed my hand and just stared in my eyes. Then she reached up and removed a delicate gold chain from her neck and placed it around mine.

"This is my promise," she said, and I just waited. "A promise that I am yours alone."

I was without words, but I leaned over and kissed her gently. Her eyes darted quickly, subconsciously, to the woman in the kitchen twelve feet away. She looked down shyly and said, "Sorry." I wanted to take her and run, run back to the mountain and hide for the rest of forever, and I told her so.

"Oh, I would love that," she said. "I miss my little cabin on the mountain so much. That was such a beautiful time."

Her mother slid open the patio door and stepped out half a step. Annie quickly let go of my hand and pulled inward. It seemed a response as ineluctable as sneezing.

"Annie, lunch is about ready."

Then she took another step out and looked directly at me. "I suppose I ought to offer you lunch, but I'm not sure how comfortable I am with that. Annie has us in a bit of a—" She couldn't come up with the word. "We're just not real comfortable with that." And then, matter-of-factly but with complete honesty: "I'm sorry."

And she went back in.

10

THE FIRST TIME I HITCHHIKED clear across Colorado was by mistake. Not that I just kind of fell off a log and into a car, just that it hadn't been the plan two weeks earlier when we jumped a slow-moving train heading west. (Jumping a slow-moving train cannot be called hitchhiking, after all.)

Like my daddy before me, I went over to pick pears in the late-summer orchards around Grand Junction. As I recall, Pete Cox and I had money to buy tickets and everything, but by the time we stood at rail side looking up at those big brown boxcars, my mind was doing a wheelie, skipping through all sorts of Woody Guthrie and Pete Seeger tunes about the rhythm and harmony of riding the rails. And right there lay two firm iron rails pointing quite convincingly off to the sunset, calling my name in lush tones. I told Peter what I had in mind, and up the ladder we went.

We were fourteen.

Two weeks of Pink Floyd and plain old pedestrian pot under the midnight stars of heaven later, three hundred bucks cash between us, we said what the heck, stuck our thumbs in the air, and hitch-hiked home. Easy as pie and just as splendid. Actually, the times waiting on the roadside were what I enjoyed the most. I would stand and stare off at cliffs and sky and mountains, breathe in pure air when no cars were in sight. The open-road silence was intoxicating. I had never felt so free and alive and autonomous. Rides, when they came, were a burden.

Traveling the open road by thumb would become part of my repertoire as comfortable as my skin. Back on Paradise Mountain I estimated that, with pure mountain or desert backpacking thrown

in, I had just rolled over about thirteen thousand miles on my six-
teen-dollar Nesco pack.

Before long, I would do nearly a sixth that many on just one
trip.

One day in early August Cris knocked on my folks' door and introduced me to a new guy, a quiet, perpetually smiling kid with strawberry-blond hair almost as long as Annie's, named Justin Bloom.
Justin was a "mountain brother," living thirty miles away in Man-
gas Park with parents who milked a pair of goats for their daily
breakfast table, made homemade peanut butter and cashew butter,
and owned a collie. He had a reddish little beard that curled up off
his chin, making him look like a half-breed between the Truckin'
dude and Narnia's Mr. Tumnus. He spent much of his time in a
twelve-foot canvas tipi of his own making.

I believe I stood there with my mouth open, absolutely in awe
of Justin's hair. I had been growing mine for perhaps a year and a
half, Justin for four. I was the shortest-haired of the trio, although
my reasonably good beard and mustache had them both beat.

Anyway, Justin and I hit it off like twin sons of different mothers,
and within days we decided to hit the open road to celebrate. Like
me, Justin had never discovered any rationale for getting a driver's
license. I could have gotten mine in May; in fact, I took the class and
got my learner's permit, but I saw no purpose in the paper as I had
no interest in driving, anyway. Beyond six well-tuned strings and a
good Dunlop pick, mechanical things never were my forte. In times
of desperation, Cris always had a driver's license, but he also had a
job, so this time he would stay behind and work while we went to
see America. Besides, three guys together would never get rides.

Oddly enough, my dad said, "Let them go—the girl's grounded
for fifty years." Which she was, more or less.

So one morning in early August, we pooled our spare change,
pulled on our backpacks, and stuck our thumbs in the air just west
of Shaffer's Garage on U.S. Highway 285. Between us we had a
ten-pound bag of potatoes, three pounds of roasted peanuts, a five-
pound bag of rolled oats, a dozen eggs in a pair of those high-impact
backpacking egg carriers, assorted utensils and housekeeping gear,
and thirty-three dollars. What with gathering fruit and wild edibles
along the way, we figured we could survive two or three weeks.

And we did.

After a series of nonevent rides to Redtail and then Shawnee and then over Kenosha Pass and into South Park, we got picked up by a guy in a tie and a Plymouth Fury going all the way to Montrose. He was an employee of the Denver Water Board on his way to meet with a bunch of west-slope people, who had all the water, to talk about the east-slope people — Denver — who wanted it.

He sympathized with our passionate yet even-handed discourse on how people dumb enough to move to the arid Great Plains — or Phoenix or Lake Havasu City or Vegas or San Bernardino — who still expected to grow Kentucky bluegrass lawns and wash their Buick in the street every Saturday with the hose running full blast the whole time should pack up their bambinos and scoot their butts back to Ohio or Pennsylvania and leave our Rocky Mountain I'll-be-damned-if-I'll-let-them-dam-them rivers alone. But after eighty miles or so, we sensed he needed some time to fully ponder our pontificating, so we asked to get out at the junction at Poncha Springs, thanked him generously, then stuck our thumbs back in the air to catch the next willing ride going in exactly the same direction he had just gone. You could hear his car sighing in relief as he went through the gears.

Passing cars, particularly willing ones, weren't exactly prevalent at that wide spot in the highway, so we wandered over to one of three buildings in town, a gas station — another of the three was also a gas station, but it was closed and boarded shut — and bought a loaf of bread and a jar of peanut butter. Then we sat down under some trees, one of which happened to be a black walnut, and made lunch.

Having known each other all of four days, Justin and I leaned against a boulder and talked. We were of a common mind on everything we could think of, except that he had never known the sweet scent of a girl's hair snuggled into his throat or the intoxicating mantra of her slender fingers stroking his arm or drawing sunflowers on his chest. And I had never known traditional religion. His was about as traditional as they get: he was Catholic.

Actually, we got into that by talking about marijuana. I just asked him what he thought about it, believing that his answer to this important question would either reveal duplicity or naiveté or confirm a genuine depth of understanding about and commitment to the natural road, the gentle path, the Higher Way that we had just been discussing. It was a risk to bring it up at all this early in the journey, but I knew from two years and a lot of miles on the road that sooner or later we would be offered a joint or a bowlful. I certainly never packed my own; hitchhiking was illegal, after all.

Justin pulled at his little beard, brightened his near-constant smile, looked off at the summit of 14,269-foot Mount Antero, which I had reached with my father on my own three-year-old legs, and pondered a while.

"My family's Catholic," he said, surprising me. "And I kind of see marijuana as a sacrament, something holy, something to be used with care and purpose. You know, I don't think someone should smoke just to get high or to party." He emphasized the final word with his fingers making quote marks in the air.

Then he laughed and looked at me. "That's such a silly word: *party*. People get all drunk and messed up and think they're having a good time." He looked back to the mountains. "This is a good time. This is sacred time. What do you think?"

Well, he'd passed the true-purpose test, if nothing else. I was fully prepared to argue the religion thing, but I'd get to that soon enough.

"That's exactly how I see it," I told him. "The Indians smoked the pipe to make peace or to begin or seal important discussions. Okay, sure, it wasn't pot, but the principle's the same."

He chuckled lightly. "Well, I don't know about the marijuana part, but it could have been. From what I've read, they definitely tried to commune with the Great Spirit."

Which took us right back to religion, so I went ahead and opened up. My exposure to formal religion had been less than convincing—or, if anything, convincing in the opposite direction. Except for one very brief episode, personal religious *devotion* had never been a topic of discussion in my home. Religion as an entry in the Dewey decimal system, sure; as a facet of history, yes; as an interesting human curiosity, yeah. We discussed every topic under the sun in my house. But as a personal commitment? As a faith? Not us.

My mother had always pretended an open mind—she was a Job's Daughter at eighteen, after all—but as far as I could remember a Bible had never been opened in our home. I don't recall that we even owned one, although our extensive library was the centerpiece of our home. Certainly a prayer had never been uttered within those walls, at least not in my presence or by anyone in my known genealogy. A couple of the names of God were used with some frequency, but not in what I would assume was a religious manner.

Faithful so-called Christians had been the ones who slaughtered the Aztecs, decimated the Caribs, drove the Five Nations across the shameful Trail of Tears and the Navajo on their Long Walk to Bosque

Redondo. The Muslims had riddled Europe and Northern Africa. Protestants and Catholics — proclaimed Christians on opposite sides of the same coin — were still slaughtering each other in Ireland. For all we knew, religion may have been why our ancestors fled the Emerald Isle in the first place.

And the Mormons, whatever they did and believed in, had driven a little girl barely old enough to drive a car into the bus stations and back alleys and basements of America.

Religion sucked.

But I didn't want to hit Justin over the head with it, so I eased in by telling him about one other kid I'd known who claimed — actually *claimed* — to be Catholic. I supposed he was otherwise a good Catholic, whatever that meant, a sincere and honest boy, but Paul was always the one we had to hold up out of his vomit after he drank too much beer at Don Carlin's backyard keggers. It was like he felt manically driven to get wasted.

"I'm not really a drinker," Justin said. "You lose control, and I don't think that's right." He laughed his little elfin laugh, a quiet chuckle that pulled his shoulders up and down. "I don't think we're supposed to get out of control."

"You're talking cosmic purposes," I said. "A plan, some greater purpose."

His smile tightened into a determined firmness. "That's how I see it."

As we finished our sandwiches, Justin told me how peanuts were a food of the gods but his mother made much better bread, and then we went back into the store for a plastic jug of apple juice, Knudsen's unfiltered. We accepted the plastic bag — not our typical reaction, due to the waste — so we could fill it with sun-drying walnuts. Then we aimed for the highway and stuck our thumbs back in the air.

I questioned Justin about his reference to the gods, whether it was offered in jest or otherwise. What did he really believe?

"There has to be a god, man! Look at this beautiful world." He looked outward, smiling, his eyes tracing the lines of the Collegiate Peaks to the north of us, Colorado's highest summits. He said it with firmness, a conviction that assumed I was right there with him, perhaps a half-step behind.

To my nonreply, he finally responded with a querying look. "What do *you* think?"

"I have no idea," I told him. "Male? Female? One of 'em? Six? I have no clue. How could anyone?"

Justin was quiet for several moments. We crossed the highway and took seats on our backpacks as the occasional driver whisked past, oblivious to and uncaring about our contemplation of the same universe they occupied. Justin pulled a harmonica from the pocket of his pack and started to rub it like a fetish stone.

"The New Testament tells the stories," he said then. "Miracles, healings, and people raised from the dead!"

"Yeah, but who's to say they're true?" I countered. "No one can know. No one can prove it. It's stories—maybe they're uplifting and all that, but maybe it's a bunch of crap." And then I hit him with the main objection that had always been used in my home, the one that overrode all the others: "Look at what's been done in the name of religion, the name of Jesus and Allah and everyone else. You got your wars, you got your conquests, you got more prejudice and anger and intolerance in the name of God than any other cause ever thought of. *Especially* the Christian God. The Christians slaughtered the Muslims in the Crusades, the Aztecs in the Mexican conquest, and the Indians in America. Those were always good Christian folks."

Justin was terribly quiet for a long time, and I was just getting ready to think I'd ruined the rest of our trip when he said, "You're right about that. It's been pretty ugly."

So we just sat for another few moments.

Part of me was all for proclaiming right then and there that I was an atheist, that there was no god. But in addition to not wanting to accept that as reality, I also knew that no one anywhere could prove that one either. We just didn't know. No one could know. It was the great mystery of life, and it pissed me off to no end to be so bereft of a solid, guiding answer to the whole thing. I really wanted to know. What the hell was my purpose on earth? Where did I come from? What was next? What was real?

But then I looked off at the same mountains he did and loved it and felt a stirring of my soul and thought: *Someone or something sure did a good job of making this planet.*

I just about let on. I was just about to tell him that I really wondered and I really wanted to know, when he surprised me with a comment I had never before considered. He said, "Maybe everybody's just getting it wrong. Maybe they're all inventing their own image of god, of religion, and they're way off base. Maybe none of

it is what Jesus really taught. Or Mohammed or Buddha or whoever."
    I looked at him then, and he finally turned to me.
    I hesitated. "So," I began, "let's just say for a minute that there
really is a God, an actual–what? An actual person or being or something. How does one find out about him? It."
    "Or her."
    "Yeah."
    "There's the Bible," he said, and I could tell he liked the book,
probably knew it fairly well.
    "Yeah, but there're a hundred and ninety-two zillion churches
that all say the Bible is it, that they read it right but everyone else is
off on a moon launch. You can't solve it by appealing to the Bible."
    "But like I said," he countered, "maybe they're all—" Within
an instant, he saw where that wouldn't take him: if the true, actual,
honest-to-god God couldn't be found by reading the Bible, then
what was next?
    I offered some alternatives. "Zen? Buddhism? Native Ameri-
can?"
    "The Indians always seemed pretty sure of themselves," he
said.
    "I like the Great Spirit concept," I told him. "At least, I like the
thing where the Indians, at least the old ones, always seemed so
committed. There is a"—I had to think outside my usual lexicon—
"there's a reverence there that you rarely see in Christians. A reverence for life. For all life. For the earth. But they're still kind of shooting arrows in the dark, don't you think? They don't really claim to
know who it is, or what he looks like, or anything about him."
    "And they kind of imply that their god is different from the
white man's god anyway," Justin said. "I've never really liked the
idea of separate gods for separate races."
    "Yeah, what good is that?" I said. "You either have a god or you
don't. You got a different god for every race, and you got the gods
fighting amongst themselves, the same stupid thing all the followers are doing: 'Hey, I'm the real god.' 'No, it's me!' "No, me!' 'No,
me!'"
    I thought of my readings in Nierhardt, and I attempted to de-
fend what I thought the Indians were doing. "I think they're just
proposing their understanding of the Great Spirit and challenging
the white man to come up with a clearer understanding. I don't
know that they're claiming a different one. They propose a real god

that they claim to know something about, the way he thinks, the way he acts or reacts, and then they challenge the white boys to stand up and be counted. It seems the Christian whites are always just quoting verses from the Bible, which are about as obscure and useful as teats on a bull."

He laughed at that one, but my dad used it all the time.

"Isn't there a white man alive who has an actual knowledge of God?" I asked. "Who has seen him or talked with him or had him butt in during a phone call. Doesn't anybody know God? Why is Christianity just in books?"

"Whoa." Justin was catching up. "You have a bit to say."

"I have a bit I'd like to know is all. Why can't anybody tell us straight out what God looks like? Living in mystery is fun for a while, but it's a crappy deal for someone who really wants to know."

"Maybe we're not supposed to know."

"You like that idea?" I was approaching apoplectic. "You think that's true? If that's as good as God can be to man, then piss on him. I want a different god."

Now Justin was laughing again. He popped up onto his feet and started wailing out a tune on his Hohner Bluesman. He could really cook, bending notes and chords like he was on stage with ZZ Top.

I hopped up too and grabbed a couple of sticks from the side of the road and started snapping out a rhythm on my backpack, banging the hell out of the thing just to get my internal flames to go down. Cars whizzed past, the boogie carried on unconcerned. We bopped along for a good twenty minutes before exhausting ourselves in the high mountain glare, and then I flopped down on my pack.

11

"The road must eventually
lead to the whole world."
—Kerouac, *On the Road*

JUSTIN MOVED HIS HARMONICA into a slow, mournful tune, and I just lay there for another twenty minutes until his pucker gave out. Every four or five minutes a car would approach and then pass without slowing, debating, or batting an eye. As if we weren't even there.

I put my thumb back up in the air for every passing car. We never cursed them, we never complained. This was the life and the reality of traveling by thumb. A ride was fortunate, the waiting merely an exigency of the game, at the moment a very pleasant and accepted one.

Then I left Justin at the side of the highway and wandered across toward the store, where a single aluminum light pole reached high into the air to illuminate, at night, the remote intersection of Highway 50 and Highway 285. It was covered with pocket-knife pronouncements, nearly every one a poetic cursing of this particular spot by other thumb-reliant travelers from around the world. Many listed the duration of their wait: *Two hours, 41 minutes, and counting. Four hours, starving, out of weed. Gave up, slept in woods.* From one spoilsport: *Worst intersection in America.*

I read the light pole to Justin while he raised his thumb high to a passing Jeep Wagoneer, smiling as pleasantly as he could. The Wagoneer never even burped in our general direction. None of the curses were older than three years, meaning that either the light post had been there only three years or the Colorado highway department repainted it every so often.

I pulled out my pocketknife and added an entry of our own, but as the day was not over and neither of us wore a watch, I merely scratched in our names and the date of our waiting.

Sometime around four-thirty in the afternoon—I could tell by
the sun—probably a full three hours after our landing there, a 1964
Chevy panel wagon pulled to the side. It was piloted by three long-
hairs in striped train-engineer caps. And off we went.

We crossed Colorado from right to left, then headed down
through Durango and across the state line north of Aztec. When we
got out, hitchhikers were strung out for half a mile on Route 550
heading south. Every one of them was older than we were, some
had a woman with them, and many had dogs, usually Aussie shep-
herd-type units. Mountain men that we were, we just walked right
on past all of them and then added a good quarter mile of breathing room just out of principle. Standing under a ragged Budweiser
billboard in the middle of nowhere, we finally got picked up by a
pair of Navajo brothers. Just like in their creation story, they were
twins.

Before the late-model pickup reached us, we watched it stop
right in the middle of the highway—without risk of impeding traffic—a quarter-mile away and pick up a lone male traveler. By its
speed in covering the quarter-mile between us, we figured we were
out of luck, but the driver hit the brake just as capably as he had hit
the gas and screeched to a stop at our feet.

The guy in the passenger seat just sat there and smiled at us, so
I asked, "How far ya headin'?"

And the guy said, "All the way." And smiled some more.

Well, we hadn't told these guys where we were going at all,
and the next town that even appeared on the roadmap was about
eighty miles away. We hopped in the bed of the pickup with the
other hitchhiker, a guy from Illinois named Gilbert, and went about
ten miles before all the fountains of the heavens opened up. Then
the guy on the passenger side opened up the sliding rear window of
the pickup cab and yelled, "Hey, you guys ought to get up front." I
was sizing up the sliding window when the pickup ground down
to an abrupt stop right in the middle of the two-lane road. The side
door opened, and the right-side guy jumped out and said, "C'mon,
man. Get in here!"

He was a big guy, with hair almost as long as Justin's. He was
carrying a beer and a big smile. Gilbert was already moving up and
over the side. I caught Justin's eye and then said back to him, "We're
all right, man. Go ahead."

But he was having none of it. "Get up here. This is a Ford!"

So up we went, five guys on a Ford bench. We were practically on each other's laps. The driver ripped into the gears as soon as we pulled the door closed, and off we went. The brothers, Will and Wolfe something or other, spent the first fifteen minutes trying to teach us to say something in Navajo, the basic good-day howdy-do: *Yatahey!* We never even got close. And the next forty minutes scared us to death.

Will had a real interesting way of crossing the desert. He would come up on the car in front of him at about eighty miles an hour, then jerk the wheel to pass at the very last moment. His favorite game was timing the pull-out-and-pass to the exact and only moment he could possibly do it between the oncoming car and the bumper of the one in front of us and survive. Once or twice we almost didn't.

We finally slowed down, and Will said he was going to show us how "the Nation" lived. The landscape hadn't changed in forty miles, still just pinyon pines and sage against the red dirt. Off in the desert, at the end of a two-rut track about fifty yards long, was a white adobe building. No windows, just a door. Justin and I were plenty nervous. We stopped and exploded out the doors, and then Gilbert walked right in.

It was what the poet Joy Harjo would call a "bar of broken survivors," a saloon, a watering hole in the desert, whatever. It was the first one I'd ever entered. Drunk Indians were lying all over the place, passed out on the tables, over the counter, victims of what Harjo would also refer to, in "Deer Dancer," as "poison by culture."

In the deep, dark corner, one old man sat and cried. An old woman moaned at his feet, rocking back and forth in her velvet dress with turquoise and silver swaying in and out from her ample bosom, slapping in rhythm to the jukebox, which was playing something really sad from Merle Haggard.

Within moments of walking in, Will and Wolfe had abandoned us, moving off quickly to distant reaches of the dark, smoky, one-room bar. One great big fella—fat, ugly, and really huge—caught everyone's attention, especially ours, when he bellowed out something like, "Look at the *belagana!* We got white boys to visit with!" He pulled himself up off the bar and headed right to us. I was sure we were about to get our white-boy scalps lifted. I didn't have a lot of experience with grownup drunks—a couple of times at my uncle's place, a Christmas party or something, but my folks would up and leave as soon as people started to slosh their words and lean into your face, going, "You know what I'm saying, my friend? Are you my pal?"

And my dad would go, "Time to leave. Merry Christmas."

Then the fairgrounds in Missouri, which made my skin crawl to remember it, the smell of booze and puke and piss and pot, all thrown together. A couple of teenage parties, but I usually split those right after pulling Paul out of his puke. Always booze and puke and idiot commentary. I guess you have to grow up with it.

Anyway, I was feeling way out of place. Me the veggie pacifist, the only fight I'd ever had was with a dog. Okay, sure, a Great Dane, but still just a dog. Me and Uriah were walking down Paradise Mountain Road one day just sniffing the spring begonias, and up and over the embankment came this freakin' horse, white with black patches, and he went right for Uriah's throat, my poor blind collie not knowing Great Dane from Frampton's Camel. Just took him right to the dirt, Uriah scrambling, scratching, actually moaning in fear. And I landed on that sucker and started throwing punches — mouth, ribs, gut. The Great Dane hung onto Uriah maybe another three seconds and then said, *What the hell, this is a human beatin' my bones!* And beat I did, pummeling the crap out of that dog until he let go of Uriah's shaggy throat and skedaddled for the woods.

Better choice than eating my dog, but still not very smart. He beat me down the embankment, taking it in one leap, but I caught him within thirty yards in the woods — *city flippin' flatlander canine* — and landed on him, taking him down into the begonias. This time he fought back, trying to sink some fang, but I busted his chops, whomping his ribs *wham-wham-wham* and then finally letting him up, actually giving him some space, saying "Come on, sucka" out loud, wanting him to just try it, ready to break his freaking neck. And he turned and split. I went back to my sweet blind dog, who was leaning against the side of the roadcut, panting, probably as scared to be all alone he-didn't-know-where as to have just been attacked by he-didn't-know-what.

To my surprise, Gilbert went straight over to the Big Guy and thrust out his hand.

"Hey brother, how are you?"

The Navajo giant took his hand, pulled him into a smothering embrace, smacked him on the back, and then came toward Justin and me. Gilbert had lived, so Justin put on his best little shiny-eyed smile and offered both hands.

"Hey, man, how ya doing?"

Same embrace, same results.

Then to me.

I can't say that I remember what my face was doing—after all, I couldn't see me. But I do remember that he reached me, the last guy in line, and just hung on, smothering me, leaning into me and through me and pressing me up against the bar, right into another guy, who didn't move and didn't care. Then he started complaining to me personally about how the white man had treated his people. "You see my people?" he said. "This is my people. This is our hope. We are the Dineh, and the white men have driven us to ruin" and on and on. *You know what I'm saying, my friend? Are you my pal?*

And I thought, *Oh man, you may be right, but it wasn't me and I wasn't here and I have no idea what to do about it and I think it's time to split. Merry Christmas.*

The whole place was a morass of misery. We found Will and Wolfe, and they were hanging on their friends, trying to comfort them, commiserating with their people. I told Wolfe that we ought to be getting back on the road—it was a long way yet to Albuquerque—but he tried convincing us to stay. It took a few minutes, but pretty soon Gilbert and Justin and I exited the front, waving a hearty good-bye to all our new friends and moving toward the highway.

Will and Wolfe came out then, and we exchanged farewells. We thanked them just as the Big Boy came out. Wolfe seemed highly offended that we were leaving, or that we hadn't solved something, or maybe he suddenly realized we were white, but it was very tense, the Big Boy coming, and we moved quickly for the highway, where nothing was passing but a slight breeze.

The Big Boy came on, Will and Wolfe disappeared back into the bar, and we said amongst ourselves, "Ya think he's mad?" And things like "Can we take him?" and "What does he want?" and, "Man, I wasn't the one who tricked Sitting Bull" and stuff like that.

And then suddenly, down the highway, far off like a speck, I could see a car coming. Better yet, it was a Volkswagen bus. The bus actually passed us as the Big Boy was reaching the highway, calling after us, but then it screeched to a stop and backed up—John Wayne in a campermobile—and let us in. We pulled off just as the Big Boy reached the dashed yellow line. Passing zone.

Well, John Wayne took us to the New Mexico town of Cuba, where Gilbert decided to cash it in for the day, go find a place to crash. We got another lift with three kids who confessed to having just stolen all the popcorn and candy from the eighteen-stall movie drive-in. From the tone of their conversation, it seemed apparent that their friends running the snack bar had let them "rob" the place. I never could see going to jail for cotton candy or juju beans. Not with what they feed you once you get there.

We eventually got to the south end of Albuquerque, just outside of town, where we hiked a hill off the interstate and threw out our sleeping bags for the night. Next day we headed south looking for wilderness.

12

"I saw God in the sky in the form
of huge gold sunburning clouds
above the desert that seemed to point
a finger at me and say, 'Pass here and
go on, you're on the road to heaven.'"
—Kerouac, *On the Road*

IT WAS MID-AFTERNOON, early August, and about 103 degrees. The ragged crags of the Organ/Franklin Mountains rippled in the heat to the east. We had gotten a ride from a salesman who told us he was going all the way into El Paso, Texas.

Not an option. ZZ Top may like the place, but we were having none of it. We asked him to just let us out at the final onramp in New Mexico, the south end of Anthony, and bid him farewell from the emergency lane. Then we hoofed it on down the side to a Texaco station, where we filled our canteens in the bathroom and pondered our options. The guy in the station told us the little gravel road out front continued east into the Organ Mountains, rugged country peopled mainly by black-tailed jackrabbits and range cattle.

My kind of people. That was our road.

The road was straight, narrow, and beautiful, ambling gently upward into the mirage that blends earth and sky into one amorphous mélange at that altitude and temperature. We went back outside and started walking east up the road, just gazing at the desert crags. This is what we had come for. The road was good, but a new wilderness, a new patch of virgin earth, was what really drew us onward.

We almost didn't hear the Mexican farmer yelling at us from back at the Texaco. When we finally looked and noticed he was calling in our direction, we merely paused, drawn halfway out of the present. He entered his pickup again and rolled toward us. Three of his brood occupied the bench seat, and another three sat in the bed. When he rolled up to us, he called over the other two passengers, "Where going?"

Justin smiled his best smile and answered, "Up into the mountains. *Las montañas.*"

He looked confused for a moment, but I suspect he didn't know how to ask *What the heck for?* in English, so he just answered, "*Venga.*" Get in. "I take you."

So we went over the back into the bed, where the others shifted to welcome us. In fact there were four people in the back ahead of us: two teenage boys and a woman holding a baby, who we hadn't seen previously. No one said anything. We just rode and smiled. The pickup climbed into the Organs, and the topography and the vegetation began to change. Soon we reached a summit, a pass, and the road stretched out before us into the eastern ranges. Justin and I had the same idea, and I knocked on the back window.

"*Está bién aquí,*" I called.

"*Aquí?*"

"*Sí.* Right here."

The old boy stopped in the middle of the road—no threat of traffic—and we got out. Thanks and *adios* and the pickup pulled away. The Organ Mountains were just a single broad ridge of rocky, desolate, frozen volcanic thrusts stretched north and south. The road was bordered on both sides by a scraggly barbed-wire fence, intended, so we assumed, more to keep the cattle off the road than to keep people off the range. After all, how many people would be picnicking in this farthest corner of the map?

We went, of course, through the fence on the north side, away from Texas. Everything was sharp: the boulders, the plants, the sun. We hiked onward toward a valley perhaps a mile away. The sun was nearly intolerable, and we sipped from our canteens often. When we pulled into the valley, the just-beginning ridge shadow was high above us and only about thirty feet wide. We found a large boulder and sat on the lee side. And sat. Soon we lay back on our packs and took afternoon naps.

When I awoke, I saw Justin wandering the hillside in the evening shade of the ridge's shadow. He was walking slowly, maybe a hundred yards distant, slightly bent over, staring at the ground. At first I thought he was sick, but then he'd throw his hair back over his shoulder and I could see that little permanent smile on his lips.

One doesn't holler in the wilderness—bad manners and bad

form — so I stood up, took my bearings, and went toward him. I was moving quickly but silently, and he saw me anyway. One's peripheral vision in the stillness of wilderness is extremely acute. Especially for one immersed in the ways of wilderness.

"Whatcha finding?" I asked him when I was close.

"There's these beautiful little flowers all over," he said, smiling, and sure enough there were. They had opened in the cool of the evening shade, as many blooms in the desert are wont to do.

"It's a vetch," I said, leaning over to inspect.

Justin recognized the similarities to the northern varieties and said, "Well, sure!" with a full satisfaction. "That's not really what I was looking for," he added, "but they're sure nice."

"What are you looking for?"

"I was looking for peyote," he said, without looking up.

And there began another entire discussion. Within minutes we discovered that both of us were carrying two books with us in our backpacks. His were *Book of the Hopi* by Frank Waters and *A Separate Reality* by Carlos Castañeda. Mine were the gift copy of the *Tao Te Ching* and *Journey to Ixtlan* by Carlos Castañeda.

"What would you do if you found some?" I asked him.

"I don't know. Just look at 'em, I suppose. Pretty scary stuff."

We sat right down in the desert dust and discussed Castañeda, an anthropologist who some years before had apprenticed himself to a Yaqui Indian mentor in Sonora named Don Juan Matus and then written books about the experience and the apprenticeship. Don Juan was a *brujo*, a sorcerer, an instructor in the ways of truth and power. Of *knowing*.

That's what it said in the books, anyway, and Justin and I wanted to know — to know the purpose and meaning of life. Same reason he was carrying *Book of the Hopi* and I was carrying the *Tao Te Ching* — the Way of Life. The only power either of us was after was the power to be independent and self-sufficient in that knowledge. But Don Juan's path to knowledge was a pathway revealed only through the use of psychotropic hallucinogens, primarily peyote, psilocybin, and mescal. It was harsh and demanding. And very dangerous. Castañeda was often at risk of death or serious impairment. Even William Burroughs, Jack Kerouac's cohort in the psychedelic beat years, had rejected "the open-ended, dangerous, and unpredictable universe of Don Juan."

What anthropologist Castañeda was learning from his Sonoran Desert medicine man, and Justin and I from Castañeda, was that knowledge, reality, and the ability to control one's life and destiny came from some esoteric key buried deep inside a mystical mystery, a mystery unraveled only by the very precise use of these plants, plants long used by the indigenous Americans. In essence, one had to be willing to risk his life to gain the truth or go out of his mind trying.

"I wonder if we're really supposed to be doing that kind of stuff," Justin said.

"You mean, whether your mother would approve?"

"No, I mean in the grand scheme of things. Should man be risking death just to find God? Should he have to?" Justin confessed that he often thought that the Coyote, Don Juan's "ally," his Shower of the Way who appeared only while Don Juan was under the influence, reminded him more of the Christian Satan than of the Christian God — he was capricious, mean, untrustworthy.

"So why would Don Juan follow him?" I asked. "Why risk your life?"

Justin looked off to the east, the smile wavering. "Why are we interested? Why have thirty thousand or a hundred thousand or however many people bought the books? Why'd we both bring one with us?"

Good questions.

I knew a lot of people wanted power, but I knew a lot more who just wanted to get stoned, get high, take a trip, and never leave the farm. A lot of people drank beer and then went four-wheeling or drag-racing down the highway, but it didn't mean they had any interest in the Big Picture. I just wanted to know Truth.

"I like the setting," I said finally.

"Mexico?"

"Well, just the desert in general."

"Yeah," he agreed. "It's beautiful." And it was. But it was also harsh, just like the stuff in the books.

Justin looked around long enough that he finally got his smile back. "I don't picture a lot of kids being able to do it," he said. "Or women. Can you picture your mother? But then, kids and women aren't really who Don Juan has in mind, I suppose."

"That's half my argument with it, though," I said. "Are only grown men, tough guys, supposed to find God? What about my mother, or my girlfriend? I think that's the part that disturbs me most, that this is some sort of private knowledge. Privileged." And then I made a confession that would soon come to haunt me. "But if that's what it takes, I'd do it. I wanna know the meaning of life that bad, man."

And Justin said, "Yeah," but then he reminded me that we didn't have a mentor, a *brujo*. "We'd probably kill ourselves."

And we kind of laughed and let it go.

We sat still then, immersed in our private, privileged thoughts, and just let our eyes wander over the land. We could see evening lights coming on in hovels and ranch houses scattered at immense intervals over the scrub desert to our east, where we were surely seeing fifty, sixty miles. To our south the first lights of El Paso, or whatever was just east of it, were just tinting the sienna sky. Heat still rippled from the earth's surface, but the distances were growing, the horizon extending eastward.

I knew Justin was a mountain boy, one who had learned the ways of the mountain. He could sit still and quiet for more than two minutes without feeling some obligation or need to talk. Most people can't do that. It's always wall-to-wall obligatory blah blah.

In fact, we sat there for right around twenty minutes without saying another word. Soon the shadows thrown by the ridgeline were long enough that I knew sunset was approaching. I stood, and Justin watched me. Then he stood and followed, as if he knew exactly what I was thinking. We walked back to our packs, unstrapped our sleeping bags so we wouldn't have to fumble with them in the dark, and took our bearings. Then we headed up the ridge. Justin extracted a bag of dried fruit from his pack and continued after me up the cooling mountainside.

I sat on the ridge top and watched, wondered, and wrote.

I had this dream that I was waiting
In some red desert all alone.
The sky was red and quickly shading
With deeper hues of night unknown.

A darker night was never heard of;
The moon took the back roads to the sea.
Morning's sight I had no word of.
Hell was left alone with me.

I'm just one man,
What can I do?
No open door to pull me through.

Must I fall or can I stand here
All alone?

I had to climb another mountain
Just to show I was a man (I had to know).
Evening found me on the mountain
Without a ledge on which to stand.

Unuttered depths fell below me;
My life was clinging to the stone.
Spent muscles would no longer hold me;
I took a breath and I rode it home.

I'm just one man,
What can I do?
No open door to pull me through.
Need I fall or can I stand here
All alone?

All alone.

I awoke in the morning just as the sun was teasing the eastern horizon. Justin was perhaps thirty yards away, sitting lotus-style on a boulder, arms laid out comfortably on his knees, palms up to catch the energy from the sun and the sky. His eyes were closed. I knew what he was doing: he was *sensing* the moment when the sun would blink its first golden ray over the edge of our world, and he'd probably get it just right. I'd done it a dozen times on Eagle's Nest.

But this time I wanted to see it happen, just like that morning on the Stonehenge plain of my childhood. I sat as Justin did, but I kept my eyes open. From time to time, for brief moments, I would let them flirt across the landscape, seeking movement, color, definition. Then back to the spot where the brilliant yolk of the sun would soon spill over the crack in the cosmic eggshell. In one of my flirtings I spied a jackrabbit doing the exact same thing we were: sitting on a boulder, ears up, watching for the sun.

I almost watched him too long. The golden pinpoint broke, then exploded over the rim of the earth, bathing us almost instantly in its glow. No sneaking up through layers of pine trees here.

It was day. In another thirty minutes it would be hot day.

We held our separate places for several more minutes—Justin's

eyes were wide open and he was smiling broadly—and then I began
to dig around in my pack for breakfast. I was pulling out some eggs
when Justin walked up quickly, saying, "Look at these!"

He was holding on a flat rock three of the largest cactus fruits
I had ever seen in my life. I knew that prickly-pear fruits were edible and even prized by some wilderness foragers, but my experience to date had been with the hard, pulpy things available on the
Great Plains or in the foothills of Colorado—certainly not a treat.
But clearly we were in the Edenic center of the cactus world, where
cactus flourished just as wild rosehips get bigger and softer and
sweeter as one rises from the Plains into the mountains back north.
These cactus fruits were dark purple, bigger than golf balls, and,
when we sliced them open, sweet and juicy as strawberries.

"Let's make oatmeal!" Justin said.

Sure enough. I put a quart of water on the stove to boil, grabbed
my pocket knife, and off we went in search of more fruit. In the
seven or eight minutes it took for the oats to get soft—we're not
talking instant anything here; that's the city way—we harvested a
dozen plump fruits and then discussed the possibilities of preparation. My dad, who once hung telephone line through this area
back in the mid fifties, had told me that you could burn the spines
off a cactus fruit—many of them nearly invisible and thus impervi-
ous to pliers—to render them edible. Or, we decided on our own,
you could slice them neatly in half and scoop out the soft middle,
like you would a soft-boiled egg or a cantaloupe. This latter method
proved perfect, and as soon as the oats were ready we each scooped
a full half-dozen desert plums into our breakfast bounty.

Feast!

We wandered the ridges, dallying in caves and crevices, for several
hours, returning to camp again at midday and then remaining holed
up on the west side of our boulder until late afternoon. We read. We
slept. Along about dinnertime, a pair of huge Texas longhorn cattle
scuffed and snorted their way into our camp. I opened my eyes
without moving and watched them for several minutes tentatively,
tense, alarmed. Then I moved just a little, and they both turned and
ran like scared kids.

Justin sat up and wondered what had happened.

The next morning we broke camp, covering every square inch to
look for scraps of litter and then sweeping the area clean of our

footsteps and people-smudges with the low-hanging branches of a catclaw acacia. We did not break the branches from the bush, of course, but used each where it grew for the footage lying within its natural reach.

Then we headed south for the fence and the road. This would be the southernmost point of our trip, and I wondered out loud how long it would be before I saw points farther south, or if I ever would.

13

"Keep America beautiful. Grow a beard.
Take a bath. Burn a billboard."
—Edward Abbey, *The Journey Home*

SOME KIDS LOOK FORWARD to the beginning of each school year: new clothes, new friends, new mayhem and malarkey. Show off their new car. Another go at the big four-point-oh.

I could hardly tolerate the thought of returning to the red-brick prison, with all its inane force-feeding and forced regurgitation of trivial schlop amassed and administered solely for the purpose of making us all the same, then throwing away the kids who didn't fit or learn that way or dig that scene or really care about trig and track and all the rah-rah crap. For me, fundamentally, it was simply a forty-five-mile hitchhike into the city and "syphilization" anyway, so I detested it on aesthetic as well as pedagogical grounds. And usually pulled in about a 3.8 GPA.

What I dreamed of was the double-diamond meadow on Paradise Mountain, Annie reinstalled in the cabin on the front of the mountain, with the view out over the South Platte River Valley. Especially Annie.

So Justin and I pushed on, up through White Sands and over the Sierra Blanca Mountains and Ruidoso, then north toward Clines Corners and U.S. Highway 285, upon which Paradise Mountain sat four hundred miles to the north. We crashed one evening in a hidden-from-the-highway mud-cliff campsite along the Pecos River. Just before sunset we wandered our nude bodies out into the silt-laden stream for a long soak, which we both cut way short when things started hitting our backsides and chewing on our toes. Many things. We jumped up and out of the water, and I pulled a cooking pot from my pack and started scooping pails of water from the stream until we knew: crawdads. Great big ones.

Next morning we continued north right up U.S. 285, with one brief shortcut up Colorado Highway 17. We were running low on funds, down to about nine dollars, so we visited a number of farm fields and orchards along the route, gleaning peaches (still a little green), ears of corn (perfect!), and even late-season chokecherries north of Alamosa (edible).

The proximate promise of not-quite-ripe peaches lodged itself in my brain: there would soon be fruit to pick and money to be made in the orchards of western Colorado. But I just held that thought as we traveled north. I was dying to see Annie, and Paradise Mountain was calling my name. Grand Junction would have to wait.

After we had stood on the roadside in Mosca, Colorado — population about twelve — for three hours, a full-fledged U.S. Marshal with a white beard halfway to his waist and a uniform and rifle in the window rack to prove it picked us up and took us right over Poncha Pass to the junction of Highways 285 and 50. We waved good-bye from beneath the Light Pole of the Many Cursings where we had sat and pondered the verities of life and God and remote highway junctions sixteen days before.

But soon enough, two more rides and home.

Besides a really nice welcome from Annie in the field west of her house, one of the first things I got after our return was a well-worn copy of Jack Kerouac's autobiographical novel *On the Road*. I finished it in three days. Then I sought out *The Dharma Bums* and *Desolation Angels*. But it was *The Dharma Bums* that wiggled its way into a crevice in my soul and took up residence. I felt I was reading about me: the open-road wanderings, the recursion to wilderness, the whole-hearted longing for a spiritual homeland.

Kerouac wrote, "I really believed in the value of charity and kindness and humility and zeal and . . . tranquility and wisdom. . . . I believed that I was an old time bhikku in modern clothes wandering the world in order to turn the wheel of the True Meaning, or Dharma, and gain merit for myself as a future Buddha (Awakener) and as a future Hero in Paradise." And as a contemporary wrote about Kerouac and his cohorts: "The specific object of their quest was spiritual. Though they rushed back and forth across the country on the slightest pretext, gathering kicks along the way, their real journey was inward; and if they seemed to trespass most boundaries, legal and moral, it was only in the hope of finding a belief on the other side."

This is what I was telling Annie one fine fall day when she said, "Sit down, I need to show you something." Then she reached into her daypack and extracted a package, a slim, brown paper bag that she handled as if it contained a Renoir original. She pulled out a book. A very colorful book, called *Hey Beatnik! This Is the Farm Book*.

She had already finished a first reading that weekend, and I could tell this was something special. It was produced by a bunch of hippies on a big commune in Summertown, Tennessee, headed by a guy named Stephen Gaskin. The first thing Annie told me was that they were all complete vegetarians — it was a rule.

She knew that would water my sprouts.

Two months earlier, the evening before we left for the music festival in Missouri, we'd had an interesting exchange while we were out cuddling in the porch swing at Bob and Larry's Bear Creek cabin. Although it was a Tuesday, we were dressed in our Sunday best: matching denim overalls so covered with flowery cloth patches that you could barely see the blue, except that hers didn't have the Rolling Stones tongue sewed over the crotch. Annie was having trouble snuggling up with my necklace, a bold hand-strung assemblage alternating the thick scales of limber pine cones with dried berries of uva ursi (kinnikinnick) and arborvitae (juniper) and featuring the skull of a small animal at the tip. (I was never sure of the animal because the fur and most of the bones were missing by the time I discovered it deep in a crevice in the rocks above my house. Probably a weasel.)

In any case, the necklace was hampering the hugging, so we pulled apart and just sat there pondering a pair of pigs in a pasture across the road.

"Oh, they're so cute!" she said.

"Yeah, and you eat them," I replied, with great caution for her tender feelings.

She told me I was rude, and I told her I was right, and she quit talking. Then she said, "You're right," and she vowed to quit eating meat, right then and there. And she kept to it. She didn't eat the bologna in the Kansas jail four days later, either.

So anyway, I'm saying, "Cool, they're all vegetarians. I knew there were more than just you and me," and she said, "I want to join them." And I said, "Huh? Who?" And she said, "The Farm. I wanna go there. You and me, baby."

And I said, "Us?"

And she said, "Us. A couple. We can get married in Old Tennessee," which to us wasn't a whiskey but a great Dan Fogelberg tune about love and longing, and she knew I would hearken and say ahoy to that.

What I really said was *whoa*. And then I said, "Marriage? We're hippies!"

And so she changed the subject. "They're gentle people. They're pacifists. They use horses to plow, and they grow organically."

"So they're Amish?"

"Look at the pictures, dummy. They're hippier than you are."

So suddenly I'm digging on the Farm, thinking, *Could this be real? Me and her, starting our life together as a "couple," settling down?* However so construed.

The Farm was definitely cool. Here was an entire community of people committed to peace, to gentle living, to walking lightly upon the earth. Perhaps the most discomfiting thing to both of us was the religious component: preachers and meetings and prayer and holding hands—yecch. I told Annie we could just ignore that part, be conscientious objectors, and she said, "Man, will I ever get away from it?"

Our little stint on the road, Annie's and mine, had kept me nervous most of the time, a feeling I never had with Justin, even though our trips were longer, our rides weirder. It was this thing of having a girl, a woman, along that made me scared half the time. What if somebody tried something, tried raping her or hurting her? Could I protect her? Me, the pacifist who typically traveled with nothing more potent than a bag of hand-harvested and home-dried spearmint for a quiet evening tea.

We'd even faced the prospect once. Some big jock dude in Missouri, so drunk he could hardly stand up, had slobbered in Annie's face one afternoon, saying, "The only thing useful about a woman is between her legs," and I had wanted to kill the S.O.B., not so much out of piss-and-vinegar hey-that's-my-girl outrage as out of fear, fear that he'd actually grab her and start trying something. Not having grown up around it much, I just plain and simple couldn't deal with drunk people. I had another guy's lawn chair within reach, and I would have beat the jock sucker's brains into pea soup, but he just laughed at her, laughed at me—*Aren't I funny with all this drool on my chin?*—and turned back to boogie in his oblivion.

What was happening was that Wolfman Jack had said, "Everybody stand up and hold hands" — three hundred thousand of us — "and tell the person next to you something you like about them." And Annie got the jock. But that was the whole scene; the whole brotherly love, peace, don't-you-want-to-kiss-my-butterfly-tattoo thing was really just grotesque. The taste in our mouth after Missouri, in fact, was one of fear and loathing. These were supposed to be hippie people, the gentle race, flower children, and maybe they were, but we were clearly a different strain. We'd left the place thinking, *Man, get me back to the mountains,* and what we'd gotten was a pair of airplane rides. Separate ones.

There was no way the Farm could be that weird; they'd stayed alive as a peaceful community for two or three years already.

A few days later, Annie said, "The ladies at the Farm have their babies at home," and she was smiling. "They give birth to their babies in their bedrooms!"

"All alone?" I asked.

"With midwives."

She was way into it. She was practically shopping for another bus ticket. But I just said, "Who wants a baby?"

Nevertheless, suddenly Kerouac jumped over into the passenger seat of my mind and the Farm took the wheel. Throughout that school year, while all the wonders of differential calculus and the Monroe Doctrine sailed smoothly in one ear and out the other, Annie and I could think of nothing else. We walked on parallel paths so close that they quickly became one path.

Our parents' response to our blooming was anything but comfortable. Or unanimous. When I quit eating meat and wearing leather at fourteen, my parents thought it was a phase. My dad told questioners — like Grandma — that I'd always been too lazy to chew my food anyway, and my mom told them she'd found a great new recipe for carrot casserole. An exceptional cook always, she became my best ally, learning a whole new palette of palatable portions.

When Annie quit eating meat, her parents saw it as one more step away from the faith they held so dear. And they saw me doing the coaxing. I'd learn later that the eating or noneating of animals wasn't quite the doctrinal dilemma they — and most other North American Mormons — thought it was, merely a cultural bias. Mormon doctrine explicitly recommended the eating of meat only "sparingly." But this sudden commitment to complete abstinence loomed large in their minds, which was just what Annie wanted. Zealous converts to the faith of only a few years, they were forcing her to be way too Mormon, way too perfect. She was suffocating, and the only way she could figure to breathe was by taking off, making some miles.

Knowing nothing more than that about their Mormonism, that and their penchant for big families, I threw it right into the pot with Ireland and the Aztecs and the Inquisition, and together we allowed it to become one more target of our complaint and our platform: down with the Vietnam War, down with dams, down with meat-eaters and beer-drinkers and hell-raisers and trash-throwers and snowmobiles and handguns and bigots and racists and rabbit-breeder population exploders and religious kooks.

During our final year of government incarceration in the public school system, our "family of choice" came together again, and this time with a vengeance.

Literally.

Cricket and Annie and I got Whopper-minus-meat on the menu at the Burger King in Lakewood. Typically we wouldn't have supported with our dollars such an exploitative industry of death with its demand for third-world environmental rapine, but we were going after the conscientious objector value. And they did say "Have it your way," after all. So we tested them.

Our hair grew long and untended. My beard filled out nicely. On the mountain and anywhere else we traveled, Cris and Justin and I uprooted signs, especially the No Trespassing type—planet earth belongs to no man privately. We disassembled split-rail fences and tossed the rails back into the woods; we pulled nails and staples and barbed wire from trees, carefully placing the nails in our shoulder bags; we sabotaged bulldozers, rolled rocks and logs onto four-wheeler trails, and gathered refuse left, right, and middle. We couldn't believe that some people were still throwing trash onto the roadside or into the woods. This was the 1970s after all!

I made myself a cane, or walking stick, from a four-foot piece of beautifully warped aspen wood, the kind that formed at the very crest of windswept ridges and rock outcroppings. Dead ones, of course—I never touched a live tree except in a fond caress or to rub some of the aspen talc into my hands as lotion. Soon I began searching the woods specifically for such specimens of gnarled wood and crafting beautiful canes. Kids at school started paying me for them, especially when I figured out a way to hollow them out the entire length and turn them into peace pipes. I started turning a reasonable buck in the creative walking-stick business.

Mostly we went barefoot, and I rarely wore a shirt. Sneakers were acceptable; leather was anathema. I hand-sewed myself a pair of denim moccasins with drawstrings. The whole thing was to get in touch with the earth, which was the title of a favorite book of Native American verse and photography. Flowers in the hair were beautiful, and twigs were really okay. Tree sap was a bit hard to reconcile in the hair, but hey, it happened.

Our clothing was primarily overalls, and for Annie and me those were primarily flowered cloth patches with a small amount of underlying blue denim. My mother wouldn't have let me out of the house that way over her dead body, of course, but I carried my freak suit in my Johnny Appleseed shoulder bag and just changed clothes in a field or the woods before arriving at the school, as Annie did from the other direction. We were a unique pair, and it was very apparent.

And we each did all of our own patching.

Which is exactly what Annie was doing when I launched into another discussion of Castañeda: adding a patch of daisies to the right buttock of a pair of blue-jean shorts.

"I don't like the drug part," she said. "It just doesn't seem right that someone should have to get stoned to find the meaning of life." And she wasn't talking Don Juan psilocybin. She was talking anything stronger than breath mints. Beyond some real meager experimentation early on, Annie had never been a toker or a drinker. It gave her a headache just smelling the stuff. I told her that even the residents of the Farm could smoke pot—it was natural, a plant—and she said, "So's tobacco. You gonna take that up?" And I said, "Lady, get real," and she said, "I am" and "I just don't like it."

I struggled with her decision, wondering if she was right to abstain, but I did not join her in it. Nor did any of the rest of the "family." Most of us eschewed alcohol, however. That remained Cricket's and Cris's private domain. As we discussed it then, theirs were the only parents who drank too, and it had been part of growing up. The rest of us, like our parents, thought it stupid-looking going in or coming out and foul-smelling either way. And somehow it was way too conventional an entertainment for our discriminating rebellious tastes. Plus, as I continually explained to all of them—I'd recently read *Diet for Small Planet*—the manufacture of alcoholic beverages, like the manufacture of meat, was an egregious waste of natural resources, taking perfectly good corn or grapes or barley and pouring them down the throats of cattle or idiots when the same acreage of any of them would feed far more mouths of either species with actual food.

Annie and I started isolating ourselves more and more from the group, even from Cricket and Cris. It wasn't so much that we saw things differently, although Cricket and Cris both liked to drink and do the occasional party in the city; we just wanted to be alone. Just she and I and a quiet place in the woods somewhere. Somewhere far away. We started talking about homesteading in Alaska or British Columbia or Montana. The Farm commune seemed a nice step forward, but we wanted privacy. We wanted another little cabin in the middle of nowhere. I just wanted her, and she just wanted me. Not another soul. But either course prompted some serious questions about our future.

We were beginning to get scared.

One day her mother found us necking on the couch and just came right out and faced us down. She said, "You're on a course to trouble, kids. Maybe you ought to just get married, at least make it legal and proper if you're going to carry on like this." We at first pretended shock, shock that she would presume some sort of heinous activity between us, but Mrs. Hawk stared me straight in the face, tears brimming in her eyes, and said, "Don't accuse me of being so stupid. You know where this leads." My heart lurched, and I felt the sting of having done something that I really shouldn't have done, harboring a fugitive and running away and getting her busted in Kansas and scaring her folks, not to mention rolling around in a sweat on the lady's own sofa.

But then I remembered my place and time and significance in the generations of earth and said, "What good is a stupid piece of paper?" And Annie said, "Yeah," and Mrs. Hawk said, "I'm not talking about paper. I'm talking about a covenant before God that you have committed your all to this person, to love and honor and cherish and defend and support." And I waxed bold and said, "I do all that!" And Mrs. Hawk said, "What about when she's old, or she isn't so young and cute anymore," and I said, "I'll love her anyway." And she said, "What about when children come," and I said, "There won't be any. We don't believe in burdening the earth with any more mouths to feed just so they can use up the water and the energy and scar hillsides and destroy the planet." And she didn't know what to say to that, so she turned just to Annie and said, "What about what's right, Annie? What about agency and choice and consequences? What about the temple and the plan of salvation and the restoration of truth and the covenants and the prophets and Joseph Smith?" And I said, "What the hell?"

To myself.

And then one day two weeks later Annie looked me straight in the eye and said, "How much *do* you love me?"

"Oh, baby, a whole bunch."

"Enough to marry me?"

I was shaken, stirred, and sifted like wheat in a stiff winter wind.

"What do you mean, marry you?"

"I mean, regardless of whether you believe in it or not, what do you love more, your freedom from convention or your lady — me?"

She was serious as a heart attack and almost in tears.

I pleaded, "I love you, baby. You know I do. I have never been untrue, I've never hurt you. I cried half the night when I got you thrown in jail. And then half the next two nights when I thought it was you — "

"I know," she said quietly. "That's not what I mean. Do you love me enough to sign a silly paper, even if it means absolutely nothing to you, if I were to want one? A marriage certificate? Would you be willing to make me your wife?"

I looked at her long and desperately, and then I said yes.

"Yes, baby. I love you enough to marry you."

"That's all I want to know," she said.

The next spring, over spring break plus a couple days extra because none of us gave a squat, the lot of us hopped in a couple of cars — Jim traded his folks the yellow pickup for a cherry-red Mustang, yee-haw! — and headed over to the incredible slick-rock country of Capitol Reef National Monument in southern Utah, an area I had never before seen. Five days, carrying our own water, eight pounds per gallon, through absolutely the most magical place I had ever wandered. The canyon we traveled was more of a chute, the flat sandy bottom between eight and twelve feet wide, and the red sandstone walls rising straight up four hundred, six hundred, eight hundred feet, far more aptly the embodiment of Ozark Mountain Daredevil singer Larry Lee's description of the Grand Canyon, wherein "the sky above was nothing more than a single thin blue line."

The night before we left for Colorado again, Annie and I climbed four hundred feet up to the cap-rock rim to watch the sun setting off to the southwest over the Aquarius plateau. We cuddled up in the soft and warm red sand under the overarching branches of what had to be the world's largest specimen of, dig this, *Ephedra viridis* — Brigham Bush or Mormon Tea — and looked out over the Virgin River valley swearing we would come back here someday. For twenty minutes we just sat and held each other, me thinking *Man, I want to go somewhere and be alone with this girl forever, just live together in peace, in privacy.*

I thought about the war in Vietnam and wondered if the damn thing would actually end before I had to claim 4-F or run to Canada. Because if I ran to Canada, which I most assuredly would, Annie would certainly come with me, and then, just like on the road to Missouri, we would never have peace, probably never even complete the trip. End up in the slammer in Whitefish, sliding my baloney back under the door.

But just as the sun settled low and went blink over the far horizon, Annie pressed me back into the dirt and we made a really cool sand angel right there under Brigham's nose.

Glory be, however, within a few months the school year ended, the troops came home, and the springtime sun climbed high in its daily arc over Windy Peak.

But something was changing.

From Zero to Zion

"In the woods we return to reason and faith."

—Ralph Waldo Emerson

14

FOR ALL THE YEARS I had lived in the shadow of Mount Kolob, I had never set foot on the peak itself. Nor had Cris. In fact, we had never even crossed the saddle ridge that led to it. It's not that it was a big mountain—only about eleven thousand feet, while Cris and I had jogged to the summit of a half-dozen fourteeners by then. But where the northwest flank of Paradise Mountain melted into the narrow ridge that led straight north to Mount Kolob, the woods became strange and magical. It was one of those high windswept ridges just below timberline that played host to weird shapes, weird sounds, and constantly shifting colors. Here the lodgepoles lived up to the claim made by their scientific name of *Pinus contortus* and the stunted sub-alpine firs directed all their growth to the lee side, as if the branches were fleeing the bone-bashing winds of winter.

On such ridges as this, the limber and bristlecone pines assume their reign as kings and queens of the alpine forest, their fantastically twisted and twirled asymmetry standing bold in the wind, worthy of trademark yet so far beyond capture by the best artistic hand of man.

Here the bold and frequent and formidable protrusions of orthoclase feldspar-filled granite for which the Rocky Mountains have their name—most perfectly eponymized in Colorado—appear maudlin grey in the morning, cuddly pink at midday, and majestically golden at sunset. The marmots whistle, the conies scream, and the Clark's nutcrackers swoop and chatter and then sail fast away on the thick winds of heaven.

One morning in early September Cris and Justin and I were determined to cross that ridge and make the summit of Mount Kolob before noon. We carried both water and food—apples, cheese, and chocolate for Cris; dried apricots for Justin; and enough gorp—trail mix—for the entire planet.

Having just left the mountain road and entered the woods on the back of Paradise Mountain, we stumbled onto a very old road climbing the ridge in just the direction we wanted to go. (Some weeks later we followed it downhill, about four miles, right to the cabin on Christopher Drive.) It was now more an erosional route than a road, and we followed it uphill through the deep, shaded woods. At a point about halfway across the ridge, it breached the summit and then slipped on and off it for the next quarter mile or so. Walking silently in awe and in reverence, we entered and then crossed a flat, open space not unlike the Stonehenge plain of my Windy Peak experience, and I knew I was on sacred ground. That's when we saw the USDA beekeeper cabin, at once, in unison.

We froze.

"Whoaaa."

Standing in full sun just beyond the Stonehenge plain, this was the most magnificent structure to date. Remote, solid, and aesthetically pure: nine-by-fourteen, one window, one door(way). Raspberry bushes—alas, a bit out of season—festooned the eastern wall. To the east, we could see the Great Plains just south of Denver, and to the west we had a perfect view of Mount Rosalie and Mount Evans. Moving left, Lionshead, Lost Park, and Windy Peak. Standing directly over the cabin was a fifty-foot limber pine, perfectly straight but leaning fondly toward the cabin, its branches reaching out and over like the ribs of a protective umbrella.

Within a week we had returned, ready to get serious with the place. Winter was coming on, and it needed some work. The first thing we did was roll a huge fallen tree across the logging road about two hundred yards from the cabin. Although the cabin had apparently not been visited in years, perhaps decades, we were taking no chances.

Cris had introduced us to a friend from work named Geoffrey Raines who needed a place to live and owned a Willys Jeep. We offered Geoffrey, who was several years older than we were, squatter's rights in return for the use of his four-wheel-drive vehicle. We drove the jeep up the logging road as far as we could—unfortunately, there was a very large tree blocking the road about two hundred yards from the cabin—and then hiked a thousand pounds of mortar mix, a hundred gallons of water, window plastic, lumber, nails, cooking utensils, spare blankets, canned goods, and tarpaper to the place, transforming it over the next two weeks into a masterpiece of unskilled but very loving labor. Then we rolled a few more fallen trees across the road, and Geoffrey and I moved in.

Geoffrey wore a full neck brace, having peeled off a rock face above Silver Creek six months before and fallen 185 feet to the ground, breaking his neck in three places. He lived because at about a hundred and twenty-five feet he entered the upper branches of a Douglas fir and then plowed his way through it Wile E. Coyote style all the way to the ground, breaking five ribs and his elbow as well but saving his life. He lay still as long as he possibly could, trying to yell, but as sensation came back into his body he realized he was being eaten alive by the red ants whose home he had disturbed, so he rolled over and pulled himself a couple of hundred yards through ponderosa pine needles to the road, where a passing motorist found him an hour later.

It was in this cabin that Geoffrey introduced me to two things: *Be Here Now* and purple microdot. One would lead me to heaven, the other to hell.

15

"Before I can say I am, I was."
—Wallace Stegner, *Angle of Repose*

THE FOUR OF US—Cris, Justin, Geoffrey, and I—decided one fall day that perhaps pot was losing its thrill. Any more it gave me a headache as often as a high, and the burnout aftermath was about as pleasant as a mild case of the stomach flu. Annie was completely clean, had been for months, and that fact sloshed around in my mind with some regularity.

But instead of joining her, we men decided we just weren't progressing in our journey of awakening, an opinion aided and abetted by Geoffrey. In fact, Geoffrey said very little—ever—but his entire demeanor suggested a confidence, a remote aloofness that never let me feel other than substandard in his presence. We couldn't even call him *Geoff*, *Jeff*, or whatever. He moved into the beekeeping cabin with a short stack of books, including all the existing Castañeda titles—four, at that point: *Teachings of Don Juan, A Separate Reality, Journey to Ixtlan*, and *Tales of Power*—and he said he had been where Castañeda had been. At least partway. He had started down that road to knowledge, that path to knowing: he had imbibed the sacred hallucinogens described in those books—peyote, psilocybin, mescal—and survived.

In addition to living through a fall that would have killed me from fright before I hit the tree.

We practically sat at his feet.

One day I started browsing through another of Geoffrey's books, a fanciful volume named *Be Here Now* that told a tale of the author's own enlightenment, including a long trip to the Buddhist monasteries of India and Nepal with a hippie guru who had no name. The type was clearly set by hand on most of the pages. It swirled around in circles and changed font sizes and read backwards and back and forth and anything you could imagine. Half the pages appeared to be made from brown paper grocery sacks. I told Geoffrey it looked like something made in third-grade typography class or while the guy was on an acid trip, which was facetious as I knew nothing about acid trips.

Geoffrey told me that the author, Baba Ram Dass, had previously gone through much of his life as Richard Alpert, Ph.D. With his colleague at Harvard, Timothy Leary, he had taken the clinical exploration of the hallucinogenic drug experience to heart, and to him it had become a religious sacrament, the religion being a New World version of Buddhism and the hallucinogenic drug of choice being LSD. So, Geoffrey said, Ram Dass probably did typeset it himself while on an acid trip.

Geoffrey suggested one Saturday that we all take a trip together, just us four mountain boys. An acid trip, purple microdot, just like Ram Dass and Leary. That was rejected by each of us youngsters fairly quickly and with not a small amount of boldness. For one, this was not a naturally occurring item but a clinically produced chemical; it broke all the rules of mountain freak ethics. And two, it scared us to death. LSD was what Jimi Hendrix and Janis Joplin and Jimmy Morrison and the folks with the beer cans in the canyon had dug on. All of us were familiar with Castañeda's peyote experiences, and each of us agreed, due entirely to his own recounting of it, that certain of the hallucinogens, even the naturally occurring ones, produced an experience that was anything but pleasant. And in the case of peyote and datura at least, probably not safe. Ditto LSD.

Justin spoke up, explaining to Geoffrey that we three, the Fabulous Furry Freak Brothers, were peaceniks, woods people, men of gentle nature and seekers of the low road, the path described so well and so often in the *Tao Te Ching*. But then Geoffrey proceeded to tutor us, mere acolytes, saying, "That is exactly what Ram Dass was after too, man: enlightenment, revelation, nirvana. And Ram Dass has found it, man—here's the roadmap. Dig."

Geoffrey sat on one log, the three of us on another. His jaw firm, his piece said. Men on the way to heaven, or mice on the road to nowhere? Cris said, "How much is too much? How do you know what's safe?" And I said, "What's Ram Dass mean by enlightenment? Is he on a peaceful path? And Geoffrey said, "Read the book."

So I did.

Two weeks later we took the microdot.

It was a beautiful fall morning when we started, probably high sixties, not a cloud in the magnificent blue sky. We sat on the newly tarpapered roof of the cabin, and Geoffrey handed around the LSD. We each took two tiny little dots of chemical. Ram Dass had explained, or perhaps Geoffrey had, that the good stuff was a derivative of morning glories, a flower, and Geoffrey had assured us that this was the good stuff: natural derivative. Then we got off the roof and took off in single file for a nice tour of the woods. We went north by northwest, hitting the lower flank of Mount Kolob in about ten minutes and then proceeding up the mountain. The blues were getting bluer, the greens greener, and something told me that these were the true colors, that I had just never seen so perfectly before. Soon I was perceiving individual pine needles a hundred yards away, then bugs crawling across rocks far down the ridge, then individual droplets of moisture in a cloud forming over Windy Peak. I reveled in my enhanced abilities to see and played games with myself, staring at rocks until I could see the cell structure of the surface lichen or the crystalline structure of the boulder's heart.

When I looked up, however, I had lost the rest of the group. At first I felt merely disappointment at not having them there to share in all I was seeing. I strained to hear laughter, talk, or the sound of movement above me up the mountain. I heard nothing of the sort. But I did hear my mother.

She, and others I could not identify, were coming up the logging road, nearing the cabin. I feared perhaps we had left some acid lying around at the cabin or some pot. I thought I would try to get there first and hide the paraphernalia, but the voices were very close and I knew I'd never beat them.

My mother was now calling my name, telling me to come and make myself visible to her. She sounded mad, and it scared me. I hated hurting my mom; she had always been so accepting and patient with me. We would sit and talk for hours, even after I became a longhair, even after I started disappointing her in front of her friends after mowing their lawns for free as a six-year-old and selling them flower seeds and greeting cards as a ten-year-old. My mother and I would sit at the dining-room table and talk for hours about anything: the Moody Blues, Deep Purple, the erosion of headlands on the Oregon coast, the sarcophagi of Egypt, the Crusades, or the Sand Creek Massacre. And now here I was disappointing her, maybe breaking her heart.

I thought again of just going down to the cabin—I had now moved around to a point directly north of it, and I could see the whole Stonehenge Plain—and talking to her. Telling her I was okay, fine, nothing wrong. But there were too many people, and I didn't think her friends would understand. Or perhaps they were relatives: my aunt and uncle from Golden, or even my favorite great-aunt and great-uncle from Scotts Bluff, the uncle who handmade me a violin. The voices were really loud, but I couldn't see the people. I moved down the slope inch by slow inch, never snapping a twig, moving with utmost caution, my every sense scanning for sights, sounds, or smells of danger. Over the course of what must have been hours, I worked my way around the east side of the ridge, coming in right under the cabin. The voices were gone now—the people must have left—and so I crept slowly up to the cabin and looked inside. No one.

The sun was halfway down in the western sky, and it was growing chilly in the shade. I could see none of my friends, so I went down the western side of the ridge until I found a wide-open spot where the afternoon sun was bearing down full, warming the ground, and I moved quickly to the center of it. I looked around me and was startled to see the entire lodgepole forest—every twig of every branch on a million trees—flipping me the bird with upturned needle clusters. It was mean, violent, and oppressively threatening. They did not like me; I didn't belong. I had broken the covenant, made game of the ethic, and I was being rejected by the fold.

I burst into tears and sat down holding my knees to my chest, rocking back and forth, back and forth. Soon I wiped at my eyes and tried to focus, tried to get my head to hang onto something rational, but I was petrified, in tears, blubbering. I crossed my legs lotus style and thrust back my head, my chin toward heaven, pleading for the great power of the universe to come to my aid, to save me. Then I leaped back up, tore off my shirt, my shoes, and my pants, and retook my lotus position in just my briefs, thinking that was more humble and acquiescent before the Great Spirit Power.

I whispered out loud, then spoke audibly, finally with some force, saying, "Lord God, if you're out there, if you're real, save me! Keep me safe, don't let me die, or overdose, or lie here in my vomit until I suffocate like Jimi Hendrix." I pled and called and then pled some more for what seemed an hour.

And then I felt some peace. Peace was out there somewhere, and I knew I would find it.

I put my clothing back on and moved slowly back up the ridge, topping it just as Geoffrey entered the Stonehenge Plain from the north. He looked at me without expression, simply nodded, and went into the cabin to start the stove. I followed him in and asked where everyone was. They'd all had a fine hike up the ridge, Cris getting clear to the top of Mount Kolob. Where had I been?

I said something about getting a little turned around, and he said, "Well, you can sleep it off now," and I said, "Will I be okay?" He looked at me oddly, then with some knowing, and he said, "You'll be fine. Just sleep it off," and he went out for water or wood or a look around.

So I took a pair of goose-down sleeping bags and a length of rope up into the loft, stretched the rope back and forth across the opening several times to function like one of those protective railings on the upper level of a bunk bed, and lay down under both bags, which could serve as padding against the roof in case I started thrashing around or going out of my mind again.

Geoffrey came back in and studied my cage for a moment before leaning back over the stove. I asked him who had come visiting; was it really my mom? And he said, "No, it was Cris's mom with a couple of their old friends from Connecticut, wanting to say hi." Geoffrey had met them, explained we were all way up the mountain, so sorry, and they had left.

Again he said, "Sleep it off," and he sat down by his fire.

16

"We are none of us good enough for the world
we have, and yet we dream of heaven."
—Edward Abbey, *Appalachian Wilderness*

I HAVE MENTIONED my Catholic friend, a good kid if not a bit too devoted to the beer keg and the Jack Daniels. For some reason Paul continued to make room for me in his life even though I often criticized his faith and his heritage as a Christian. To my mind, the fruits of Christianity were well documented: the Crusades, the Inquisition, the bloody conquest of Mexico and a hundred other unfortunate peoples. I'd read *National Geographic*, and I'd had all those talks with my mom, who had read everything else. So one day, in the midst of a particularly spirited discussion with five other friends sitting around listening, Paul pulled me into his ring and hit me with something no one else had ever used: he bore a witness.

As a fourteen-year-old boy, he once fiddled around with his steady girlfriend in a camping trailer parked in front of her house. They fiddled around long enough that they ended up going all the way, right there in her folks' driveway.

Paul regretted it immediately, immeasurably. He went home tormented and for weeks afterward could hardly function. He was scared to death. When the girl missed her period two weeks later, it was more than he could handle and he nearly cracked up.

Right there in front of everyone, he told me through sixteen-year-old tears that he had pled to his God for forgiveness, for a miracle, for a way out of a trap with no apparent exit.

And the miracle happened. The girl resumed her normal cycles, and the two of them resumed the life of normal—and post-haste chaste—teenage kids.

The other kids laughed, congratulated him, went their way.

I was stunned. I had no reply, and I just sat there looking at him.

He couldn't know what I was thinking, but there was a deep stirring in my soul, hoping against all hope that what he had said could
possibly be true. That a God really lived, that He or She or It listened
and loved us—perhaps even me.

That was the first time, or maybe the second if you count my
sun-god experience on Windy Peak. But the third had been right
there on the ridge to Mount Kolob. Something had happened. I'd
been collapsing into the earth, imploding, and suddenly it had all
gone away, all the irrational fear, all the sheer panic. I had remained
concerned, but I knew as I laced up the safety net on my upper
bunk that I'd probably live. I looked out the plastic-sheeted window
at the woods turning golden in the late-afternoon sun, and I knew
there was peace out there, there was peace out there somewhere for
me.

Cris had come in some time later, and I'd asked him if he'd
mind keeping an eye on me from time to time, because I wasn't feeling real chipper. He smiled and said sure, he was feeling just fine
and the top of Mount Kolob was "absolutely far out." He'd found
the upper end of the overhead cable system that led down to the old
sawmill in the valley where Cricket and Annie had come face to face
with the elephant of their imminent demise.

I was happy for him. I really was.

I was happy for me. I was going to be okay. I didn't feel sick, I
was no longer seeing through walls and staring at the cell structure
inside my hand, and my paranoia had subsided. But as I lay there
watching the red-hot sides of the oil-can stove through my safety
net, I thought to myself, *What the hell am I doing?*

I had a good family; if my dad and I weren't close, I did know
that he cared. He was faithful to my mother, he was faithful to his
children. I had a peaceful home. Heat in the winter, water in the
taps, two-ply toilet paper, my goodness. My mother and I were
actually close—a Nebraska girl who had never tasted booze and
slapped my dad the first time he touched her above the knee, and
her disappointing hippie boy.

In all my travels, in all my dreams, I was really just going nowhere. Annie and I had pored over current and back issues of *Mother Earth News* looking for cheap land in Alaska, Arkansas, Missouri,
anywhere. Problem was, nobody anywhere was handing out free
land, especially in four-hundred-acre parcels. And free was all we
could afford. I was going nowhere, and I didn't have the financial
wherewithal to even buy my own traveling shoes.

Facing reality better than I was, Annie applied to college. Following a summer stint at J.C. Penney, where she'd had to wear not only a lady's dress but pantyhose under it just to answer phones in the catalog department, she had said, "This is what I get for thirteen years of public ed?" and started looking around. What she found was Colorado Mountain College, two hundred miles away, stuffed into the woods above Carbondale, down the road from Aspen.

But she hadn't seen it until after fall semester was already booked, so she was applying for January as a graphic arts major. I knew this as I lay there, and I said, "What about me?" I had no inkling of what college meant, or where it would get you, or what I wanted to do as a grownup. I was sick of school and classrooms and walls and algebra "teachers" who couldn't give you a single answer as to where this particular strain of institutional pour-it-in-spit-it-out sludge was used in the real world. The only vision of the future I had entertained for four years was living in a small cabin in the woods somewhere, picking my guitar and loving my girl. Here I was in the best cabin in the woods I'd ever found. The girl was leaving, and the woods wanted me out.

The boys were back from their trip. Geoffrey was starting a huge pot of chili, and Justin was outside wailing some blues on his Hohner — *You got that right, boy, blow that harp!* — so I got up, unlaced my padded room, and went down the ladder and outside to take a leak.

A waxing moon was rising in the west, sitting right on top of the dusk-rose snows of Mount Rosalie like a vanilla-dipped cherry on a strawberry snow cone. The weather was cooling but pleasant. The sky was clear. Everybody was mellow; everybody was whole. I had lived.

I hesitated, then looked at the trees. They were calm but still held for me a pose that would haunt me for years. I went back in to look for a Fig Newton or something, and Geoffrey was stirring the soup. On the shelf above him was *Be Here Now*. For a moment I almost took the book and threw it into the cook stove, but it wasn't mine and one just doesn't do that to books.

"So what did you learn?"

It was Geoffrey, and both the sound of his voice and the question he asked startled me. And pissed me off — so tutorial, so arrogant. But I believed that the ingestion or use of drugs to a seeker always resulted in a message; the seeker doesn't do it just to get high. So I took his question seriously. Yet perhaps it was premature.

"I don't know."

"You have a bad trip?"

"It sucked. Most of it."

"Hmm. That happens." And then again, "What did you learn?"

What I had learned was that Geoffrey fancied himself a sort of Don Juan, a teacher, always a challenger of the first thought that came to one's mind, and frequently a challenger of all the others. So I didn't give him one to challenge.

"I have no idea."

Monday morning Geoffrey and his sister left for New York to visit friends. Cris and Justin, being a year behind me in school, had that commitment to keep. Annie was still answering phones; my dog poop scooping gig was over. (The dogs still pooped, but with the arrival of fall Cliff didn't care about the lawns anymore.) So, with my blind but smiling collie I had the cabin to myself and plenty of time to, as Kerouac once said, "monostate and meditate." It went okay during the day. I read, I wandered, and I wondered. Uriah joined me in all but the reading. An oft-contemplated solo up Mount Kolob intimidated me. The west side of the ridge scared me to death.

I'd go up and sit on the cabin roof, just staring to the east for hours, out over the Great Plains. Where Annie lived. And beyond that, Missouri. Or to the south—Lost Park, Windy Peak, the ponderosa high prairies around Woodland Park, and beyond that—and beyond my line of sight—the Sand Dunes, Raton, and New Mexico. The Lands of My Pleasant Wandering. But at dusk or before, we headed home each night, usually before, and I'd just play my guitar for hours, turning the tips of my left-hand fingers into calluses an eighth-inch thick.

Finally, about midweek, I could again sit on the cabin roof and turn to the west, letting my eye carefully trace the horizon to the right, from Windy Peak and up the slope of Rosalie to Mount Evans, its bulk forming the only—but total—impediment to seeing most of the way to Grand Junction and the mighty Colorado River.

Cris came up a couple of evenings, and we talked freely of my bad trip with the microdot. He had weathered a few paranoiac moments of his own, he said, especially when his mother showed up, her sharp crow-cackle voice zipping up and down the mountainside. In general, it had been all he had hoped for. But he wouldn't be doing it again.

"A little too heavy for my tastes," he confessed. "There were definitely times when I wasn't in control. Not a great feeling. Coulda dug having some Pink Floyd up here, though!"

"You know that's not all the book is about," I told him then.

"What book?"

"*Be Here Now*." I reached over to the shelf for it. "It's really pretty inspiring. This Ram Dass gets into some pretty heavy trips. But he has a very inspiring message."

"I thought you didn't like the trip," Cris said pointedly.

"I didn't, but that's not what I'm referring to." I then said, "He even quotes Christ, I think. He calls him a great guru." I'd read that kind of thing a couple of times lately, in books coming from way outside the traditional Christian perspective, a perspective that always seemed so pompous, so inflexible and exclusive. I couldn't reconcile the fact that every Christian told you Christianity was the truth, the whole truth, and nothing but the truth, and yet every Christian I knew had a different set of realities, and they all rejected everyone else's. They especially rejected the non-Christians. The good Christians had the Muslims and the American Indians and the Hindus and the Buddhists frying in hell without even asking them what they had in mind.

That kind of doctrinal arrogance, that kind of absolute, immutable cancellation of the eternal rights or value or potential of other humans, which had been put in effect all over the globe, just blew cinders out my afterburners.

"I ever tell you I was raised a Christian Scientist?" Cris asked.

I laughed at him. "Yeah, right, you and Dr. Demento, physicist of the absurd."

"No man, Christian Science. It's a religion. A church. First Church of Christ, Scientist. My whole family is. It's mostly in New England, I think." And then I remembered something about Kerouac's friend, Philip Whalen, having once been a Christian Scientist, although he had eventually abandoned it as "theologically a very vague position" and opted for Buddhism. But when Cris said, "You wanna read about Christ? I'll bring up a copy," I said sure.

After all, even Ram Dass had said the dude was cool.

Cris looked at the book a while longer, then said he had to go to work, Friday night down at the Highlander. Now he was cooking instead of washing dishes.

"You staying up tonight?"

"Yeah."

"You want me to take Uriah down, or is he okay up here with you?"

"Nah, go ahead and take him down," I said. "He gets kinda nervous up here at night." He liked to lie near the fat dog at night and bark at the squirrels first thing in the morning, and there weren't a heck of a lot of squirrels at the cabin's altitude.

So Cris took Uriah and headed off down the road, promising to be back up midmorning tomorrow.

I just sat and watched the stove glow red, the wash water in the bean pot starting to bubble. I grabbed the little bottle of dish soap and squirted in a dab, just enough to cut the grease but not enough to offend the woods when I poured it out over the pine needles.

And that's when the roof started coming apart, something up there, invisible, evicting.

As I grabbed my lantern and my rascal beater and headed off down the road, not fifteen minutes behind a good ride with a friend who cared and a dog who loved me, I thought to myself: *There it is again. Something's trying to kill me.*

17

WITH ANNIE WORKING and Justin and Cris still in school, I spent the rest of that winter in relative hibernation on the mountain—reading, playing guitar, and reading some more. I had come to love silence, or the gentle rustling of the woods, more than any other sound. In fact, to one raised in wilderness, silence is really a misnomer, a lie. I suppose the city dweller at first thinks the woods or open prairies are silent, devoid of music and life and nuance and clandestiny, but given any time and acceding any degree of patience he will learn that the wilderness plays a full-bodied symphony any time of day or night, with more range and color and instrumentation than the craziest city street—as Thoreau put it, "the finest imaginable sweet musical hum." What is more, and more important, he will begin to hear his own mind, the messages it sends and the questions it wants answers to. It might even find the answers.

That winter my mind began a nearly incessant conversation: What is life all about? What is real? Do I have a purpose? Am I the only consciousness that really exists, everything and everybody else serving merely as props in my play? And if so, why? This particular one really pissed off Cris, my suggesting he was just a figment of my imagination.

But the questions continued, and the answers were few. I had no idea why I was a walking, breathing consciousness on the earth, but I renewed my conviction that I'd best use my time intelligently, devotedly, lest the Big Answer arrive and find me wanting.

I reread *Diet for a Small Planet* and discovered E. F. Schumacher and his "Small Is Beautiful" philosophy, which melded admirably with Thoreau's own philosophy that "a man is rich in proportion to the number of things which he can afford to let alone." I read the *Farm Book* over and over, wondering if that environment was really what Annie and I would be comfortable in. At the top of our minds was simply the population of the place, the whole Magic-Bus-everybody-together thing. It was its own city, in a way, like the experience in Missouri. And like Missouri, it was right in the heart of the old racist South. We were Pacifist Zen Vegetarian Great-Spirit No-Boundaries Mountain Hippies, after all; what would it really be like in a place that had once treated humans as property and still acted that way half the time? And then there was the open marriage matter, or at least a social construct that was still defining itself at Summertown—I didn't want anybody but Annie, and she didn't want anybody but me. We were simply not available to other creative configurations.

I was suddenly living at some sort of arm's-length impasse with the woods, glad that it was winter but not at all sure where I stood on the planet that birthed and bred me, or how tall, or how welcome. One day, out of the blue, while I was just sitting in the afternoon sun on the silent road pleading for the woods to speak, the wind to stir, the Great Spirit Mother or Father or whoever ran the joint to do something please dammit, to let me know I was yet a valued soul on the earth, a gray jay landed five feet away, walked right over to me, jumped up onto my head, and sat there a while, pecking lightly, pulling my hair. Then it flew off.

And I thought of Kerouac and the little bird who one time blessed his ugly stay in a Los Angeles railroad yard, and I said, "I'll be all right."

I finished Geoffrey's copy of *Be Here Now* and found myself surprised throughout at all the Ram Dass–praised gurus quoted in that book, including Lao Tzu and Jesus, the latter of whom he quoted extensively. At least, he attributed the quotes to Jesus—I wouldn't have known an authentic Bible verse from the photo captions in an Ice Capades program. And then there was a sketch toward the end of the book, on page CVII (107) of the paper-bag pages, a close-up of Jesus getting what looked like railroad spikes driven through his hands or wrists. I'd heard that part; I lived in America, after all. But in this telling the artist had modeled a look of peace on his face, and Ram Dass had claimed one further attribution, Jesus pleading for his killers with "Father, forgive them, for they know not what they do."

I wondered aloud about that one winter night, Annie two hundred miles away now in Carbondale. Cris and I were sitting on his south deck watching the moon ride low over Pikes Peak sixty miles to the south. We were just sipping Lemon Zinger from mugs and waiting for the moon show to hit its stride. It was probably 9:00 P.M. with an air temperature of around fifteen degrees. Living at this altitude for very long, you became immune to that kind of thing for at least short periods of time—say, thirty minutes. Also, it had been one of those perfect standard-issue Colorado winter days when it reached maybe sixty degrees in a cloudless blue sky at around 2:00 P.M. It would hit probably thirty below by three in the morning, but right now the heat was still emanating from the solid log walls of Cris's house.

Cris said, "You know, I was raised a Christian Scientist, and—"

"You've told me."

"And I'm really starting to believe that Jesus is the—what, the master teacher? The main guy?"

"The guru of gurus?" I offered.

"Yeah."

I waited a few moments, trying to listen to my own head, which was sort of grumbling, and said, "You serious? With all you've read and everyone you've seen quoted?"

"Yeah. I really do."

"Why, 'cause you grew up with it?

He was sober, serious. "No, man, because—" But he couldn't find it. So he turned on me: "You say you're wondering too. Why? You didn't grow up with anything but Eddie Arnold and the Tijuana Brass."

I shrugged. "That's what's interesting about it. Here I am reading *Buddhist Bojangles and His Peppy Dog Skip Go to India* and I end up wondering if Jesus Christ is the guru of gurus. It's really a trip."

He swallowed the last of his tea. "Let's go in. Good night for some Strawbs."

So we went in and down to his room. He put *Hero and Heroine* on the turntable and cued up "Out in the Cold." Then he pulled a copy of *Science and Health with Key to the Scriptures* from his bed. He'd been reading.

And so we started holding regular mental jam sessions like that for a couple of weeks—Strawbs, Mary Baker Eddy, Pink Floyd, a bowl or three of our own fall harvest—mountain grown, the richest kind—Mary Baker Eddy, Ram Dass and Uriah Heep, Mary Baker

Eddy, another bowl. It was fanciful writing, but to me Christian Science sounded just like Ram Dass–Kerouac Buddhism with Jesus thrown in: the one Big Sky Mind thing, all of us just anonymous, amorphous parts of one great big cosmic omniscience.
Kerouac:

Life is like a dream
You only think it's real
Cuz you're born a sucker
For that kind of deal.

Ram Dass:

No Mind, Never Matter,
Never Mind, No Matter.

Mary Baker Eddy:

Mind is all and matter is naught.

Matter, or body, is but a false concept of mortal mind. Mortal mind
and body . . . must be destroyed by immortal mind.

Even the *Tao Te Ching* taught that "misfortune comes from having a body." I often thought to myself, *This beautiful world, this mountain, this sacred winter night and I'm supposed to believe it's all a dream? An illusion? Something to overcome?* And to overcome so I could become part of the One Big Cosmic Consciousness, pain and individuality and death and golden lupine and mountains and love and French kissing, none of them real, all just illusions on the road to heaven, which was starting to sound kinda like one big Ultimate Blah Blessing.

But if it was right and proper, count me in. I just wanted to be kind and good and pick flowers and hug trees and look off into the purple distance from a comfortable rock. But convinced of the theology or not, understanding it or not, this Christ seemed to lodge in my throat—that one thing: Christ. I couldn't get around him.

As we read, Lao Tzu and Ram Dass and Black Elk and Don Juan faded and this Jesus started occupying my thoughts like none of the others ever had. Thoughts of Jesus seemed to swell in my mind. Although I knew very little of him through personal experience or study, every citation any other writer made of him was one espousing love, kindness, the gentle way. And I wondered aloud, "Why have so many wars been fought in the name of this guy?" And Cris said the same thing Ram Dass was saying, that perhaps most of his "followers" had in fact never gotten it right; they'd misunderstood or improvised on their own. That's exactly what Justin had said too: the "Christians" were misreading their own religion. My academic exposure to Jesus was the historical context my mother had laid out, warning me it was clearly too fantastical and outlandish for a rational, educated son of Ireland by way of New York, Wisconsin, and Iowa. But certainly not prohibited, if I was of a mind.

End of January I hitchhiked over to Colorado Mountain College, two hundred miles at an elevation averaging over nine thousand feet, hitting twelve thousand at the Eisenhower Tunnel and eleven thousand at Vail Pass. I got a ride over Loveland Pass at the tunnel, but I had to stand for thirty-five minutes on the top of Vail Pass when a pair of mid-twenties city kids pulling a flatbed trailer full of snowmobiles let me out at their favorite place to go screw up the snow, pollute the air, scare anything that breathed, run over rabbits, and scar the land. Not that I told them what I thought; I just said thanks for the ride and walked upwind before sticking my thumb back in the air.

I finally stepped out of a VW bus at the CMC dorms at around three-thirty in the afternoon. Annie was in class, but her roommate, Pam, a Chicagoan with long silky brown hair falling over a white turtleneck sweater that was doing a poor job of concealing breasts the size of Cook County, let me in and asked me if I wanted a cup of tea or something. The room was two beds, a hotplate, and a full-wall closet.

Sure, I was a bit nipped.

"Don't you have a car?" she asked, incredulously.

"I don't even have a license," I told her, but I was giving it some thought.

Pam was busy packing up her sleeping bag and some toiletries. Going somewhere. I took a seat on what must have been Annie's bed, as I recognized the quilt.

"We knew you were coming," she said, "but no one was sure just when."

"Yeah, that's the nature of hitching," I replied as I watched her move. Beautiful. Lovely.

In a minute she finished packing and sat down on the other bed, facing me. Smiling. Perfect teeth. Annie had told me she was from Chicago, moneyed and well traveled. But she looked right at home here on this little campus in the middle of pinyon woods three miles from the paved highway: Vasque hiking boots, faded jeans—really tight ones—and that wonderful turtleneck. She looked marvelous, but I changed my focus to the posters on the walls: Ansel Adams, Susan Polis Schutz, and a photograph of a kitten hanging by his front paws from a wire, the caption reading *Hang in there, baby!* Musta been a college thing.

I had never been untrue to Annie. Since our first kiss in the summer snows of '74, I had never touched another girl or even seriously considered it. The prevailing thought: my dad was faithful to my mom, and that was the only kind of relationship I wanted in my own life. The temptation to jump Pam and wrestle her under the rug was not an unknown temptation, but I refused to let it go any farther and got up to put away some highway gear in my pack, just as Annie walked in.

She came to me quickly, hugged me close, and then planted a little peck on my lips. Discreet. Modest.

And then Pam grabbed her stuff and headed for the door.

"Well, you two have fun. Good to meet you, Kit."

And out she went.

So then I jumped Annie, dropping her back right on the bed and going for her neck. She giggled and gave a little, but then she was up, pushing me away. I toyed with her for another half-minute, but she was serious. She even said no.

"What's going on?" I asked, but she just changed the subject and said, "Come see the coolest college campus in America. Bring your pack."

So I followed her out, wondering. The campus was in fact very cool, just a handful of little buildings, most of them round, surrounded by juniper-pinyon woods. On the far west end of things, a one-hundred-foot depression, round like the buildings and probably their inspiration, occupied much of a small wooded hillside. Jumbled basalt lined its edges, the boulders poking their heads through the snow and reminding me, somehow, of my Stonehenge Plain back on Windy Peak. I said, "Maybe it's an old sacred site of the Indians." Annie said that everyone called it the crater, but no one really knew whether it was meteor-formed or not. Then I saw the tipi. A big one.

Annie whistled in warning, and out came a guy, long hair, beard, wearing jeans and flannel. He was smiling and walked right toward us. His name was Wayne, and that's where I'd be staying nights. I was very welcome.

Once I'd stashed my gear while Wayne took a breather from carving a flute out of river birch, Annie and I headed back to the student union, where she introduced me to everyone in sight. I was still her man, and she was very pleased with me, but along the way she'd explained that staying in her room just wouldn't look good and could maybe get her kicked out. I said I doubted that, look at all these hippies, and then told her I hadn't planned to you-know-what anyway.

She said, "That's not the point, baby. It doesn't look good," and then she started to cry, just before we got to the little cafeteria. I said, "Let's talk about it after. I'm starving."

So later she tells me the way things are: she loves me, but she's had a lot of time to think, and our relationship has got to change. I said, "What's with Wayne? How good a friend is he?" Kinda frosty like. And she said, "Don't even go there. I'm your girl, baby, and you're my man, but we're just not living like we should be." And I said, "Heck of a time to fill me in."

But that night till late we talked in her room. I held her tight, she kissed me deep, and I said, "You're right, dammit, I think we've made a lot of goofs." And she said, "But not about us." And I said, "Oh, baby, not about us. I really love you."

And I went alone to the tipi by moonlight, a nice little walk in the woods.

What Wayne had was an eighteen-footer, hand-built to Northern Cheyenne specs, except it had a wood floor. It was a warm night, and in the morning Wayne and I chatted for a good hour until he left for class. Then I just sat outside in the morning sun, lotus position, breathing in through my nose, out through my mouth, and then leaned back against the tipi and absently fingered my on-the-road copy of *The Dharma Bums* and wondered, *Is this the end of Summertown and Alaska and Canada?* And then I remembered, *Oh, yeah, there's always marriage.* And I thought, *Oh, good Lord, I'm seventeen years old!* So I wondered some more.

I opened the book haphazardly and looked down at page thirty-nine and read:

Colleges [are] nothing but grooming schools for the middle-class non-identity which usually finds its perfect expression on the outskirts of the campus in rows of well-to-do houses with lawns and television sets in each living room with everybody looking at the same thing and thinking the same thing at the same time while the Japhies [Japhy Ryder] of the world go prowling in the wilderness to hear the voice crying in the wilderness, to find the ecstasy of the stars, to find the dark mysterious secret of the origin of faceless wonderless crapulous civilization.

Having no idea at that point what *crapulous* meant, wondering in fact if Kerouac had made it up, I said to myself out loud, "Man, I like the way that sounds." The whole paragraph. And, on my way back home twenty-two hours later, I wondered what to do about the whole crapulous deal.

By the third week of the quarter Annie had switched her major from graphic arts to outdoor education, the wilderness training track. Her twice weekly letters to Paradise Mountain told me of cross-country ski journeys, snowshoeing clinics, rock-climbing seminars, about beautiful sunsets and walks at dawn and how she finally had a place to call her own, kind of, in the woods, and she didn't need to worry about getting kicked out, the rent had been paid and she was getting straight A's. She always had.

In one long letter she told me about how she really had thought she was going to die on Paradise Mountain twenty months earlier in that big summer snowstorm and especially how she thought Cricket was going to die. Cricket even told her, "I'm just going to lie here, the snow swirling all around, it's very peaceful, I always thought I'd be scared, you go on without me." And Annie shook her awake and said, "Get your butt vertical and help me think," and then each of them told the other for two hours straight—seeing nothing but white and tree trunks—just put one foot in front of the other and move your ass, girl, or we're gonna die right here right now in the summer freakin' snowstorm woods of Colorado. She never felt closer to God in her life and started wondering, *Is he real? How much does he love me?* And then they found the road and the cabin, and I came down out of the swirls to take them home and make her a cup of Red Zinger tea.

But she didn't tell me everything.

• • •

So I just said hmm to myself and sat on my mountain. Cris and I were halfway through *Science and Health*. Justin joined in for a while, but it just didn't click. When the snow began to retreat, he was going to live in his twelve-foot tipi and follow the Native American way.

So I sat on my mountain and wrote:

I don't really know, babe, just what I need
A guide or a lover or pity.
But I do have some pictures
All stuck in my head
Showing me how it must be.

Old cabins and moonlight
On a backdrop of pine
Snow falling slowly and clean.
A smile every morning, gentle words every night
With a lady who'll make my heart sing.

And Annie wrote me back, better stuff than mine:

at the height of my emotions
    I loved you
at the height of my soul
    I touched you —
and you touched me

And:

    soaring —
never darting
never stopping
    as i ascend higher,
inspirations and dreams
        before me
love and beauty
        beside me
i have nothing to fear
        nothing to hide from
for i have you.

Never much punctuation, usually only lower-case letters, Annie the epitome of humble, always in real creative layout on the page, and I'd think *Man, she's an honest-to-Robert-Frost poet, but it sure wouldn't fit to music.*

Then the first week of March Cris told me he was going to Israel. His uncle back in Connecticut ran a Christian Science school that Cris had attended as a child—something I'd never heard about before—and he was leading a tour to the Holy Land. That's what Cris called it—*the Holy Land*—and I felt a strong stirring to see the place too. I was feeling a serious need for some sort of pilgrimage. To someone. Something. Somewhere. I wanted answers, and I wanted them real soon.

As it turned out, for spring break Cris went halfway around the world, Annie went halfway to heaven, and I went all the way.

18

"How many a man has dated a new era
in his life from the reading of a book."
—Henry David Thoreau, *Walden*

HERE'S HOW IT HAPPENED, after all: Sometime on the evening of March 20, 1976, Carlos Castañeda, Baba Ram Dass and the Mormon prophet George Albert Smith met in my bedroom. Oh, they never knew about it, of course.

Until now.

It was a Saturday morning in 1951 when my grandpa took in a trade at his car lot and gas station in Gering, Nebraska. Under the front seat was a Book of Mormon, copyright 1948 by George Albert Smith, Trustee in Trust for The Church of Jesus Christ of Latter-day Saints. Never one to pass up a freebie — having survived the Depression, after all — he stuck it on a shelf. Three years later, when my mother, then eighteen, moved to Denver with a college scholarship, she took it with her.

Twenty-two years after that, I was sitting on a couch in the front room of a red-brick suburban house in Lakewood, Colorado, preparing to apologize to a lady whose life I had terrorized for two years as the long-haired hippie lover of her wavering Latter-day Saint daughter.

Just me and her. Me and her and the click of the clock. We were equally terrified, but I was meaning what I said and so I said it all.

I said, "You know I really love Annie."

And she was meaning what she said, so she inhaled deeply and gave it all she had. I could see a masterful amount of courage coming out of her eyes. She said, "I think we believe you, but you have to understand . . ."

"And we want to do what's right," I continued. "What's honorable." I really think I used that word.

She hesitated. Then, "Well, I think you both know . . . Annie certainly knows that there are proper ways of doing things. Love means . . ."

Then I hesitated. This had to be perfectly honest. "Pardon me, Mrs. Hawk, I don't believe that she *has* known," I said meekly, "but I know that she wants to. We want to do what's right. We're committed to that. We're committed to each other." I remember my eyes brimming with tears then, although I was a self-sufficient mountain man who'd slept in a cave and caught a trout with a stick, and here I was sitting in front of a mere suburban woman. "We're just a little confused. We don't know what's real or what's right. We just know we want each other, and we want it to be right."

Then she got a little teary, and so I began to open up. I told her how I'd been reading about one Jesus, and I understood she knew something about him because they had pictures of him on the walls. I confessed that the texts I was reading were volumes on Zen and the Tao and metaphysics and Native American thought, which were a little more to my tastes than the Bible, but even these referred to this Jerusalem Jesus as the Great Prophet, the Master Teacher, admired and honored by the spiritually inclined throughout the world and across the centuries. And I told her that every time I read of Jesus — even in the midst of all the other thoughts and philosophies — I felt myself wanting to know him somehow. I just couldn't get him out of my head.

She sat quietly, and I could see that she was shocked. Finally she asked, "Have you told Annie?"

I said, "About Jesus? No. She knows I'm looking, though. I've been looking forever. But no, I haven't mentioned the Jesus part. I don't know how she'd respond to that, and I don't want to lose her."

She hesitated again. There were definite tears in her eyes, and she said, "I think she'd take it okay. You ought to tell her."

And I said, "Okay, I will." And then I told her, sitting there on her sofa, that I was sorry. I wanted to change my life. Annie and I had modified our relationship. A lot. We wanted to set things straight. Could she forgive me? Us?

She did more than that. She got even.

In what I would someday understand to be one of the bravest things any Mormon will ever do in this life, she asked me if I would be willing to speak to a couple of Mormon missionaries. I said "Who?" and she said, "I don't know. Let me make a call."

But then she just sat there, awaiting my permission, I think. For a couple of moments I looked for a way out. But the course of honor was to see the thing through, and so I said yes, I'd be happy to do that.

She excused herself, went into the kitchen, and made a phone call. I sat in the living room quietly, surveying the walls, wondering what in the world I'd gotten myself into. After a few minutes she came back in, then she went back out, then she came back in with a small plate of Oreos. I took one, and not a minute later the phone rang.

It was for me.

On the other end of the line was a very friendly, cool guy named Reefer, Elmer Reefer, or something like that, and he wanted to know if he and his "companion" could come up and see me that night, and where did I live? I told him Paradise Mountain, and he said, "Just give us directions. We'll be there at seven."

So I went back into the living room, finished a couple of Oreos, and said I'd better hit the road, it was a couple of hours home. Mrs. Hawk said, "Just listen to them. Just listen with an open heart—don't make any judgments for a while." And then she said thanks for coming down and actually shook my hand. Lady who'd probably wanted to walk the dog over my grave, let him pause a spell at the headstone, shook my hand.

When I got home a couple of hours later, I asked my mom if we didn't have one of those "Books of the Mormons" somewhere in our big library. She said we did, an old one her dad had found under a car seat years before. She told me she'd read it once, and then she found it for me. I went upstairs and started to read.

During spring break at CMC each year, outdoor ed students took "Mountain O," or Mountain Orientation. It's a grueling expedition through the high Rockies west of Aspen ending in a spectacular climb of one of Colorado's most challenging fourteeners, Capital Peak. Unlike Colorado's tallest, Mount Elbert (14,331 feet), which had actually been summited by a guy on an old bike, Capital Peak is sheer granite, the final three hundred feet to the summit a knife-edge ridge so narrow you rip your pants, since everyone is roped together and scooting inch by nervous inch on their fannies, your legs dangling down opposite twelve-hundred-foot super slides on either side. You screw up in the middle of the rope, you just get nauseated, someone straightens you out, and you move on. You screw

up on the ends of the rope chain, you play pendulum with your face
in an arc across the granite wall, back and forth until enough people
can get a grip and the strength, their arms and legs shaking, maybe
getting nauseated themselves, to get you back up to the knife edge.
One of those suckers makes guys like me get a stomach ache
just because it's there and eighteen-year-old kids from Cincinnati
and Petaluma cry like babies and wish they'd never heard of this
damn college or this program or this entire damn state, can we go
home now and why does my head hurt?

So at the meadow just below timberline, 11,500 feet, where the
trees suffocate and quit growing even as shrubs and the real climbing starts, the Mountain O instructor, Dave McAllister, says, "Do
you mind if we begin with a prayer?" Like he always did, the kids
used to it. Only this time he asked Annie to say it.

Annie had met Dave the day she changed majors. He ran the
outdoor education program. She sat across the desk from him, one
of the kindest, most gracious men she'd ever met, and thought there
was something weird going on here. Dave was clean-cut, clean-
shaven, in the very midst of a very free-spirited mountain hideaway
with pot plants in every dorm window and an acoustic guitar in
every classroom. They met again a few days later, after a few days
of classes, mapping out her course of instruction, and Annie said to
herself, *There's something even weirder* — certain words he used, certain phrases, just like at home. So it was Annie who called the third
interview, just walking in out of the cold and saying, "Dave, I gotta
talk. Can we close the door?"

And Dave said please.

Annie just stared at him for several moments, Dave smiling his
gentle smile, and she said, "I'm a Mormon" and started to cry.

And Dave said, "I know. I appreciate you coming in."

Annie asked him, "What, did my parents call?" And Dave said,
"No, I just knew. But I sense you're not entirely comfortable with it
at the moment."

"You're one too, aren't you?" she asked.

And he said, "I am. How can I help?"

And she burst into Big Tears.

Here she had come two hundred miles to get away from everything in her past — parents, the Mormon religion, even me in a lot of
ways — to start fresh, to start clean, to look down an open road with
no lines, no signs, and no stoplights and say, *What is real, what do I
want, what is right, and how can I find it?* And this perfect and gentle

man who was supposed to direct her life for the next two years was head of the regional Mormon missionary force.

She told him everything. She cried all over the place. She even cursed once or twice and said, "Why do I feel so lost and so bad, and why is it so damn hard just to grow up and find peace and love and a course of life that fills your heart with gladness?" And he said, "Why don't you come to dinner, meet my family. We'll talk."

By the time they stood in that meadow under Capital Peak, Annie had been through it all. She'd sat there on the McAllisters' couch and taken the missionary lessons, just like an investigator because that's what she was. She'd gone out with missionaries in Glenwood Springs as they taught others. She'd done everything but pray in public or acknowledge to any of her CMC crowd that she was a Mormon, that she was converted, that she was *back*. Or tell me.

And then Dave asked if she'd pray for that group as they began their ascent of one of the great and awesome mountains of America. She looked at him sharply for some moments. He offered only that same gentle smile he always displayed. Then he bowed his head and waited. Annie continued to stare at him for some moments, but then she couldn't help but turn to watch as twenty-three mostly freewill hippie kids removed their hats and Carlos Santana kerchiefs, bowed their heads, and waited for her to pray.

All the fountains of the soul burst forth, and she prayed then, not a long one but as real and as deep and as knowing as any prayer ever offered. As she blubbered through her few lines, she suddenly knew that God was real, that he lived, that he loved her immensely and wanted her back. The feelings flooded through her, and she could hardly speak. She said amen and remained staring at the ground for several moments, alpine forget-me-knots blurring blue all over her boots. Several kids touched her shoulder as they passed on their way toward the high peak of their purpose and said, "That was beautiful," and one girl, crying, wanted a hug. Annie finally looked up and found Dave staring at her from thirty feet away. His own tears were running freely, and he was smiling. He knew exactly what had happened. He had been there himself.

So when the doorbell rang at 7:31 P.M.—I knew they'd get lost a couple of times before finding our house—I could hear it all the way from my third-floor room. I knew my mother would get it. I had explained who was coming, Mormon missionaries, and she had said,

"Hmm, I'll let 'em in but your dad and I aren't interested," and so I just waited at the top of my stairs.

I first saw them, two clean-cut twenty-year-old boys, from directly overhead. The one in front was wearing a navy-blue suit with pinstripes, the other a solid gray. Both wore Florsheim wingtips. At the upper landing, Pinstripe offered his hand and said, "Hey, Kit, I'm Elder Reefer, and this is my companion, Elder Edwards."

"You're both named Elder?"

"Nah, the Elder part is just a title, like mister or minister, or whatever. It's our missionary title."

And then I said, "Reefer, is that real? That's really your last name?" And he said yup, and then yuk-yuk-yuk, he laughed with me.

And I said far out. I had honestly been expecting a longhair, a hepcat whose nickname told the whole story: Kit, this is Reefer. Reefer, Kit. Wink wink. But these guys were right out of CIA school. The experience of the last few hours served to temper my disappointment, but I did swallow one final dose of *What have I gotten myself into?*

So we went into my room, where I'd already placed a couple of desk chairs, and my sister stepped into the room and said, "Mind if I listen?" So we all took a seat, me on the corner of the bed because I was fresh out of chairs, and off we went: Mormon discussion number one.

I listened as Elder Steven Reefer taught me about Joseph Smith, the Book of Mormon, and what the Mormons call the First Vision. It's a story of angels from heaven, angels visiting the earth, speaking to man, revealing themselves in actual form and body. Speaking in actual voices. I knew that what they were saying was true. I hadn't been there, but I absolutely knew it, it was inside, I could feel it, and I longed with all my soul for such a vision.

And then suddenly Elder Reefer was asking me if I would be willing to repent of my sins and follow this Jesus by being baptized into The Church of Jesus Christ of Latter-day Saints that next Saturday, six days away. Elder Edwards, a farm kid from Utah not long in the field, was rocked up on the back legs of his chair, his hands cradling his head, trying to look cool, casual, and very at ease. When I said yes, that was the desire of my heart, he went over backwards, right into the wall.

Then Reefer asked Michelle the same question, and she said, "Sure, why not?"

Once Edwards rearranged himself, both of them blushing, Elder Reefer taught us the pattern of Mormon prayer, how one simply opens his heart and humbly talks to God. Simple. Direct. No beads or prescribed positions or prayer books. He said, "You just talk to God and tell him what you feel and ask him for what you need and ask him what you want to ask. Ask him if what we've said is true." And then he asked me to pray.

I said, "Me?" and he said, "You. Please." And then he got down on his knees, Edwards following, closed his eyes, bowed his head, and waited.

I was just a skinny little teenage hippie kid with a funny name. I'd stolen some shotgun shells from a 7-Eleven when I was twelve so we could drain the black powder, make a pipe bomb, and stick it under a truck muffler, and boy, did we fly that thing. I'd lived wrong with a girl and smoked dope and used bad words and even put a quart of ice cream in my pack at a City Market in Durango one time and walked out without paying, and it all flooded in, hot and shameful and in full-living color. I had not a single claim to honor or fame or stature in the world, and even the grownup hippies were cutting their hair by then.

But Reefer and Edwards just stayed there, their heads bowed, in complete reverence, and I said in my heart *Oh, my god!* And he said, *Speak to me, boy, come back, I'm here. I'm real and I love you* and I could almost hear a real voice and I kneeled down and I said, "Oh, god, if you're real, let me know, I want to know, and I want to change and I want to know if what these boys are telling me is true, they asked *me* to pray, and I'm really sorry for everything I've ever done, and I didn't know some of it was wrong, I just didn't know, I really didn't, but some I did and I'm really sorry and I've been looking for this forever and I wanna come back, amen."

And then I stayed there on my knees blubbering and Reefer did too, his hand on my shoulder, and then Edwards got back down and said sorry and started to cry himself. And we just stayed there for a while.

Then finally we got up and shook hands and Reefer said, "Can we come back Tuesday," and I said please.

By late that week, I believe it was as late as Friday, I had worked up enough guts to call Annie—two hundred miles away—and tell her I was joining, quite willingly and determinedly, the very church she hated, the very one I had accompanied her in taunting, boycotting, and bad-mouthing for two years. Would she come to my baptism and maybe still love me?

She said, "Oh, baby, I am so happy; I have come to know for myself that Mormonism is the true way of God. Let me find a ride— I wouldn't miss this for anything." She had been fretting and crying for two solid weeks about how she would tell me and what it would do to our dreams of forever. She'd asked Dave, and Dave had said if Kit is really worth it, he'll take you as you are and maybe even listen. And if not, move along, he's not worth it.

So Saturday morning, after I'd completed the discussions—seven of them—and my first reading of the Book of Mormon, Elder Reefer called me by name, said a prayer, and immersed me in a big tile bathtub of chlorinated city water in a Mormon stake center in Lakewood, and I became the world's newest Latter-day Saint, six weeks before my eighteenth birthday.

When I came out of the font, Mr. Hawk was waiting. He came to me nervously, then pulled me into a hug and said the exact same thing I said: "I don't know what to say."

And I had no idea what to *do*, either.

19

> "I had raged purely among rocks and
> snow . . . raged and been a fool when
> I shoulda loved and repented."
> —Kerouac, *Desolation Angels*

I'D HAD ONLY FIVE and a half days to learn how to be Mormon, so I
didn't come in with a full doctrinal deck, so to speak. Take marijuana, for instance.

My new pastor was what they call a branch president, because
he presided over a branch, or a small congregation. Bigger con-
gregations are called wards, and the guy who runs one of those is
called a bishop. In fact, the Silver Creek branch of The Church of Jesus Christ of Latter-day Saints was so small in 1976 that most of the
members called it, very fondly, a twig. So one day about three weeks
in, my branch president, Raymond Goode, had me in for a personal
interview. I was learning that Latter-day Saints are in for interviews
a lot; a good shepherd knows his sheep.

President Goode, who pursued a career as a pilot and served in
his church role without pay, as do all other local Mormon clergy, had
been kind to me from the first day. As I heard it years later from one
of his counselors, Ernie Davis, the first time I walked into a church
sacrament meeting between my two missionaries, Ray Goode had
said, "Go back and shake his hand. I've gotta start the meeting in
a minute," and Ernie had said, "Oh my goodness, do you think I'll
catch anything?"

So anyway, Ray Goode had me in, I supposed, to congratulate
me on my new haircut—sixteen inches to find my earlobes, Graham
Nash's lyrical scolding echoing in my mind: "Almost cut my hair!"
My mother, who I'd asked to whack it off, was quite fond of it herself. But what he really did was ask me a lot of questions: Any problems with liquor? No. With tobacco? No. Did I have a girlfriend,

and were we having any sort of sexual relations? I said, "Is French kissing okay?" And he said, "Is that all?" And I said, "Yes, sir, it is," completely honest, and he said, "Well, be careful, but I think you're all right."
    Then he said, "Marijuana?"
    And I said, "They never mentioned that one."
    And he said, "Whoa."

He took care of the one little piece of the baptismal interview no one else had thought to cover—it was 1976, and I had hair halfway to my butt, and no one thought to ask me about pot?—and I went home from church with a decision to make. I went straight up to my room—my dad saw me go by and laughed, "Hell, I ain't ever seen the kid in a tie!—and went right to my stash and pulled my favorite pipe-cane from the closet and headed outside with a match.
    I wandered out onto the south slope of our little knob of Paradise Mountain. It was mid-April but the slope was already completely clear in the warm Colorado sun. I found a peaceful little nook under a leafless aspen tree, sat down in a lotus position with my peace pipe, loaded her up, and stared out at the southern memories of my life. They were good, but I'd been heading right to this spot for half my years, maybe all of them. I looked at the little bag of homegrown, at my beautiful pipe—a dark walnut-stained length of lodgepole with a perfect snakehead bulge at the upper end, the place where I drilled out the half-inch bowl and then cured it with honey and concealed it with a stopper made from the branch of another tree—and said to myself, "Well, well. The end of an era."
    Then I packed the bowl, lit it, stood up, and took one toke over the line to Sweet Jesus and each of the cardinal directions of the compass, broke the peace pipe over my knee, and threw the pieces into the woods. Then I scattered the remains of the bag into the dormant skeletons of golden lupine and green gentian and candytuft and spring beauty and went back inside to read the Book of Mormon and listen to the Ozark Mountain Daredevils.
    I never smoked pot again.

President Goode had told me something else after, "Man, you can't smoke marijuana now, you turkey." (He always said "turkey" in comradely conversation, and only those who had never smoked it called it "marijuana" in the first place.) He said, "You gotta start over. This is like a rebirth, your baptism and all. A second chance.

A new beginning." Then he opened his Bible and found a pair of verses, Matthew chapter nine, verses sixteen and seventeen:

> *No man putteth a piece of new cloth unto an old garment, for that which is put in to fill it up taketh from the garment, and the rent is made worse. Neither do men put new wine into old bottles: else the bottles break, and the wine runneth out, and the bottles perish: but they put new wine into new bottles, and both are preserved.*

I was that new bottle, he told me, and I'd have to fill up on something new now.

So the pot thing was one of the few cards missing at rebirth, but the tools for dealing with it and the other two would be functioning fine by the time I got to each of them over that first few weeks. On one hand I could say that I came in with an open mind, a new bottle, a clean slate, saying, Okay, I'm humbled, write on me here; whatever you say, I'll believe it. But that's not really the way it was. Not even close.

What had happened was that I ran back up to Paradise Mountain that fateful Oreo afternoon and started to read the Book of Mormon. The book's introduction claimed right there in the first two paragraphs that the account I was about to read was "a record of God's dealings with the ancient inhabitants of the Americas . . . the principal ancestors of the American Indians." And my first thought was, *Just try pulling that one over my eyes,* but my second was, *Annie never told me this.*

Engraved or etched into metal plates "by many ancient [American Indian] prophets," the record was eventually hand-delivered by one of them, as a resurrected being, to a young man named Joseph Smith, who then translated the account from the ancient language and published it in 1830 as the Book of Mormon. Eleven other men swore in print on the following page that they had "seen and hefted" the plates from which Smith translated and that the plates had "the appearance of ancient work and of curious workmanship."

So I started to read, just bopping around at first, getting a feel for the thing, but within pages I was glued to it, both the story itself—the tale of a family of Israelites who fled Jerusalem for America in about 600 B.C., as recorded by a son named Nephi—and the doctrine. The text was using language with which I was familiar, referring to "the Great Spirit," and then one prophet expressed his desires to "walk in the path of the low valley," to be "strict in the plain road," which was practically right out of the *Tao Te Ching* or *Black Elk Speaks*. Then I hit a section on the reality of and, in fact, the need for "opposition in all things," which was the best explication of the duality of the universe—Yin and Yang—that I'd ever read. It was better Buddhism than Ram Dass ever pulled off.

The whole of the first sixty pages or so was a warning and a prophecy that the descendants of the people writing the book, the American Indians, would "be scattered, and smitten, and hated" by an invading people from across the sea, "smitten on every hand, and driven and scattered to and fro, even as a wild flock is driven by wild and ferocious beasts."

And I said wait a minute and checked the copyright page, thinking this thing was published in 1830; we didn't start driving and plundering the Indians until years later—the Trail of Tears in 1838, Sand Creek and the Long Walk of the Navajo in 1864, Wounded Knee in 1890—how could an 1830 writer have known what would start happening years down the road? Sure, the colonists had hassled the Indians, including my own Seneca ancestors in western New York, but this was language referring to a definite and large-scale driving, a plundering, a near-extinction by an invading people that would eventually "possess the land."

But then instead of just saying the Indians were going to be reduced to ashes by the invading Europeans, the Book of Mormon narrative testified that the "Lamanites," the Indians of the Americas, were "of the House of Israel . . . the covenant people of the Lord" with promises of glory. This was their book, the affidavit of their covenant and the promise of their redemption!

I was stunned. I had never heard another Christian religion—and this one was definitely Christian, the name and words of Jesus were all over the place—acknowledge the Indians as worthy "children of God," let alone bona fide human beings. It seemed to be the whole message of this book.

I stuck my thumb in the page and looked up from a verse, my eye going naturally to the light of my southern window, and the room was spinning. I mean physically spinning, and I almost got nauseated, but then I realized that I could see straight and clearly through my southern window. The room just went around and around the window like a river flowing swiftly around a firm, translucent boulder. It was clear only in that one direction and only through the window; everywhere else it was as if I were trying to look through spinning pop-bottle glass. Then I noticed a buzzing in my ears that soon came to sound like a voice, a tiny voice. It was talking about the book! The book was testifying of itself, speaking in my mind, and it wasn't even my voice. Suddenly I absolutely and completely knew the book was a true record; wherever it came from, and whatever it said next, I knew it was true.

So that night when Elder Reefer told me the rest, I was really going backwards: *I know this is all true, but give me some detail. What is it that I believe?* I would soon come to recognize this as the very core of the authentic Mormon conversion experience, and the converts are not few. Some, as I would learn first hand in the next few years, let themselves get talked into it: *Okay, sure, I'll play along for a while, sounds good.* And they play along until someone else sings a tune they like better or they get bored or they can't keep up the regimen or, plugging onward on half-empty, they finally have The Experience.

Others, like me, have The Experience first. Right from the start they hear these voices in their heads telling them things they've never heard before, or giving specific answers to specific questions they've had in the backs of their minds since they were ten, or confirming dreams they had as a kid. Or they have actual beings from another world visit them in the night and stand in the air at the end of their beds all glowing like white-hot glass and talk to them in a real voice and say, *Shape up, Buckwheat, there's work to be done and here's what it is,* laying it out like a battle plan.

Those are the ones, like me, who end up saying I Know, capital K, that it's true; I heard the voice, I saw the light, you can spit and spatter and sputter hell and doo-doo all over my life, but I'm not budging. And these are usually the ones who end up going through hell just to see if they mean it, like running their new bottle through a really hot dishwasher. Again and again.

Like me.

What Reefer and Edwards told me that first night was that Joseph Smith, a fourteen-year-old boy in rural New York—I knew it, a country boy!—had listened to all the local preachers and proselytes and wondered to the depths of his soul where the truth was, which church of all the churches was true, or which god of all the gods was real, or whether god was real at all. Was there ultimate truth? And what on earth should he do?

Raised in a Bible-reading home, Joseph turned to the book for answers. Then he talked to the local preachers, every one of them saying, *I've got the truth! No, me! No, me!* And finally he decided that all the preachers understood the same passages of scripture so differently that it would be impossible to solve the thing by just appealing to the Bible, which is exactly what I had said to Justin two years before.

So Joseph took his cue from the Apostle James, who had written: Just go ask God yourself, nothing wavering, with a pure heart, real intent. He went far out into the woods to pray, to find god, and something tried to kill him. He could feel himself being pressed into the earth by some great power of darkness, but then a brilliant light descended upon him, and the dark power fled away. And I said to myself, that's exactly what happened to me up on the ridge, except for the light thingy! And Joseph looked up into the column of light and saw two actual beings, human in form but so blinding in their glory that he could hardly look at them. One of them called Joseph by name and said, pointing to the other: "This is my Beloved Son. Hear Him."

It was that Jesus, the same one I'd seen nailed to the cross in *Be Here Now*, that Buddhist paean to LSD consciousness or vice versa; the same one Christian Science said was really just an amorphous consciousness sort of thing, both books having led me straight into Mormonism and a Jesus with hair on his arms, standing there looking just like a man, with "keen penetrating blue eyes," according to one early chronicler.

Elder Reefer said the Being of Light who first spoke retreated, and Jesus remained to speak with young Joseph, a mere boy, calling him by name and speaking in an actual voice "like the sound of rushing waters" and telling him that not a church then on the earth had the authority of the Creator to be doing what they were doing in his name, that some had a form of godliness but none had the power, none had the whole truth, none had it right but taught mere philosophies of men, mingled with scripture. And Joseph would be the Prophet who would restore the ancient church to the earth.

This is exactly what Cris and Justin had said: Maybe none of the Christians had it right, and everybody was improvising on their own.

And then Elder Edwards started to tell me about the Book of Mormon itself, and I grabbed my copy from my pillow and said, "I know, this is so cool!" And they were surprised, but he went ahead and told Michelle and me how Joseph was led to the buried plates by another man, an angel without wings who came right through the wall, *whoosh*, into Joseph's log-cabin bedroom and then stood in midair talking to him and quoting Bible verses and saying they were being fulfilled before Joseph's very eyes. And then this angel, a man named Moroni who had been the last ancient American prophet to write in the record, gave Joseph tools and the power to translate them into English, coming out in 1830 as the Book of Mormon.

And I asked, "Have they rewritten this thing much since 1830?"

And Reefer said, "Whaddya mean?" And I said, "You know, the Indian part, 'cause in 1830 the Indians hadn't been driven and annihilated yet, but it talks about that in the earliest pages." And Reefer said, "No, they've added chapter headings and footnotes and corrected some grammar here and there, but it says exactly what it said in 1830. And then he said, "But listen to this," and he read me some verses from another scripture book, the Doctrine and Covenants:

> *Verily, thus saith the Lord concerning the wars that will shortly come to pass, beginning at the rebellion of South Carolina, which will eventually terminate in the death and misery of many souls. . . . For behold, the Southern States shall be divided against the Northern States, and the Southern States will call on other nations, even the nation of Great Britain, as it is called, and they shall also call upon other nations, in order to defend themselves against other nations. . . . And it shall come to pass, after many days, slaves shall rise up against their masters, who shall be marshaled and disciplined for war.*

And then Reefer said, "That was written on Christmas day . . . in 1832."

And I just looked at him, waiting for him to smile and say gotcha or something; but he was firm and serious and then said, "Joseph Smith was a prophet."

Elder Edwards went ahead then and told us about an account in the Book of Mormon of Jesus Christ visiting these ancient prophets in America after his resurrection in Jerusalem. Had I read that? Not entirely sure what *resurrection* meant, I said, "No, wow, tell me more."

I'm not sure I needed half of what they said after that or even heard it, at least not at that moment anyway, because my head was way elsewhere, thinking, *Oh, man, here is a real God, a tangible being who came and spoke to a boy and to others after him, appearing in actual*

*form and reality, though glowing like the sun, and said it's all messed up,
the preachers and popes have all rewritten the story, so I'm starting over.*
That was the claim! Reefer said, "We don't interpret anything or
wonder or rewrite or argue. He came and told us, face to face, man
to man. We know. We have no question. There is no mystery. Joseph
and others stood there and talked to him. And another prophet lives
today."
I said, "What else did Joseph do?"
And Reefer said, "He did a lot. He restored the ancient Christian church to the earth again, with twelve apostles and everything.
But then they killed him when he was thirty-eight, the people who
didn't like Mormons. They shot him to death in Illinois and then
ran all the Mormons out of the country, twenty thousand of them,
in the middle of winter, hundreds dying along the way." And then
Elder Edwards, the Utah boy, said, "Actually they ran them out of
Missouri first in 1838, drove about ten thousand of them right out
of the state in the middle of winter." And I asked why, and he said,
"'Cause they were growing too fast. Local preachers and politicians
got everyone stirred up and drove them right out of the state, the
Missouri governor even issuing an extermination order, leave or
you're dead." Then he said, "But they killed a passel of 'em first,
even little kids, the soldier in charge justifying it by saying nits
make lice."
It was the exact same phrase the other preacher, John M. Chivington, had used twenty-six years later in Sand Creek, Colorado. And
one side of my head was thinking, *Bad year for minorities 1838 was,
the Cherokee Trail of Tears happening four hundred miles to the south that
very winter,* but the other side was thinking, *Well, here it is, someone
else who got treated just like the Indians. In America.* In fact, I must
have said something out loud, because Elder Edwards said, "Oh,
yeah, my ancestors were among them, the ones who lived, walking
thirteen hundred miles to Utah pulling everything they had left in a
handcart, a little wooden wheelbarrow thing."
And I had never heard about that—in all my book larnin' in
school and *National Geographic* reading and discussions with my
mom and everything, no one had ever told me about the Mormon pioneers and why they were pioneering in the first place. As
Brigham Young had once put it, they came to Utah voluntarily because they had to.
But I had one final question for Reefer and Edwards that first
night. I said, "Tell me about heaven." And Reefer said, "Well, we've

got a whole discussion on that, but basically heaven is for families."

And I said, "What, you mean as actual people?"

He said, "Yeah, actual people, arms and legs and hair and—"

"Not just part of the ooze in some Big Sky Mind?"

"No, brother, you and me and the people we love, all individual people with eternal potential to grow and be glorified, united as families. How else could we call it heaven?"

And so I joined, and I kept reading, and I said to myself and to Annie and to anyone else who would listen, *I have found it, I have found the Truth, great big T, and this is the best news in the world.* I couldn't wait to tell Cris! And Cris came home from Israel, and I ran down and said, "Cris, I have found the truth, and it is in Mormonism!" And he said, "That's incredible, Kit, me too. I have found the truth of life, and I am returning to Christian Science."

And I went back up the hill, where Uriah took my thumb in his mouth and followed me in, then I climbed the stairs to my third-floor room and sat down on my bed to look out the window at the southern memories of my former life and said, "Now how on earth did this happen?"

Children of God

"Is this the way to the Celestial City?"

—John Bunyan, *The Pilgrim's Progress*

20

"It is possible for the human spirit to win after all!"
—Kerouac, *On the Origins of a Generation*

TO ONE WHO HAD crisscrossed the West on the motive power of the thumb, a driver's license was superfluous and a car expensive. But suddenly I was going to church three times a week.

In those days Mormon church meetings were spread all over Sunday, a remnant of a time in which all Latter-day Saints lived in Utah. Of course, every Latter-day Saint never lived in just Utah at any given time, but that was kind of the thinking: Here we are in Zion; who else could there be?

Well, as far as Paradise Mountain Mormons went, there was only me, and I had no car. So for a number of months I got a ride. The missionaries actually came and got me for a couple of weeks—twenty-three miles each way—but soon the Mormon take-care-of-our-own thing kicked in and a couple of local brothers agreed to bring me in each week. On Sunday mornings Oliver Butler would leave his home in Pine about 6:55, drive four bone-jarring miles of washboard and hairpin turns up the back side of Paradise Mountain, fetch me in his old red pickup, and then descend seven miles of the same down the front of the mountain, then onto the highway and on the next fourteen miles to the Presbyterian church where we rented space.

I thanked him graciously for coming all the way up the mountain for me, and he said, "Heck, I'm sleeping in. Until two months ago we were still renting space in the Elks hall, and I'd be wiping beer off the chairs and throwing away pizza boxes about now. So you're welcome."

We'd attend an hour of priesthood meeting for males over the age of twelve, and then Oliver would take me home. That afternoon, Paul Gardner would come up from Elk Meadows and do the same thing, taking me into Sunday school and sacrament meeting, the main church service.

Due in large measure to the unpredictable nature of the side trip up Paradise Mountain, we were frequently late to the meetings. Fortunately, due in even larger measure to a habit so common it has long since gained status as a unique Mormon time warp, most everyone else was always late too. It didn't matter how far they had driven. This time warp functions today in Utah wards that are three blocks square. It happens to lifers and converts, in Milwaukee and Moldavia. It's part of the faith. We call it Mormon Standard Time.

Then after the meetings—which, of course, ended right on the dot—Paul would take me home again, frequently making an effort to say hi to my folks and inquire as to their well-being. The other Mormon standard: missionary work.

Besides my own baptism the day before and priesthood meeting that morning, the first LDS worship service I ever attended was a fast and testimony meeting, where the members come having skipped the last two meals so they can donate the money to the poor; the Mormon welfare and humanitarian program is huge, reaching all over the planet. On this first Sunday of the month, many fasting members stand and bear testimony of the things they know to be true: Jesus, living prophets, the Book of Mormon, that sort of thing, just off the cuff, out of the heart, lots of people crying, the little kids saying, "I know Mommy and Daddy love me."

As soon as I understood what was going on about twelve minutes in, I stood up and gave mine. In those days you could either go to the pulpit or stay in your seat, where one of the twelve-year-old deacons brought you a corded microphone. I stood up near the back, took the microphone, and the whole congregation turned to stare at me, Kerouac's "nature boy saint in beard and sandals"—although none of them had probably ever heard of Kerouac—thinking, *Who left the door open?* And I blubbered with the best of them, with absolute conviction of the things I was saying. I even said thanks for letting me come in, and then I sat down.

It was about two weeks later that Cris's mom said to me, "I could never join a church that doesn't allow women or Negroes in their clergy," and I said, "What are you talking about?" And she said, "Ask your preacher," really pissed that I'd become a Mormon. She hadn't cared quite as much if her own kid and I became bong-sucking Buddhists or roamed the back roads and byways of America

with a harem of chickies in a VW bus. But become a Mormon? She
was incensed.

Her response to my Mormonism surprised me more than her
claim that the Mormons were racist misogynists.

So I asked my preacher.

Ray Goode looked at me like, *Well, here goes another one; in one
door and right out the back.* But he just said, "That's right, men of African descent have been barred by the Lord from holding the priesthood."

And I said, "Who says?"

And he said, "The prophets, from Brigham Young right down to
Spencer W. Kimball," who was the guy then running the church. But
this was before I held the priesthood either, so I just said, "Why?"

And he said, "We don't know why; the living prophets have
taught it to be so, and we sustain the living prophets."

"So blacks can't go to heaven?" I asked.

He laughed and said, "No, you turkey. We let them join the
church, and we believe they'll go into heaven right there with us,
as long as they keep the commandments. Just like us." And then he
said—probably thinking, *Well, I might as well dump the whole load;
he's gotta sink or swim sooner or later*—"Women don't hold the priesthood either." And he paused, looking for a reaction. Then he smiled
a rosy-cheeked smile that I would come to love and said, "Except
when my wife gives me a hug, then she's holding the priesthood.
But they go to heaven too. If they don't, brother, I'm coming back!"

And I went ahead and laughed a bit with him, rolling it around
and not finding anything to get angry about, not that I was black or
a woman and had any right to a valid objection anyway. But still I
asked why.

And he said, "That's the way the Lord set it up. Men hold the
priesthood. Women don't. It doesn't make them any less valuable in
the eyes of God; it's just the way he set up the program." And then,
as if to give the women some comeuppance, he said, "But women
can bear children."

I thought of Annie and how she'd chewed me out once that
winter for being so anti-kid. I'd said the usual: "Having children
should be a crime; we're destroying the earth." And she'd said,
"Well, we're just kids, somebody had us, and anyway I want to be
a mother someday." I was shocked. The thought had never crossed
my mind: she and I producing a kid, a family. It had always been
just me and her, saving the world.

So I asked Ray Goode, "What's the big deal with kids? Why would that be important?" And he said, "Children and families are central to the Creator's plan. We like big families!" He was proud of it, and he meant it, and I thought, *Oh, my goodness, what do I do with this?*

And then he interviewed me for the priesthood and that was when he asked me about marijuana and I went home with two things to think about, one that had been working its way to the surface for over a year — pitching the pot — and another that pierced me right to the core: the big-family doctrine. A single thing drove my reaction to both: I knew, I absolutely knew, that I'd found the truth of God and that a living prophet led the Saints today, a day when it was obvious to anyone that humans were destroying the earth.

I'd even seen him, Spencer W. Kimball, the eleventh man in succession from Joseph Smith. He was a little old man who had lost most of his vocal chords to cancer and now uttered things only raspingly through a microphone that hung around his neck. I saw him on television the weekend after I got baptized, sitting in the Hawks' family room with the whole family — five kids. I sat and watched ten hours of the church's 146th annual world general conference from Salt Lake City, Utah. And I'd read others of his words since.

The challenge to give up pot was in fact a relief. Every time I had smoked recently, it was like I could feel memory cells frying in their own grease. My head would be lethargic for days afterward. It was like, finally, a valid excuse that no one could refute unless they were wrapped in the colors of bona fide bigotry: No, I'm sorry, I don't smoke. I'm a Latter-day Saint, and we don't do that.

But the baby thing . . . I was a Latter-day Saint, and we *did* do that. Oh, how I struggled with that one. Human beings were the cause of nearly every terror on the earth, as far as I could see. It was humans who clear-cut forests, poisoned the rivers and the sea, waged war and slaughtered innocents. It was humans who threw their trash on the roadside, shot animals for sport until the species disappeared from the earth, fouled the air with their Fords and their factories, and carved up mountainsides with their dirt bikes and snowmobiles.

How was I to accept this? What was the logic?

I was feeling no sudden pressure to go and make a baby with someone — the act was forbidden in my current condition, and I was determined to adhere by it. It wasn't that, but it was the theology

itself. I intended to swallow Mormonism whole. I *had* swallowed
Mormonism whole, hook, line, and sinker. Overnight. And now this
one piece was stuck crosswise in my craw. I'd even finished reading
the Doctrine and Covenants, that other book of Mormon scripture,
which said that meat eating was allowed, although the doctrine suggested it be used "sparingly." Whether used for food or "raiment"
or just to occupy hillsides, animals were fulfilling "the measure of
their creation" just by being and would be herded into heaven without passports. I liked that. No other religion I had looked at besides
Native American ones had any clear statement on the afterlife of
animals.

Mormonism even said that the earth was a living spirit, a spirit
entity that would be resurrected just like the humans and hippos
and the tiger lilies and live forever in a glorified state of perfection
I liked that a lot.

Once I understood that animals had souls and would live forever in another realm but had a purpose on earth that might just
include getting served for dinner, the eating or noneating of meat
assumed a lesser critical mass in my mind, although I happily continued on my present vegetarian course, even confirming it with
Ray Goode. But having kids, once I was married, was a stout pole in
a stiff wind. The living prophet had said that husbands and wives
should "live together normally and naturally and let the children
come." The larger church doctrine taught that people who "under-
take to curtail or prevent the birth of their children . . . are going to
reap disappointment by and by."

Keeping the rather large and uncompromising and very hard-
to-swallow complaint to myself, I went to my knees again, saying,
*Oh, Lord, I know you are real, I know you have a prophet, and he has said
we gotta have a bunch of kids, once I'm married, we gotta let 'em come, but
that makes no sense!* And I went on and on lodging that complaint for
days, ten of them to be exact, trying to reason with the Lord and saying, *What could you possibly have in mind?* but really wanting to know
and to do it the right way, at least in my heart since I was at no risk
physically, anyway.

And my concern over the doctrine went away. It just melted.
Over the next little while I would begin to understand the doctrine
behind it, and my opinion on the topic would even reverse directions in the next few years, a process Latter-day Saints refer to as
personal revelation and testimony. But it was my first experience
with solving a doctrinal or administrative challenge in the church.

One pivotal verse would refer to it as a "burning of the bosom" and another as a peaceful feeling, a satisfaction.

Which is exactly what I got.

There would be other challenges to work out over the next couple of years. The blacks and the priesthood thing would remain a bit of a lump in the sock for a couple of years, as it would in the hearts of many Latter-day Saints, right up until the day, June 8, 1978, that the church prophet Spencer W. Kimball would say, "The Lord has heard our prayers, and by revelation has confirmed that the long-promised day has come when every faithful, worthy man in the Church may receive the holy priesthood . . . without regard for race or color." Mormons worldwide would breathe a sigh of relief over that one—not every single one of them, of course, but I swear that everyone I talked to had just been sucking in their guts, holding their breath, praying that no one ever asked, and they were absolutely thrilled when the prophet spoke.

The priesthood ban had been a very unpopular doctrine, but subordinate to the higher doctrine: We didn't run the Church, God did, and it wasn't our prerogative to name the rules. Same way with polygamy: It was practiced for sixty years in the nineteenth century, stopped in 1890 by the prophet then leading the church. That was then, this is now. Certain so-called Mormon fundamentalists would cruise right into the twentieth century and then the twenty-first still forming plural unions and then expressing surprise and ire when the church excommunicated them or never let them in to begin with, when in fact plural marriage had never been a fundamental practice but a situational one. The fundamental doctrine was that God led his church through a living prophet. You believed the prophet, you went to your knees until you did, or you checked out.

One other thing that President Kimball did was gave a talk just a few months after the priesthood revelation that decried hunting for sport, the indiscriminate killing of "little birds" and other wildlife, the bloodthirsty ways of men, really laying it out and pleading for gentle ways, gentle hearts. He quoted the original Mormon prophet, Joseph Smith, who told of once finding a nest of prairie rattlesnakes on the trail he and some colleagues were following. The others gathered to kill the snakes, but Joseph said: "Let them alone—don't hurt them! How will the serpent ever lose his venom while the servants of God possess the same disposition and continue to make war upon it? Men must become harmless, before the brute creation." And then he lifted the snakes one by one on a stick and moved them off the trail.

Then Kimball quoted Joseph's nephew, Joseph F. Smith, who became the sixth church president:

> *I never could see why a man should be imbued with a blood-thirsty desire to kill and destroy animal life. I do not believe any man should kill animals or birds unless he needs them for food, and then he should not kill innocent little birds that are not in-tended for food for man. I think it is wicked for men to thirst in their souls to kill almost everything which possesses animal life. It is wrong, and I have been surprised at prominent men whom I have seen whose very souls seemed to be athirst for the shedding of animal blood.*

I was in the Lakewood regional meetinghouse, the stake center where I had been baptized, with six hundred other guys watching the talk from Salt Lake City on a closed-circuit system, and I almost stood up and cheered. I wanted to catch a plane to Salt Lake City and go hug the guy, kiss his feet. But grown men all around me were chuckling, actually scoffing at the prophet's comments about their favorite bloodthirsty pastime. I wanted to raise my open hands to heaven and say, "We thank thee O God for a prophet," and most of the rest of the crowd was saying, "Well, that was out of line."

Believe, go to your knees, or check out.

What I did was I said, *Okay, Spencer, I'm gonna believe everything you have to say: women, kids, priesthood, whatever — I know you're a prophet.* And that's exactly how my mind and heart dealt with doc-trinal matters from then on.

In July, a casual friend from high school, Rusty Corwin, took the missionary lessons and joined the church. Within days he and I had decided to move to Provo, Utah, where we could learn how to be real Mormons and prepare to go on missions for the faith. Provo is the home of Brigham Young University, the church's flagship in-stitution of higher ed, and it boasted the most homogenous LDS population on earth, ninety-eight percent in 1976. We'd live off our art — he would paint and draw caricatures, and I would sell canes, just not the hollow ones.

Rusty's folks were kicking him out of the house anyway — *damn Mormon scum* — so we loaded our packs and hit the road, our tools on board. We spent six weeks trying to get anything to work, and nothing much would. By the end of the stint we were doing day labor, including picking fruit—some for pay, some for food— and looking at jobs bussing tables down at Zion National Park. I said, "But we're here in Zion to prepare to be missionaries, not to work three hundred miles away in the national park." And Rusty said, "Let's just go home."

So we did, Rusty showing signs of bitterness.

As soon as we returned to Colorado, Rusty checked out of church and never checked back in. That's about the same time my sister Michelle checked out too, saying, "There's no one my age in the branch to socialize with." And I went, "*Socialize*? What the heck does socializing have to do with the truth?" I don't even recall if there was anyone my age in the branch. It never crossed my mind. Oliver Butler was fine: he was fifty-four. Paul Gardner was good: he was thirty-five and had six kids. But then I just went to church to worship, not look for a date.

Anyway, I went back to my little mountain congregation and got my first calling, or church job. Every congregational role in The Church of Jesus Christ of Latter-day Saints is done by volunteers, only you don't volunteer; you're *called*—everyone, including the bishop and branch president and right up the chain.

I got the worst calling of all, though: I got called as scoutmaster. I was eighteen, and they handed me seven thirteen-year-old and fourteen-year-old boys and said, "Now go make them perfect." Well, at first I expected it would be a chance to take seven impressionable young minds and teach them the ways of the woods: environmental thought, recycling, survival, edible and medicinal plants. Leave nothing but footprints; take nothing but pictures. But I was in for a rude awakening.

I would schedule a nice evening trek through the woods, but they'd rather do dodge ball, which in the six years since I'd played it had turned into slaughter ball. And instead of giving a nice sting from a volley ball, these boys played it with little super balls. I took one in the neck one night and opted out for the evening.

And then I got them on Sunday too, as their deacon quorum advisor, charged with preparing a lesson each week from the church manual. Sometimes I wondered if they would have preferred to play slaughter ball in class too.

I attended church down in the city a few times with Annie's family. Home from college for the summer, she introduced me, with some fond emotion, to her bishop, the big-city equivalent of my branch president. He was Hank Ibarra, a Yáqui Indian from El Paso, Texas, who had busted his guts getting his little family out of an environment of dead-end poverty and alcoholism, converting to the church along the way and becoming a well-respected insurance executive. He called the two of us into his office that first Sunday and looked at me and said, "So you're Kit."

And I looked at Annie, who was smiling, and then, with no one else in the room to look at, I looked at the bishop, thinking *I bet he knows everything.* Because that's what the faithful—or those who were really trying to be faithful—did with their priesthood leader, they told them everything. They said, "Bishop, I've made some mistakes, and I want to start over. What do I do?"

Which is exactly what Annie and her priesthood leader had already done. And they'd already run the course of counsel, just like I had forty miles to the west. Tears had been shed, prayers offered, encouragement poured forth from the generous reservoirs of a faith that had seen its share of hard times. And what Bishop Ibarra ultimately said to me was, "God bless you, brother, you've got a great road ahead of you."

And what I thought was: *I have found my Yáqui wise man.*

Sometime that winter the Hawks moved to Fort Collins, where Brother Hawk took a faculty position at Colorado State University. When Annie returned from another semester, that's where she went. It was a seventy-mile hitchhike, but I did it as frequently as I could, or sometimes Annie would borrow a car and come down. I met her in Lakewood one time, and we went on a real date, our first ever—we dressed up and went to a Mexican restaurant and then a movie and then smooched in the back of her Toyota until she said, "Whew, we better separate." Then she dropped me off at Conner's place and drove all the way back to Fort Collins alone, and I laid in the upper bunk at Conner's and talked long into the night about my new faith, pleading with him to check it out, and he said, "Maybe I will."

One time Annie came up to Paradise Mountain, and we went down to a restaurant in Pine that had vegetarian food, Will O' the Wisp. My mother took a photo because it was so bizarre, me in a fancy shirt and Annie in a dress. I was still trying to figure out what the hey to do with my hair, clear above my ears and all. I even tried on some of my dad's Old Spice, and Annie said, "Is that necessary? You smell like an old man."

And then one time we found a Mexican restaurant in Indian Hills with huge veggie burritos and Red Zinger tea. We went there three or four times, but it was a really long way for Annie to come for a date, and afterward we'd always have trouble keeping our hands to ourselves, just us in the car. Annie said, "Why don't you come to Fort Collins more. It'll force us to have a curfew." So I hit the road again.

I became a zealous promulgator, a highway heaven hawker. One ride was with an older couple living in a Christian village north of Boulder. Mrs. Schuster chewed me out big time for becoming a Mormon—there it was again, as bad as being a Muslim or a Buddhist, she said, and how could I be led so astray? I testified back with everything I knew, especially the part about Mormons being Christians—Jesus Christ was in the name of our church, for goodness sake—but she was having none of it. A week later I received a Bible in the mail, with a verse in Isaiah marked with a highlighter: "To the law and to the testimony: if they speak not according to this word, it is because there is no light in them." And I said to myself, *Absolutely right, sister.*

It was a great Bible; I kept it for years.

Then one time I got a ride from a cowboy couple who could not keep their hands off each other. She was right up on his lap as he drove, and I was on the pickup bench next to her hoping they didn't get it on right then and there or drive off the road. When I told them about my new faith, she said, "Do you wear that funny red underwear?" and I hoped she didn't start checking. I said, "No, what underwear are you talking about?" And she said, "All Mormons wear it, clear to their wrists and ankles," and I said, "Well, I'm new."

So when I asked Elder Reefer about it at church one Sunday, he got a little smiley-eyed look and glanced at his new companion, Elder Wiemann, and said, "Oh, she means temple garments." And I said, "Huh?"

"Temple garments," he repeated. "When we go through the temple for our endowments, we get a sacred garment that we wear from then on. But it doesn't go clear to your ankles."

"And they aren't red," said Elder Wiemann.

They taught me more about temples and how I'd go there if and when I decided to be a missionary or when I got married.

I wondered which one would happen for me.

21

"We watched the seasons pass, we were crystalline
as snow and melted gently into newer forms
as stars spun round our heads."
—Lenore Kandel, from "Enlightenment Poem"

BY THE END OF THAT SUMMER, Annie and I were talking marriage seriously, me eighteen and her one up on me, a July Fourth Independence baby, thinking, *Yeah, this will complete the circle of our love, so to speak.* We even looked at rings once, walked right into a jewelry store at a mall and said, "Show us the goods." Then they showed us the prices. Later Mrs. Hawk said, "A job would come in handy, Kit." But we didn't even like the rings. We didn't like anything about the rings: so conventional, so trite. And compared to turquoise and tiger's eye, a diamond was kind of a boring stone anyway.

But then I did get a real job, thirty to thirty-five hours a week as a janitor in the dorms at Colorado School of Mines in Golden. (Twelve years of public school—I was skipped a grade along the way—and that was what I got?) The boss asked if I had reliable transportation, since my house was thirty miles away. I said no problem, and it never was. Working regular American laborer hours, I always found lots of traffic on the roads.

I got assigned to a trainer who could move through toilets like he was wiping warm butter off Teflon. He would barge right into the girls' dorms like he was part of the sorority; he'd yell "cleaning service" on his way through the bathroom door and just keep on moving. We caught a few sights.

I told him all about Joseph Smith and Moroni and begged him to just read the Book of Mormon, and he said, "Maybe I will."

That fall Annie left for CMC again, on her way to becoming a college graduate. Cris decided to go too. They both tried talking me into it. I applied and actually got a scholarship, but then I decided I couldn't handle one more week in a classroom ever in my life.

Justin was off in his tipi with Geoffrey's little sister, digging the native religion and practicing his harmonica.

I wrote a letter to my old Catholic friend Paul, telling him I had found that Savior he had so humbly told me about. I asked him to listen to the missionaries and read the Book of Mormon—heart pure as his, he was sure to find out as I did—and he wrote me back and said thanks but no thanks, his parents raised him Catholic and he could never break their hearts. Not even "Maybe I will."

Pretty soon I was thinking I could really dig a better job with better pay. Swabbing toilets was honorable and all that, but day to day it sucked. I mentioned it to a lady at church, and she said, "There's an opening where I work. Paradise Finer Foods."

Paradise Finer Foods was the grocery story in Pine Dell, walking distance from the big Hot Dog and only nine miles from my house. There weren't many jobs right there in the mountains.

"Doing what?" I asked her.

"As a meat cutter trainee."

Well, I didn't want to offend her, and I didn't really want to get into the vegetarian thing; lots of Latter-day Saints think Mormon doctrine requires the eating of meat just because one verse instructs us not to "prohibit" it. So I just said, "Oh, really, what's it pay?" and she said, "Three-fifty an hour." Well, three-fifty an hour in those days was way above minimum wage. I thought about it all week, then I went in Saturday morning, a nice clean-cut Mormon boy. The guy hired me on the spot.

So for the next year I learned how to cut meat. It was one of those full-service counters, just like *Petticoat Junction* or *Andy Griffith* or something, and I got to know half the population of the region. With time I could tell them which cut served this or that purpose, how long to cook it, which was tender, which was flavorful, which cut down into sandwich meat best. However, I never tasted a single piece. One old lady came in every week and bought a beef kidney for her cat; there's one hanging right inside the fat of every hindquarter. With four or five hindquarters broken down every week, however, that was four or five kidneys: one down, four to go. Where they went was in the freezer case. We'd wrap them in butcher paper and write on them with a grease pencil: KIDNEY. People'd ask, "What do you do with a kidney?" And I'd tell them, "Oh, for your cat or certain foreign dishes." Bob would tell them they were good eating and easy to cook too. "You just boil the piss out of them."

Bob was a piece of work. One day he went into the cooler to lift a hindquarter off a rail hook, squatted down to get a good head of oomph for the one-hundred-sixty-five pounds, and crammed a wall hook right up his rectum. It took thirty-seven stitches to keep him regular, so to speak. The other guy and I said, "Have a great week off," and then didn't miss him at all.

But I got my own stitches a time or two. Once, I was cutting the nylon strap off a box of bull meat, the ornery full-muscle stuff you throw in to make ground beef lean—and you thought it came off the rump!—and I ran the knife through the strap and then through my forearm, right under the arm bone, all the way through. Weird how you watch the blood spurt out purple and then throw the knife and yell "Hey!" to anyone who will listen. Then another time a lady had me try four different cuts off three different tenderloins—expensive stuff, that—and then rejected them all, saying "my" meat was too fatty, and I got huffy and rammed my seven-inch boning knife back into my scabbard, only I missed the scabbard and drove it down into my thigh. Seven inches.

That was a piece of work.

On my days off, which included Sundays, I'd prepare Sunday school lessons or read or pick my guitar and write songs. The songs were taking on a slightly different hue and cry:

Do you really believe in eternity?
Does it sometimes make you change your mind,
About living the way that you ought to be,
And not doing everything just for time?

Then one night I had a dream. I'd been called as a missionary to serve in the Bogotá, Colombia mission. I looked it up in the encyclopedia and wondered. Then I wrote a tune, a slinky-slidey Skynyrd-type thing, although I set it in Brazil just because the lyrics fit better that way. (What do you rhyme with "Bogotá", pray tell?) I called it "Dancing on the Amazon."

Way down in Rio
Where the Sugar Mountain stands
There went my brother
With the good book in his hands.

He came from Arizona
Way up north around Gila Bend

He had turquoise on his fingers
And a smile that wouldn't end.

They sent him to the mountains there
Righteous men to seek.
Some said he was German,
One old man thought he was Greek.

He said, "Brother, could you spare some time?
We're here to plant the seeds."
Old man said, "Boy, hey, what you speak?
It sure ain't Portuguese."
But I can try, yeah.

BRIDGE

Cockroach drumsticks in his soup
And lizards on the wall.
You almost hate to go to sleep
When nighty-night time falls.

Bus rides there are just a gas
The kind that makes you think
About gettin' gone and far away,
It's like cleanin' out the sink.

But now everything ain't all that bad,
The work it pays you well.
But you gotta keep your head up high
And let your spirit swell.

Just stay away from the Amazon
The crocodiles and snakes.
Keep your self where it belongs
And don't make no mistakes,
No, heck, no!

Come early November I'd had about all the time away from
Annie I could possibly take, so I got a few days off, loaded up my
backpack with my cross-country skis strapped vertically, and hit
the lovely lonesome highway for Glenwood Springs. It was the first

time I'd ever gone that far in the dead of winter. I almost got myself dead on the way over.

I left Paradise Mountain fasting—not a real Mormon fast, where you don't eat food or liquid for twenty-four hours, because I took along a twenty-ounce apple juice just in case. Turned out I used it. Rides were only so-so, and I was barely making Vail by the time it was getting dark. I headed into the woods above town to bivouac on the north side of the interstate. No tent, but I had a survival blanket and my winter sleeping bag, a Slumberjack Hollofil that had once kept me alive at forty-six below zero above Granby. So I found some sheltered woods, dug a snow trench, and climbed in. I hadn't ever slept in a trench before. I'd slept in a number of snow caves— they get so warm the place is melting all over you by morning—but never in a trench. Read about it once in *The Freedom of the Hills*.

Fitful night, to say the least, especially with nothing in my gut. About five A.M. I awoke feeling really weird. I could tell it was nearing daybreak, but that's about as coherent as I could get things. The woods were running around, oozing back and forth like the blobs in a lava lamp. I could hear the highway and see an occasional set of lights, but I'd try staring at something and it would go away. Actually it'd come at me fast and then go right through the back of my head. I said, *I think I'll try that apple juice now,* and since I'd slept with the bottle stuffed into my crotch, it was only mostly slush. I sucked on the juice, then scrambled out of my stiff-frozen bag and began trying to pack things up. I couldn't do it. My fingers wouldn't work, my mind wouldn't focus. I knew I was slipping into a pretty good hypothermia—I'd seen plenty of it—so I just speed-lashed everything to my pack, got it over one shoulder, aimed my skis downhill—that part was relatively clear—and slid into Vail, numb and mumbling. Had a tall stack with blueberry syrup at the pancake house. Made Glenwood by 9:00 A.M. and CMC by 10:30.

It was Friday, and neither Annie nor her new roommate, Beth, had classes. They were right there in the apartment, Beth making no plans to go anywhere, and she asked me how my trip had gone, so I told her. She said, "Maybe you should buy a car," and I said, "I guess I have to get my license first," and she said, "Sure, that would help." So Annie and I just wandered around campus for two days, trying to play it safe with each other but really wanting to go roll around in something soft. We hung around with people as much as we could or sat in public places like the library. But we couldn't really talk there, so pretty soon we were out rolling in the snow, then onto a dry patch under a pinyon tree. Lots of warm clothes on. Goose down and wool.

It was very tense and very hard, and we ended up talking marriage again, me with energy, Annie sort of half-hearted. I mentioned it to her, still thinking, *What's up with Wayne?* Annie said, "Baby, I love you, but what about a mission?"

You can only go on a mission before you're married. Even young folks who have been married and then maybe divorced, still just twenty-five or twenty-six, are out of luck. And I said, "Yeah, I really want to go, but I got no dough." You pay your own way. Two years, no salary, all volunteer.

And we didn't know what to do about that, so we went and looked up some friends, kids we'd gone to high school with who were right there at CMC. Annie said two of them had talked to the missionaries and one had joined the church already, a couple weeks before. Like me, Annie was a real zealous convert, smitten with faith, and the word had gotten around that she was helping organize Jesus talks. She'd held several so far with a handful of students. Dave McAllister was always involved since his calling was as a local missionary, as opposed to a full-time one in some place like Rio or Bogotá. But when we found Sharon McCollum, the one who had just joined the church, she was really cold. Beautiful, but really cold. Natural platinum hair, baby-blue eyes, and a nose worth biting in public.

She lit into Annie like Pasteur pursuing the plague, calling her names and dissing Joseph Smith big time and dragging up all kinds of sewer slop that an entire global religion of anti-Mormon "Christians" always throws at us—always has, always will—and I stepped in and said, "That's all a bunch of sewer slop, proven false a hundred years ago, and who's been teaching you your Mormonism, a moron?" And she said, "My folks' pastor." And then she said, "I believe him," and I said, "I don't," and Annie started to cry, and I said, *Well, piss on your perfect complexion and that really nice sweater*—to myself—and we split.

We called up some friends of Annie's from church, and they picked us up on Sunday for meetings and then took us to their house above Carbondale for dinner. Ten years before he was set to inherit a beer fortune back in Wisconsin, the man joined the LDS Church and got cut right out of the will and was told to hit the road. Now he made wood furniture and lived in the woods.

I slept in Wayne's tipi for three nights. Once I tramped back in late at night, he and I stayed up trading a guitar and a harmonica back and forth. About midnight the first night, he lit up a bowl of really sweet-smelling stuff, and I said, "No, thanks—egad, I don't do that anymore," and then we howled at the full moon until one, two A.M., telling stories of the road, and he promised—because I asked—no way, no time, no how with Annie. Not that he hadn't been interested in a sweet, gentle girl with lovely hair and really nice legs. Finally one morning I told him, "Peace, be cool," kissed the girl real long, and headed back to my other world really messed up.

Lordahmighty, I missed that lifestyle real bad. I missed living on the road and sleeping in a tent or under a pear tree or in a mountain cabin, with or without the girl, and just hanging out on a warm aspen-gold hillside watching the sun roll across the sky, the Clark's nutcrackers dipping and diving on the circuitous currents of heaven's soft wind. I missed being with Annie night, day, and forever. I missed that the most. But in fact I'd never had her night, day, and forever. We were just two disparate souls in desperate times seeking solace in the arms of eternity.

So what I did was I poured out the wine and threw away the bottle.

22

THE END BEGAN AS SOON AS I PROPOSED. You see, come June eighth, the third anniversary of our snow-storm-lovely lullaby-beginning, Annie was home from college. Back to Fort Collins, a mere hundred miles away. We'd been together already a couple of times: walks around the lake, sprout-and-avocado sandwiches at Avagadro's Number. I wanted to get her alone, and she wanted to stay right out under the vault of all-seeing heaven and the public eye—not that I was going to lay her out; I just wanted to be alone. It was as if she was scared of me, really down deep wondering who I was.

One day I looked at the Paradise Mountain sun and said it must be June, then at the calendar in the house to confirm it, and I set my sights on the sacred date of the eighth. Even got the day off at the grocery store.

June seventh it was seventy-one degrees on Paradise Mountain, butterflies flitting around on the little candytuft blossoms; June eighth, ten A.M., it was looking to snow, just like sun-calendar clockwork. It was cold and gray when Annie pulled up the driveway in her dad's little Toyota, city tires on the back. She came on in and did the little chitchat thing with my mom that she'd never have dreamed of doing two years before, talking Steinbeck and the fall of Rome and potato salad over the making of a bag of sandwiches. Then I lent her a coat to supplement her light flannel shirt, put a couple of nice blankets in my daypack, and told Mom we were going for a hike. Then we putted my Volkswagen over to the trailhead leading to the Kolob ridge and started to walk.

The snow still lay in broad swatches up that shaded northern slope, and by the time we topped the ridge our hands were getting stiff. I opened the heavy plank door and welcomed her with a flourish. The whole thing—cabin, wilderness, memory, alone—drove us into each other's arms, and we locked in a long and desperate kiss. I think it was nerves more than anything, but Annie was shivering and wondered aloud about the environmental ethics behind starting a fire in the stove midday. I wasn't sure of that myself, but I knew that if I stayed in there another five minutes I was going to drop her to the floorboards with flannel flying, and so I said, "Let's go up on the roof."

See, I'd been up there before, and not just when I was checking for claw marks. Cris and Justin and I had spent hours on end sitting on the roof talking or looking. Summertime we'd sit in the woods, on a rock, or right down in the kinnikinnick, but when enough snow was on the ground we knew the black roof tarpaper absorbed the daylight heat and held it. We would often remain there comfortably until past sunset.

So Annie and I went up on the roof, me on the ridgeline, her snuggling right back into me, pulling my hands across her jacketed belly. I buried my face in her hair, now butterscotch sweet from the ponderosa pine, and looked out over the mountain, then closed my eyes, seeing all kinds of visions: the winter-red glow of the little oil-heater stove right below us, the macramé-draped boulder-through-the-wall in the cabin on the front of the mountain, Annie in every scene and longing in every memory.

And I said, "Baby girl, I want to get married."

And she stopped breathing for a moment, then said, "Really?" Not yes, not no, just really. She released her grip on my hands, then tightened it, then released it again. She turned to look at me, and confusion was in her eyes even though a smile played about her lips.

Confusion was probably in my eyes too, but I looked back at her as if I knew what I was seeing: Annie wanting me. Annie straddled across my chest as we lay in the Double-Diamond meadow, leaning over and swishing her hair back and forth across my face, Annie leaning back with her eyes closed as I kissed her neck in the pickup on the road to Missouri, a full-moon-and-cornfield Kansas night just flying by outside, throwing a honey-golden glow over all we did. Annie stepping out of Jim Mason's lemon-yellow pickup with her long hair drying in the mountain breeze and pulling my mouth up to hers.

I had known enough of love's pleasures to not waste another wit of time pondering alternative philosophies of fulfillment. The love of a girl was the best there was, and it was time to move forward. But I also knew I was right in between two worlds, the new and the old, and I was feeling an overwhelming, anxious fear, a desperation. I could sense the same from her, but I read it all wrong.

Somehow, she took my silence as the last word and I took hers as enough and pulled her to me for a kiss. She came only grudgingly, so I pushed the issue and then pressed her back down on the roof. She let me, her scared, wounded soul rising back to the surface, and I let it rise and started on her buttons, getting halfway to paradise before she pushed me away and sat up crying. The look of hurt in her eyes, a look of total and complete betrayal, exploded in my soul, and my own conscience exploded in return.

She buttoned her shirt and stood up, saying, "I'd better go."

And I just sat there alone on the tarpaper as the clouds rolled in and the snow started to swirl.

23

"I am now on the road to Heaven."
—Kerouac, *The Dharma Bums*

THE FOLLOWING MORNING I called Merrill Schneider at Paradise Finer Foods and told him I had the flu. Then I put Uriah and my guitar and my Slumberjack bag in the Volkswagen and headed west.

I had finally come off the roof in time to catch Annie and offer her a ride when she was only a half-mile from my house. She declined the offer, bawling her eyes out. I got out of the car and tried to talk to her, to apologize, to hold her one more time, but she just said, "Kit, I don't know what's going on, but I just need to go home and think." I said, "Please just let me take you back up to the house."

She never went inside the house to say good-bye, but she did hold my hand and let me give her a discreet little peck on the lips. And then she went away.

Next night about eight P.M. I was sitting on a high slick-rock wall above the Garden of Eden—no kidding, that was the real name of the place in Arches National Park, Utah. I was just staring out at the distant, jagged rim of the San Rafael Swell—the reef—tracing it visually down toward the V-shaped gap at Hanksville that leads to Capitol Reef, sacred ground to Annie and me.

Uriah sat and stared with me, seeing a lot less but probably knowing a lot more. He had struggled climbing the ridge, and I knew he wasn't well.

We sat there for another hour, and I watched the sun set right smack in the middle of the Capitol Reef gap, going down, blinking out, like the end of an era. In the twilight I could see images of Annie dancing around the redrock ridges, images of us. I could smell her hair, feel the curve at the base of her back and where it went from there. I could feel the perfect smoothness of her shoulders. I felt her press into me, and I had to stand up, Uriah searching for my thumb.

I felt a bead of sweat trickle down my chest, and I shivered in the wind.

Something inside me said, *What the hell is happening?* And something else said, *Let her go.* I was completely lost and lonely and inexplicably forlorn.

New wine in new bottles.

I hiked my heart out the first day at Arches, then drove on over to Capitol Reef. But there I could only sit in the car and stare, in the car or on a rock not far from the car. I had nothing left inside. Plus, Uriah wasn't doing well at all.

I drove home all day Sunday, missing church for the first time in two years, and arrived back in Paradise inconsolable. I put on the good face, not wanting my parents to think I was going to hell in a hand basket or to heaven just as sad. So I put on the face and then took it upstairs to stare out the window and listen to Dan Fogelberg crying about the woman he had thrown away, the woman who haunted his songs for a full decade. And I thought, *Will I ever get over my loss?*

So I worked: work and home, work and home, church, work and home. There were days I just couldn't go to work, my mind assailed with thoughts of *What have I done?*

Ray Goode, kind and thoughtful in all he did, told me it was probably for the best and dug around looking for a statement from church president Spencer W. Kimball counseling the convert and the person on his way up and out of a shadowed past to clear out everything in his life that tended to bring back the old days. Everything.

So I went through all my record albums, pulling out everything I owned by anybody I knew had ever taken a drink or smoked a joint or packed a bong or written a song about any of it, took them all down to Blue Spruce Records in Silver Creek, and traded them in for cash. The guy said, "Hot damn, a DJ cutout of the Outlaws' first" and "Hoo-whee" to the actual gold vinyl *Made in Japan* live set from Deep Purple and stuff like that. Seventy-five bucks. I tried to look like I really didn't care—I'd kept all my Fogelberg, of course—but told myself over and over that the Lord knew my sacrifice, and some day I would know the recompense for my penury.

I worked a forty-hour week at Finer Foods, studied scriptures or church books twenty to thirty hours a week, and played my guitar till my fingers bled, sometimes with Cris Wilde, home from Colorado Mountain College but not wanting to talk about religion at all.

I found Justin Bloom still living in a tipi above the Colorow Inn, his hair as short as mine, and we climbed Long's Peak together, a famous fourteener in Rocky Mountain National Park. Then I climbed four more fourteeners solo, Grays and Torres in the same day, running.

Then Ray Goode called me in one Sunday for an interview, asking all the questions: pot, alcohol, honesty, full tithing. Sexual promiscuity, at which I actually laughed. And then he said, "I'm recommending you for the higher priesthood, the Melchizedek priesthood. You'll become an elder."

It didn't mean I'd be a missionary yet—that would be a separate calling and process somewhere down the road—but that Tuesday night I had another interview with his boss, the stake president, and the next Sunday I had hands laid on my head and was given the authority to call down the powers of heaven to heal the sick and cure the infirm, and I thought, *Maybe it will work on me.* And then the stake president said, "President Goode has also recommended that we submit your papers to Salt Lake City for a mission call."

I said, "I'd love to do that, President, but I don't have any money," and President Clarke said, "I think that's taken care of."

"What do you mean?"

And he said, "The people in your branch, they want to support you on your mission."

So we filled out the paperwork and sent it in, and I had no clue when, where, how, or what was next, except that I did really wish to go. Especially now.

On Paradise Mountain I sat and read every church book I could get a hold of, and I told my parents I wanted to go on a mission just like Reefer, whom they had liked a lot. My mom said, "To where?" and my dad said, "Do they pay well?" And I said, "I don't know where, you never do, and no, they don't pay at all—in fact, you pay your own way."

And my dad laughed and said, "Well, that takes care of that. You don't have a pot to piss in or your own window to throw it out of," and my mom said, "That nice Elder Reefer, he paid his own way?" And I said, "Yeah, they all do, except Ray Goode has offered to help me on mine."

And at that my dad put down his newspaper, and they both just stared at me.

Mom said, "You really mean it, don't you."

And I said, "Yeah, I've even sent in my papers."

They knew enough not to ask about Annie; my mom had seen her drive away.

Then my mom said, "How much?"

"How much does it cost?"

"Yeah."

"It's two years, you never know where. I've got about a thousand dollars saved." Scrubbing toilets, scooping poop, and whacking carcasses, all for the glory of God, should he want my meager efforts.

And my mom said, "I think you'll be real good."

My dad looked at her funny, then back at me, then back at his newspaper, and said, "You let us know. We can probably help a little bit."

That was the week Cris left for the Christian Science college back in Illinois and Uriah died of leukemia, off to the big beautiful wilderness in the sky where bears don't taunt and big dogs don't bite and vision is perfect, Mormon doctrine saying, *Yep, that's right*, and me saying "Hallelujah," actually saying it to the trees below Eagle's Nest, looking out over the successive purple ridges of my pleasure and my pain. But something inside me was saying, *Dear God, I'm lonely and I'm scared.*

Annie and I met in Fort Collins one more time. She was leaving for summer term at Brigham Young University in three days, a full academic scholarship. Ostensibly she invited me up to a "fireside," what the Latter-day Saints call a Sunday-night devotional talk. Sometimes they're really good; sometimes you're just thankful there are cookies afterward.

It was okay, but our minds were really elsewhere. Coming home, I pulled to the curb a block from her folks' house and just kept my hands on the wheel. We both stared through the windshield for a while until she started to cry. I turned off the car and looked at her and took her hand. She was the finest thing I had ever known. Every cubic inch of me hurt.

I said, "I have loved you, Annie, with everything I have."

She squeezed my hand and blubbered through, "And I you, Kit." Then she turned to look at me and asked, "Do you think we're just on different roads to heaven?"

And then I couldn't look at her at all, and I started to cry. Finally I said, "Annie, will you please just kiss me good-bye?"

But she never did.

Full raging rising moon
Our own private sky
She held me soft and tender,
Whispered lullabies.

She said she loved me, and I saw it in her eyes.

We waltzed into the night
Love called the tune
She held me tight and told me
Forever would be too soon.

Don't ever leave me, you've got me hypnotized.

She wouldn't let me touch her lips
But I swear
That she kissed me with her eyes.

We walked the edge of darkness
Into the light
We talked of dreams and she said
That she just might
Love me forever . . . and it felt so right.
(Yeah, it felt so right.)

It's silly
But I like to think
That she kissed me with her eyes.

Man, she was a number
Eyes of emerald green
Hair that flowed like honey nectar
How could I have foreseen
That we weren't forever –
Was it all a dream?

You told me that you loved me
You said it with your touch.
You spoke the words and you danced the dance,

Would it have been too much?
I'll never know, girl,
Because I never got the chance.

It's all I have
So I'll always think
That you kissed me with your eyes . . .
When you said good-bye.

24

"I wandered lonely as a cloud . . .
Beside the lake, beneath the trees,
Fluttering and dancing in the breeze."
—William Wordsworth

THE PAPERWORK WAS in Salt Lake City and all I could do was wait, so I worked, I studied, and I saved every dime I could.

My mom and everybody at Paradise Finer Foods kept saying, "Where do you think you'll go?" None of them understood the missionary process. I could only say, "You never know—no one ever does." But I kept remembering my dream of eight months before, Bogotá, Colombia, and my song about preaching on the Amazon.

My dad was real nervous on an occupational level, saying, "Damn, boy, I had a career for two years by the time I was your age. When ya gonna settle down and get serious?" I tried to share a scripture, Matthew 10:39, about losing one's life in the service of the Lord so that you can find it and carry on in even better shape later on. I really trusted that, but his eyes kind of glazed over and he said, "Bull, this is the real world."

Ray Goode met with my folks a couple of times in the next few weeks to ask if they'd help support me on my two-year nonpaid mission, which would cost between five and ten thousand dollars for the two years, depending on where I went. My folks said, "We just don't have that, Ray," and he said, "The branch will come up with the rest of it. We love Kit, and he's gonna be great. How much can you do?" And my folks committed to a third, more than I could probably give it from my own funds. My dad finally told Ray Goode, "Hell, I'll pay that just to keep his hair short."

Sitting around the mailbox, or actually sitting in the living room with my mom and grandma watching *Six Million Dollar Man* reruns and kind of glancing down at the mailbox on the road every thirty minutes or so, one day I got the letter.

I didn't know it until I walked down for it, of course, but on the way back to the house—big white envelope from 47 E. South Temple Street, Salt Lake City, Utah in my hand—I couldn't help but think: two years ago I was on my way to rock 'n' roll stardom when a Book of Mormon intercepted me on my way to the Fillmore.

Scared to death.

When I came up to the living room carrying it, my mom just sat there in shock, thinking, I suppose, *This can't be real.* She was in a kitchen chair so she could lean right up and stay tense, and I was on the couch, and we just looked at each other for what seemed like ten minutes. We discussed waiting for my dad to get home from work but quickly decided no way. I tried joking around a bit, then said, "Well, here goes." I opened it slowly and then pulled the front piece of several sheets out, scanning to see if it was a letter or an ad for the church magazines, the only thing I'd ever gotten before from Salt Lake City.

Nope, this one started *Dear Elder West,* and I knew it was real. *You have been recommended as one worthy to serve the Lord and are hereby called to serve in the Colombia Cali mission.*

From there it was perfunctory, other than the date: *You should report to the Missionary Training Center in Provo, Utah, on August 5th, blah blah blah.* I had five weeks until liftoff. It didn't really hit me until my mother said, "Colombia? That's in South America. Oh, my goodness."

And I thought, *So I got it that close.*

I went out back to sit right down plop in the flowers and look south at Long Scraggy and Windy Peak and then west to Lion's Head and Mount Rosalie, shut off from the world in my surl of silence, thinking: *Just about everything I've ever known or loved has come to an end, been poured out on the dusty ground of sacrifice. I've got nothing left to lose.*

Bull. This was the real world.

Part Two:
On the Road to Heaven

Mormon Standard Time

"He that findeth his life shall lose it: and he that loseth his life for my sake shall find it."

—Matthew 10:39

25

ON SUNDAY THE TWENTY-SECOND of April I gave one of the first talks from the pulpit of our beautiful new building and became the first full-time missionary to ever leave from the Silver Creek Branch of The Church of Jesus Christ of Latter-day Saints. Annie was there with her folks, and we both shed a couple of tears. Also there: the owners of Paradise Finer Foods, a number of our customers, and an assortment of friends new and old.

The Wednesday before—the same day a guy gave me nine hundred in cash for my VW, doubling my effective contribution—the local weekly paper had run a couple of paragraphs written by my mom, the headline saying "Elder West to South America."

And so I left.

We loaded up the camping trailer and hit the road three days early, taking the scenic route—the only kind my folks knew—to Provo by way of Arizona and Arches National Park. My dad had wanted to go through Capitol Reef on the way north, but I begged him off, saying I'd been there only a few weeks before.

So in the evenings my dad and I ambled around on red-sand twilit trails trying to find something to say, my mom and I sat in the trailer early mornings, her talking a hundred lines a minute and me wishing she would slow down a bit so I could think; she was more nervous than I was. And then finally up to a Utah County KOA where I walked out into a field south of Provo and just sat down in the weeds to stare up at Mount Timpanogos to think, over and over again: *Now what?*

The next morning my folks and I entered the Provo Missionary Training Center, also known as the MTC. I stood by nervously while the workers checked my haircut, completed some paperwork, gave me my black plastic nametag—in Spanish—and directed us down the big hall, along with another hundred or so kids, guys and girls, entering the same way, doing the same thing in one-hour shifts, seven hundred kids every Wednesday of the year. Some other folks, all smiling, directed us into a large lecture hall where some MTC honcho named President White gave a thirty-minute talk about "the best two years of your life" that were about to begin. Then he said thanks for coming and invited the missionaries through one door behind him and parents and significant others through another, behind me.

With mothers all around us kind of gasping and going, "Oh, heavens, my baby," the three of us stood up, my mother crying freely and giving me a smothering hug. I looked at my dad, his thumbs hooked over his wide leather belt with an enormous steers-head buckle, blinking at a couple of tears of his own, and wondered, *What are they really thinking?* We shook hands. He said, "Take care of yourself." Then he gave me a hug.

I moved off into the long line shuffling toward the back of the room, looked back once, and walked through the Missionary Door.

Out the back we entered a long hallway, where the occasional guy got pulled from line, sat down in a chair, and his hair trimmed to standards, some of them probably thinking two minutes before: *I'll go in here and show all these other guys what an individual I am, what a rebel, what a cool cat.* But the powers that be said, *Not here, not now, and not for two years, Alfalfa — you're ours now.*

By the time we got to the housing-and-companion-assignment table, we were all just one guy: *Elder.* There were, in fact, a few young ladies thrown in, sister missionaries. I had never met one of those before.

I met my MTC companion right there in the housing line, Elder Travis Ruff, who was reluctant to walk with me or even say much—a tough guy, probably still reeling from a fresh hallway haircut. Then we all wandered off to our respective accommodations, dorm-style rooms in four-story brick buildings scattered across a fifteen-acre compound surrounded by a high chain-link fence. We were all to find our rooms, pick a bunk, and return to the main auditorium within forty-five minutes.

Before the end of the day, we were all organized into MTC districts and directed to our classroom with the district's name taped to the door, our home for the next eight weeks. Our district Armenia, named for a city in our mission, consisted of ten people: six guys going to the mission based in Cali, Colombia, including me; two guys going to the one based in Bogotá; and two sister missionaries heading to Santiago, Chile. With our two returned-missionary instructors presiding, we spent some time introducing ourselves—I was the only convert in the bunch—and then headed as a group to the MTC bookstore to pick up our training materials, which included the little white missionary handbook, our operator's manual for the next two years.

That night we had our first district testimony meeting, where everybody was invited to share their thoughts on Joseph Smith, the Savior, the restoration of the gospel in these latter days. I was amazed at how perfunctory some of these seemed. Kids. Most of them not really converted yet, even though Great-Great-Granpappy and Mam and a hundred other progenitors had walked the trail, sailed the seas, blah blah blah, the pioneer-heritage hullabaloo I'd heard so many times, always wondering if any of it meant diddlysquat until one learned to give up, walk away, sell, abandon, lose, reject, forsake everything and everybody and every place that didn't fit—which seemed to fit me a lot more than it did a single one of them. A couple of the guys were even joking, saying, "Well, it's easier than college."

Which is not to say that most of them weren't committed and sincere. They just hadn't faced the flame yet. They hadn't had the Experience. For the duration of the MTC stay, eight weeks if our visas came through okay, we would mostly sit in a small classroom ten hours a day, studying the language and culture of our destination country, memorizing the lessons we would be expected to teach in the field, learning how to teach them, and starting to learn how to live with a constant shadow we didn't pick. Among the first things drilled into our heads was that our companion was to be chained to our wrists, figuratively, for the next two years. Even when we were in the bathroom, our companion was to be waiting right outside. They said it was for our own protection, but they didn't explain from what. I'd learn that on my own.

I got to know Elder Ruff in one fell swoop one evening during our companionship inventory. It seems that while I spent my available teenage years on and off the back roads of America, he spent his up and down the back streets and alleys of small-town USA, primarily Roy, Utah. Street fights, drag racing, high school brawls. He had a knife scar on his left hand where his thumb was practically severed. And a couple of chunks of gravel were embedded in the skin just under his lower lip from where he slid across the pavement on his face after being slammed to the street by a van filled with rowdies from the rival high school one Saturday night.

His buddies had helped him up and stuffed him, covered with blood, into the back of their '69 GTO and screamed down the street after the van. They closed in on the van, which had stopped at a red light near the center of town, and the driver of the Pontiac spun the car to a halt right in front of the van in the center of the intersection at two in the morning.

As everyone scrambled out of the van, Ruff pulled a loaded twelve-gauge shotgun off the floor of the GTO. The traffic light turned green, but with no other cars in sight he proceeded to blast the still-idling van, blowing out three tires, while his friends clubbed in the windows with a two-by-four and a length of chain.

Just another small-town Saturday night in peaceful northern Utah.

"And the other guys?" I gasped, my eyes big as golf balls.

"Most of them I didn't know," he said. "But the guy driving the van is here in the MTC. I saw him yesterday." In fact, we later learned that the guy driving the van was going to Cali, Colombia, two weeks ahead of us.

I told Elder Ruff that, other than fighting a dog once, I'd seen only one or two fights in my life on the playground and I'd never even held a gun, let alone blasted the tires of a running vehicle. Where I grew up, I told him, for excitement you went outside in your shirtsleeves to watch the November wind snap off the aspen trees. Or took full-moon walks around the south side of the mountain with my collie, rest his soul, howling in chorus as we went. Or scavenged the northern slopes for edible mushrooms: chanterelles, *Russula emetica*, puffballs. Or gathered nice wildflowers to press in my journal. And loved every minute of it.

"Wow," he said. And I could tell he meant every word of it.

My Cali group included several interesting people. Tom Barrett was from Los Angeles, where his daddy was a dentist and probably a well-to-do one, as would be shown months later. Barrett liked to race motocross; he was brash, self-assured, and kind of mouthy. He was packing about six hundred dollars of camera equipment to Colombia.

Enrique Calderón was Mexican-American, from Fresno. His parents were converts, and little English was spoken in the home, although the children had all grown up bilingual. He served as the introduction to most of us of what a Lamanite was, one of the Book of Mormon peoples whose descendants Latter-day Saints believe are among the indigenous occupants of North and South America: "Indians." In Calderón I soon came to see an entirely unique and not altogether logical mix of humility, passion, pride, and innate faith in spiritual things. And I wondered, *Is this what Colombians will be like?* (Yes.)

Chris Pfeiffer was a happy-go-lucky Utah boy, stout as a postal drop box but tenderhearted and jocular. Clay Caldwell was ever smiling, even when his brow was furrowed with frustration, a state that would become a regular facet of our lives. Like Pfeiffer he was kind-hearted, but unlike him he was very quiet, rarely offering a peep or an opinion. I thought, *Man, how's he going to do as a missionary, so quiet?*

We would all be plenty surprised over the next two years.

For missionaries going to non-English missions, day five in the MTC is known as Silent Sunday. That's the day, with three days of language training under your belt, that English ceases to exist. From then on it's the new language or nothing. Mostly nothing for another week. Companionship inventories were one of the few times we could speak English, unless we were talking with someone going to a non-Spanish-speaking mission, and in the lunchroom or the gym you'd find kids going all over the planet.

So everybody talked as much as they could those first few days, especially back in the dorms or in the cafeteria, everybody hearing everybody else's story. Ruff'd tell his and everybody would go, "Whoo-wee, man, you really were crazy," and I'd tell mine, short a few details, and everybody'd be totally silent, and one time Elder Knowlton, our language instructor, came around and stood behind me while I was talking, putting his hands on my shoulders and saying, "Elders and Sisters, don't you ever forget this story. This is who you're looking for the next two years."

And I'd think, *What'd I do?*

In those days every Mormon boy of sufficient age — nineteen in most nations — was expected to prepare himself for a mission call. Young ladies can go at twenty-one, but the onus is on the males. They aren't forced but rather *expected*. And they have to be not just

willing but also worthy. Such worthiness is a package deal: no alcohol, tobacco, or illicit drugs; no beyond-kissing sexual activity;
no serious criminal activity of any sort. Must be paying an honest
tithe—ten percent—on any income.

The worthiness determination is made by the youth's bishop
or branch president, in consultation with the youth, preferably
through a course of evaluation, assistance, and correction—when
needed—that has occurred regularly over a number of years. Yet
the expectation to go on a mission has historically been so great,
especially for Mormon boys and especially for those living in the
Mormon Belt of southern Idaho, Utah, and Nevada, that some have
sort of fudged their way through the interview process. Back then,
sometimes a bishop would submit mission papers to church headquarters knowing full well the kid wasn't entirely worthy to go but
thinking the mission field would reform the kid, turn him around,
maybe even convert him. When standards were tightened decades
later, Ruff and the kid driving the van probably wouldn't have been
able to go.

But some of these kids, I would soon come to know, never
seemed to have even spit wrong: never did drugs, never left home
until their mission call came, had a paper route or sold Girl Scout
cookies since they were nine, made the honor roll every year, Eagle
Scouts at age ten or something. Never tasted beer or cigarettes or a
bologna sandwich with mustard on white bread at the county clink
in Lawrence, Kansas, thinking, *Man, oh man, am I gonna get skinned
when I get home.*

In our weekly culture class we learned the unique nuances of
politeness, safety, commerce, history, and such of our destination
country, taught by either a native of that country or, in most cases
like ours, a returned missionary who had served in that country.
One of the culture-class teachings was to never speak English in
the streets and homes of Colombia and especially to never laugh,
because it would be rude and the Colombians would think we were
laughing at or talking about them and that would hurt the work
of the Lord. They were a very cultured people, our instructor told
us. Sophisticated. European mannerisms. It was right there in the
book.

So I made that my rule, not even speaking English in the dorms,
with the entire building reserved for Spanish speakers. One day I
asked one of our daily instructors—again, always returned missionaries—if he thought I should take my English scriptures and church

books to Colombia. He said, "Here's the deal. If you want to learn the scriptures really well, take them in English. If you want to learn the language really well, send 'em home." So I sent them home, thinking, *Lot of good that will do my parents*. Practically the only thing I would carry into Colombia in English was my passport.

We'd be up at 6:30 every morning, seven days a week, and go straight through till 9:30 P.M. with language classes, memorization, teacher training, more memorization, more Spanish, lunch, an hour in the gym, then back to class. One day a week was P-day, or preparation day, the day to throw on a T-shirt and jeans and write letters home, do our laundry, maybe even go for a hike up nearby Rock Canyon. Back in the tie, white shirt, and nametag by 4:30, and back to class for the evening. Sunday was the Sabbath, of course, with time spent in regular church meetings, a devotional fireside with a church General Authority in the evening, but the rest of it in the classroom, study study study.

What we studied: the Spanish language and the discussions, *charlas* in Spanish, a series of seven prewritten lessons or conversations that would form the backbone of our teaching for the next two years. Topics included Joseph Smith and his First Vision; the coming forth of the Book of Mormon; the commandments, including chastity, marital fidelity, tithing, the Word of Wisdom health code; faith in Jesus Christ; the life, death, and resurrection of Christ, including his visit to the American continent as recorded in the Book of Mormon; commitment to the Christian lifestyle; and what was called the baptismal challenge, the thing that Reefer had chosen to use on me the first night, which wasn't normal, the thing that had knocked his buddy into the corner of my closet.

In those days the dialogue of the discussion was to be learned verbatim, including the typical questions or arguments that the listener could pose. For all of us, this approach helped us bone up on correct doctrine as opposed to cultural doctrine, which was not an unknown problem, especially in Utah. For trainees in a new language like us, this approach brought the added benefit of embedding us with grammatically correct and functional language skills, some getting more functional at it than others. As we memorized the dialogue, we would also learn to flip the pages of a three-ring binder of illustrations—called the flipchart—to show photos or paintings of things like Christ being baptized by full-body immersion; Christ's appearance in the Americas, with this particular painting revealing a backdrop of Machu Picchu, which is highly unlikely but very pretty; a father giving a priesthood blessing to a child; and so forth. If you got stuck on the dialogue, you could glance at your flipchart to remind yourself where you were—if you had the pictures in the right order. Learning to coordinate the dialogue with the flipchart was an exercise in mental dexterity that some of the guys wouldn't figure out for months.

These were all the same discussions and pictures I had received from Elders Reefer and Edwards three years before, all in Spanish now, of course. We would practice the missionary part and then practice with our instructors all possible responses and how to deal with each. A great way to learn the language, frankly.

Whether going to English-speaking or foreign missions, missionaries were expected to learn by memory, perfectly, all seven forty-five-minute discussions before they left the MTC. So we practiced, we memorized, we gave each concept to our companion in chunks. Then when we thought we were ready, we gave it to one of our instructors. If the selected concept was close enough to word-perfect, we could check it off and move to the next one, each discussion consisting of six to ten concepts. Eventually, we had to try and pass off the whole discussion at once to our instructors.

A couple weeks in, I was called as second counselor in the branch presidency to President White, the honcho who'd welcomed us all to the MTC and a retired military officer. The first counselor was another missionary with four weeks in the field, Elder Brad Morrison. Our branch consisted of about sixty missionaries, and it was our job to stand as examples of what a missionary should be. The weird thing was that I'd been a Mormon only a couple of years and Morrison only seven months.

No one ever got sent on a mission until they'd been a member at least a year. However, Brad Morrison had joined the church against the wishes of his parents, wishes dashed decidedly enough they told him not to come home. But Brad hung onto the faith. In Idaho, a good bishop saw a young man burning up with testimony and commitment, reading every church book in sight, and turned in Brad's mission papers five months after he was baptized, thinking, *Well, heck fire and gol-dang, he's got no home and no family and he's gonna go someday anyway, why not now?* The stake president had interviewed him and agreed, sending the papers right up to HQ, kind of staying away from his phone for a few days. At HQ the papers made the rounds of church leaders, clear to President Spencer W. Kimball at some point. Eventually one of the General Authorities had Brad in for a personal chat in Salt Lake City, fully prepared to tell him to go home and wait a little longer but then changing his mind right there in the interview and saying, "Young man, we're gonna make you a missionary."

So Brad and I, we were a pair. One time in branch presidency meeting, I asked President White why he'd called me to be a counselor, and he put down his pen and said, "Oh, I asked Elder Morrison here to recommend someone he thought was really on fire, knew the scriptures, had a testimony. I figured he knows the troops at ground level a little better than I do. And Elder Morrison came to me one morning and said, 'I know who it is, but I don't know his name. I saw his face in a dream.'"

I kinda smiled at Morrison, but he didn't blink.

"So we pulled out the branch roster," President White continued, "and he pointed right at you, saying, 'That's the guy, Elder West.' And then I prayed about it, and yours was the face."

I just sat there looking at them, remembering my dream about Colombia two years before. Then President White finished: "Welcome to the mission field, Elder."

Over the next few weeks we got shots for everything from yellow fever to typhoid to small pox to ringworm, scurvy, nose hairs, and bunions, not to mention jet lag and ring around the bathtub, the gamma globulin for hepatitis hardening up in your bum cheeks like concrete in a balloon.

Unlike some of my companions, especially Ruff, my Spanish was coming along just fine. I had studied it every quarter of public school since fourth grade and gotten A's all the way, and the MTC regimen didn't pass up every single thing I had ever learned in eight years of top-flight public schooling until day thirteen.

But suddenly, about three weeks in, I developed a photographic memory for text. Elder Morrison was seeing faces, but I was seeing whole paragraphs and eventually whole pages: Look at it up and down, read it through a couple times, stare at the wall — got it. We'd practice a concept together as a district, reading it out loud for the instructor — all together now, class — and then break off into our companionships and start to practice together, only I'd tell Ruff, as soon as we pulled our chairs into a corner, "Okay, I'm ready," and do it, not a mistake. I did that twice, and he actually threw his book against the wall, yelling "Frick," the poor guy still having trouble with "*Buenos días, Señor* García."

We'd eventually do another concept as a class and break into companionships, and the instructor and the other missionaries would just sit and look at me. I'd close my eyes and give the concept, maybe a hundred and fifty or two hundred words. Nothing like that had ever happened in high school. I told Ruff it was like closing my eyes and seeing the whole page right there, like reading the back of my eyelids. I also told him I hoped I could do it with my eyes open in a few weeks.

On P-day, the domestic chores completed, we'd have a few hours to relax or go play. Options included things like hiking up Rock Canyon, going to the mall to slurp Orange Juliuses and discreetly stare at chicks, wandering the BYU bookstore, or just lying around the shack and daydreaming about days gone by. Lying around wasn't a real option, because everyone knew that if they did that, they'd start thinking about home: the girlfriend, the car, the guitar, the passed-up scholarship. And no one wanted to hike up Rock Canyon with me, so I learned how to go malling. The education at work here, not that we discussed it openly, was to develop one's skills in looking at girls without being seen. Mirror sunglasses were effective, so we all looked like junior G-men.

But the girls weren't the only target of our stealth: no one wanted his companion to know he was looking at girls, because that was part of the two-year bargain, and no one wanted to be seen as so quickly overcome by the lusts of the flesh. Along the way we learned the Missionary Maxim, taught to us by a senior church leader in one of those Sunday-evening firesides and met with great applause: "If you don't look once, you're not a man. But if you look twice, you're not a missionary." (Each of us later addended this maxim to include: "So just take *one* lo-o-o-ng look."

However, at the same time that you were looking to see if your companion was looking to see if you were looking at girls to see if any of them were looking at either of you, you both noticed something mighty peculiar: girls in Provo, Utah, didn't even know that MTC missionaries were alive yet. You were still just the embryonic stage of a future life form. Manhood was somewhere around two years away—it was written all over your baby face. What really complicated matters was the fact that there were probably twenty-five thousand eligible *returned* missionaries—their two-year stints completed—right there in Happy Valley. And they were all in line in front of you.

An additional complication was that if any locals saw a missionary staring at girls, they would be ashamed, the missionary would be ashamed, everybody would be ashamed, the church would fall apart, Brigham Young's statue would topple, and Brigham Young University would have to relocate to Pittsburgh. Nobody wanted that, so we all wore reflective sunglasses. Even inside the mall. The sister missionaries never went with us, but we were all naive enough to believe they were taking in something "cultural," like staring at guys at the other end of the mall.

I really dug the MTC overall. I would wake up, look at my companions in the other bunks, and then out the window at the Wasatch peaks; I would walk out and look at the buildings, at fifteen-hundred guys in white shirts and ties, little black nametags in their pockets, and say, sometimes out loud, "I am here! I made it!" I was a missionary, just like Reefer—I was gonna follow in his footsteps. Like Paul and Peter from the Bible, Alma and Ammon and Amulek from the Book of Mormon, and Samuel Smith and Parley P. Pratt and Brigham Young from 1800s church history. I was very stoked.

At about the one-month mark, President White called in Elder Morrison and me and told us one of our boys was going home, his mission over. The missionary's stake president back home in Burley, Idaho, had called President White to tell him the young man's girlfriend had just confessed to being four months pregnant. The church was releasing him immediately as a missionary, a dishonorable discharge. He would likely go home to church disciplinary action—perhaps excommunication, perhaps less severe—but he would certainly go home in disgrace.

The day after I "passed off" the last of the discussions, the first one still floating right there behind my eyelids, Elder Brad Morrison's group left for Colombia, visas right on time, and I was called to replace him as first counselor in the Branch presidency. I figured I'd have about four weeks in the saddle, and then skedaddle for points south. It wasn't happenin'.

26

WE HAD WHAT WAS SUPPOSED to be our final district meeting one night, everybody shedding tears, all of us wondering, *But where are our visas?* The sisters had theirs. We went through the whole farewell thing the next day, districts all over the MTC knowing the Colombians were packing their bags, along with two groups going to Italy and some assorted statesiders.

Some clown from our branch stood up right on the table in the cafeteria and made a farewell speech to us old boys about to take to the friendly skies. Then he pulled a crumpled letter from his pocket that he'd clearly stolen from his companion, who scrambled to grab it as the clown read out loud for eight hundred people to hear: "Dear John . . ." Only it was addressed to *Dear Rick*, the guy standing there crying, then slumping into his chair and covering his head, written by the girlfriend, the one, the only, the promised who had hung on lonely for as long as she possibly could, a whole five weeks, but just couldn't take it any longer, poor poor pitiful her, so she was announcing her engagement to another "perfect young man." She was sure Rick would really like him.

I'd hear another dozen of those over the next twenty-two months, the girl back home who couldn't wait, but none of them read from the rooftops like that one. At least I didn't have that to worry about.

Next day we waved good-bye to our two sister missionaries, loading their two bags each onto a van heading to the Salt Lake airport, then we went back in for mail call and lunch. The only thing in my mailbox was a little blue slip of paper: *Please inform your group that you have been delayed. The Colombian government has not given permission for you to enter the country yet. We will keep you informed of developments...."*

We walked over to the travel office and asked what they knew. The gal there said, "You just hang tight—visas could be here any day," but then she asked where it was we weren't heading. Ruff said, "Colombia," and the lady said, "Oops." She excused herself for a minute and came back with an older man who got right to it: "We have some problems with the embassy in Colombia, Elders. They're not letting any Americans in right now."

I said, "Another district went down just four weeks ago," knowing they'd made it because Morrison had dropped me a postcard. It took twenty-two days to get to the States, but it got here.

The guy said, "That appears to be the last group for a while."

We grumbled and moaned and stood around dumb for a bit until the guy said, "There's a good chance you'll go stateside for a few weeks."

Ruff said, "Stateside, like you mean Iowa or something?"

"Nah, I mean Texas or California, most likely. Spanish-speaking."

And so there we were.

At the end of eight weeks, the planned, scheduled, foreseen, prepared program kind of dries up in the MTC—as in, The End. For a week we attended classes with another group, most of our district still working on the *charlas* anyway. But our instructors had already been reassigned, and the team momentum began to dissipate. Some of the elders began to get a bit rowdy and act like hot shots, both in the classroom and out. Tension in the dorm escalated as well, and tempers strained. We simply were not where we had intended to be, and we did not have much worthwhile to do.

Toward the end of week ten, President White called me in and said he was going to release me as his first counselor; it was time for someone else to have a shot. So on Sunday I was released, our second counselor moved up to first, and a new kid came in at second. I had batted, and now I was out.

Meantime, we weren't going anywhere, not Texas—thank the Lord—and not California, because the travel office kept getting told our visas would clear any day. Nobody was getting any letters, of course, because everyone thought we were in Colombia by now, and they were waiting for word and a new address. I started thinking I was going to go absolutely nuts, if not automatically then intentionally. Elder Pfeiffer and I actually discussed hitting the road, hitching our way out to Salem or San Luis Obispo, looking up a mission office, and saying, "Hey! Put us to work. We're trained." Work with the migrants or something.

I'd sit in the dorm room and just stare up at the Wasatch mountains, humming Outlaws tunes — "Breaker, breaker, take me ho-o-o-me" — and doing Skynyrd riffs with my air guitar.

And then the news that we were still in the States finally got delivered, and we all started getting mail again from home, and cookies, and the latest photos of the fam and the farm and the new niece and the old dog and the little brother taking over the GTO and the shotgun.

But I was the only one who got a letter from Annie Hawk.

Very level, emotionally; very cautious; very tame. *Hello, Elder West, best wishes on your mission, I'll pray for you.* That kind of thing. The only heat in the entire letter came when she told me she had signed up for BYU's famous thirty-day desert survival course. She'd be gone the entire month of August, walking three hundred miles across the canyon country of our childhood fantasy era. I hoped I'd be long gone to South America by then. I didn't even write her back at that point. But with nothing else to do, I sat and remembered.

That final visit in Fort Collins, I had put my arm around her when we walked around Lake Sherwood, but it just wasn't there. Two warm bodies, two sets of feet going forward on separate roads. I wondered then and a hundred times in the years since what would have happened if I'd never tried forcing it up on the cabin roof. Or if maybe we'd met that day somewhere that qualified as neutral ground. Not on the mountain, not at the cabin — someplace where every memory was not so infused with the passion we had known.

That day I had asked her to marry me.

That day she had said good-bye.

And so I'd gone to Fort Collins the next week, a place so neutral it was entirely sterile. Joe Walsh had said it perfectly, and I wandered around blitzed with the tune in my head for most of three days: "In the city . . . nothing grows and life ain't very pretty." And "There's nothing there to catch you when you fall."

Not if. When.

But what if I had never broken Annie's heart? And I wondered: Had I plain and simply broken it forever? After it had known a fire that carried us, moved us, consumed us.

Oddly, both in the weeks after that cabin roof assault and again right there in the MTC, I wanted to hurt. I wanted to cry. I wanted to punish myself for being unfaithful, untrue, or—as Kerouac would have put it—emotionally crapulous. A glutton. A pig. Selfish.

As I lay there in my bunk in the MTC one afternoon, I ultimately confessed to simply not understanding what had happened between Annie and me at all—the flame just going out like it did, poof.

All I could think about was Annie, until Ruff had it worse. One day he got a messenger, the new first counselor coming to our room. "You're needed in the administration office. Bad news."

I said, "Oh, crap, Texas?" and the guy said, "No, it's not mission stuff."

So off we went to the Big Office, chained together and all, but when we got there they asked me to just take a seat and led Ruff in to talk to the MTC president, our branch president already in there and looking morose. Elder Ruff was in about four minutes, and I was thinking he was about to go home and be a daddy or something, and then the door opened and he came out fast, heading right past me. He actually slammed the wall with his fist and yelled the F-word on his way out the door, and I don't mean *frick*. The secretary said, "Well, that's a first."

I ducked out, and Ruff was already fifty yards away, walking fast. I called out to him, and he took off sprinting and left me in carpet dust. I started to run after him but then pulled up, thinking, *Jeez, do I let another one go?*

President White came out then and asked, "Where'd he go?" and I said "He ran," and President White said, "Bad news from home." And then he said, "Let him go for a while. He's a strong young man. I think he just needs some time to think."

I asked, "Did somebody die?" and President White relieved me of that one, saying, "No, but I'll have to leave anything else up to Elder Ruff. I don't know how much he'll want to say."

Ruff said enough when he showed up at the room just before dinner. He'd been crying, and his tie was off, wadded up in his pants pocket, but now he was pretty much just stone-faced and mean-looking. He told us all, saying, "Well, everybody's talking anyway." His father, a high priest in the church, had just admitted to having an affair, and he was probably going to lose his membership in the church and maybe his wife. Elder Ruff's mom had been on that phone, a conference call along with the home bishop and stake president. Through them, Ruff's dad had asked for an opportunity to come down and meet with Elder Ruff to apologize and explain. Ruff told us, "I'm gonna punch the so-and-so right in the such-and-such face, bust his such-and-such jaw with my such-and-such fist." That was probably another first: seven F, C, and A words on the fourth floor of the Missionary Training Center within about thirty-eight seconds.

That night Elder Ruff put a chair up next to the window and just stared out for hours, while I swept chipmunk litter out the back door of the old, leaning cabin down on Christopher Drive and then rehung the shelf where we used to put our sandalwood candles. Just before midnight I looked again—he was still staring out the window, and so I went ahead and caught a ride down off Paradise Mountain and headed west, down Crow Hill through Redtail and on through Shawnee and Grant, the blue penstemon painting the valley like a quilt. Then up Guanella Pass, stopping at the top just to breath in the air for twenty minutes, the leaves of the quakies rattling happily in the breeze, then continued on down into South Park, over Trout Creek Pass and into the Arkansas River Valley. When I got to Poncha Pass, I saw that the Light Pole of the Many Cursings was once again painted shiny and new, and I opened my eyes to the moon framed in the center of the MTC dorm window. Ruff was asleep right there, his head resting on the windowsill, and the window was open about three inches, letting in a delicious Rocky Mountain breeze.

I lay there looking at the moon for ten minutes, my head running all over the Western states, then I took my pillow and switched ends on the bed, my head down where my feet had been, so I was unable to see the moon any longer but closer to the breeze. I'd have gotten up and laid down right under the window, but Elder Ruff was already there.

The day we hit three months in the mission field—every day of it in the MTC—we decided to hold a group fast for visa clearance, skipping all food and liquid for twenty-four hours, maybe longer if we could handle it. Three or four of us had already fasted for the same purpose independently over the last couple of weeks, but we'd never done it as a group.

It was the Brazilians who inspired us. One day in the cafeteria, eight hundred kids sitting around playing with their whipped potatoes and using their forks as launching apparatuses for corn kernels and lima beans, eight guys in blue suits had walked in at the far end of the hall, and the place went silent. Elders of Israel. We'd all heard about them; the word had spread rapidly. Eight young men who had received mission calls to Brazil, then never gotten visas. So at eleven weeks the church had sent them to Boston to work the Portuguese neighborhoods. Finally at eight months their visas had come through. So now they were back at the MTC for five days to freshen up their vowels, get another round of shots, and go south, where most of their hearts had already gone. They didn't play with their food, they spoke only Portuguese to each other, and they said very little to anyone else. They stood straighter than the rest of us. Their whole demeanor said, *We are real, you are children.* They came, they polished, they prayed, and they left.

On the morning the Brazilians caught the van for Salt Lake International, Elder Barrett said to our group: "Time to grow up, kids. We've been fighting and lying around and dreaming of home, and we're ordained servants of God. Let's act like it." And everyone said amen, and Elder Pfeiffer said, "How about we have a fast, all of us, together? For visas." And then he said, "I don't want to go to Texas." And there was a big amen to that.

So we had a very solemn, very quiet, no-games no-giggles no-options fast, thirty hours straight, district prayer in the morning, at noon, at night and again the second morning.

At 3:16 that second afternoon, President White came to our dorm room and said, "Your visas just got here."

And Annie and Lynyrd Skynyrd and Paradise Mountain and the Light Pole of the Many Cursings all suddenly went *whoosh*, right out the MTC window and on down a long crowded road to get jumbled in a heap with a million other monuments of the world gone by.

And suddenly we were scared.

27

"As I have always held it a crime to anticipate
evils, I will believe it a good comfortable road
until I am compelled to believe differently."
—Meriwether Lewis, May 26, 1805,
Across the Continent

THE FLIGHT FROM SALT LAKE CITY to Los Angeles International was on
a Western Airlines 727 that turned back about thirty minutes out
because of mechanical problems. Within about fifteen minutes,
though, the pilot must have figured he had it fixed, so we hung a
U-turn around a cloud and continued on to L.A. From there it was a
nine-hour flight to Panama, then Bogotá, and finally into Cali on the
Colombian national airline, Avianca.

On the Bogotá to Cali hop, we got a preview of the next twenty-
one months from a group of guys in the back of the plane who were
obviously taunting us, although I couldn't understand much beyond
the tone of their remarks. And the tone was anything but friendly.
Soon, ignored by us and obviously drunk, one of them began yelling. The other passengers kept their eyes glued to their magazines
or out the window, and the flight attendants stayed toward the front
of the plane as much as they could.

Then I heard Ruff responding to the guy, and I turned to look,
Ruff with his Spanish vocabulary of about twenty words.

The guy would yell "*Americanos, imperialistas*," clear enough,
and Ruff would answer back, "*No hermano, me llamo* Elder Ruff,"
and then the guy would yell "*Abren las ventanas* blah blah blah" — I
understood almost nothing—"*para que* blah blah blah," and the other Colombian guys would all laugh and Ruff would say "*Como?*"
and then repeat the giving of his name. A couple of minutes into
this exchange, Ruff very aware that the Colombians were itching
for a rumble, he started answering the guy with really basic street

commentary in very basic Spanish, saying things like "Your mother is what?" and "You did what with your dog?" And our Mexican-American companion, Elder Calderón, said out loud in English, "Cool it, man, he's not joking." And Ruff said to Calderón, "He sounds kind of stupid. You think he understands international hand signals?" and he flipped off the whole group, right in their faces. They just sat there wondering what that particular gesture happened to mean.

And then we all just rode quietly, meditating, until the plane taxied to a stop in Cali. This being one of those jets where the stairs exit out the back, the Colombian boys beat us out, thank goodness. But as I entered the stairwell, the Colombian air hit me in the face, and I thought I was going to suffocate on the heat and humidity. I actually had to cough. As I cleared the stairwell, there stood the Colombian greeting line, each of the men spitting on our shoes as we filed between them. The tall one looked at each of us in turn and said, "Go home, *gringos.*"

I got the vague suspicion they didn't like us.

Many of the other Colombia passengers came down the stairs smiling at their compatriots, and a young jetsetter with sunglasses hurried past us saying, "Hey, *gringos*, welcome to Colombia!"

And I thought, *Well, buenos días yourself.* No one had ever mentioned this in the MTC.

Also, no one even vaguely resembling a Mormon missionary or an American mission president was anywhere in sight. Calderón bummed some change after a while, and we found a phone number for the *Iglesia de Jesucristo de los S.U.D.* The mission secretary said the president was tied up, sorry, so why didn't we just catch a taxi—or rather a *buseta*, or small bus—and they'd pay the guy when we arrived at the office.

We finally got there, and the two elders doing their temporary stint on the office staff took us down the street for lunch at Wopper King. Never mind the name similarity—this wasn't food like I'd ever seen before. The *hamburguesas* were simply a slab of chopped-up beef—not ground, certainly not pressed or formed; just hacked off, whacked up like an old boot, and stuffed between two pieces of thick, crusty bread. There were, of course, sliced tomatoes, onions, and lettuce available, but it was all just tossed into three buckets hanging there actually nailed to the wall, open air, flies having a heyday. We had learned in the MTC, of course, to never touch unwashed vegetables or fruit. And I still hadn't eaten a piece of meat in seven years.

The other elders ordered their burgers, intending to eat them plain. I stood there looking at the menu, the finance secretary saying in English, "C'mon, Elder West, whaddya want? They've got big burgers, little burgers, or blah blah blah," me not having a clue what else he'd just referred to.

"What's in that last one?" I asked, "that one you just mentioned."

"*Empanadas?*" he replied. "They're like big, fat tortillas. With meat and potatoes in them."

So I ate my first meat in seven years at Wopper King, Colombia. It was not an auspicious reentry into the world of the carnivore.

We spent that first night in the mission home, and I experienced my first diarrhea, very likely from the strange vittles in my gut. The mission home was a residence leased by the church for the mission president, a banker serving three years with his family, which included five children aged six through nineteen. The church just called these guys up out of the blue, and said, *Your turn, pack your bags.* And they rented out the house, sold the dog, and went.

There were iron bars on every window, multiple locks on the doors, and 24/7 security guys walking the neighborhood. It wasn't a fancy place—nice, but mere suburban dime-a-dozen in the States. The banker, President Wayne Bills, had served his youth mission in Peru, back when missions were thirty months long, and his wife was a native Spanish-speaker, from the Mormon colonies in southern Colorado. So when she gave us all a hug, mine included commentary about the homeland.

That afternoon we were all interviewed one by one by President Bills, then we enjoyed an evening meal of mostly American-style food with the Bills family, and then we held a testimony meeting, everybody getting up one by one to say he was here to change the world, even Ruff, still unconvinced about the religion part and his place in it but having seen miracles in the MTC. He'd witnessed me seeing pages before my eyes and a kid getting healed right in the middle of an epileptic seizure one night. So he was willing to give it a shot, and his dad could go to hell—he actually cussed right there in the living room in front of the Bills kids.

We all said amen, and there were tears in everybody's eyes, including the president's, and then he said, "Elders, I have your first assignments ready. You leave tomorrow morning for your various

fields of labor." And nobody said amen then; we just sat there thinking, *Here we go.*

And the next morning we went.

28

"So we saunter toward the Holy Land."
—Henry David Thoreau, *Walking*

WE GOT SCATTERED all over western Colombia the next morning, two staying in Cali, one going south a hundred and fifty miles to Popayán, a couple heading north to a pair of little Cauca River Valley towns. I got on a bus heading halfway to the Venezuela border, eight hours north to the big city of Pereira. All alone. Okay, not all alone—there were probably forty other people on that bus with me, plus two piglets, five or six chickens, a horrendously ugly little dog, and a goat. But not another person was blond, *gringo*, or scared to death.

I rode fitfully, to say the least, on a bus that would continue all the way to Rio Negro, "sixteen to twenty hours"—that's exactly what the schedule said. I had no idea what Pereira looked like. I was just hoping we were near a city when eight hours had passed and I could make myself understood to the driver, the lady next to me, *someone*, when the time came. In fact, I eventually held a reasonably coherent conversation with the very motherly lady next to me, who not only made the trip more enjoyable but also alerted me from a half-slumber when we arrived in Pereira. The Spanish actually worked, although people from all over the bus stared at me like I was from another planet and probably took the lady's autograph after I got off.

The bus pulled into a narrow side street lined with trash and winos, and the lady said, "This is your stop, hurry." I got out to a really amazing smell, a mixture that singer Bruce Cockburn would later refer to lyrically as "dust and diesel." But he forgot to mention the rotting fruit and vegetable refuse that lay behind the stalls of every open-air corner market, or the stench of raw sewage that coursed down every canal and some of the rivers, or the smell of whiskey and beer and coffee that infused every breath.

I called for a taxi—easy enough: "*taxi*"—and handed the guy
the address. He too looked at me like I was from another planet.
And I was.

We soon pulled up to a block of front doors, all stuck together
and sharing common sidewalls like in San Francisco but a lot smaller, and got out. It took me a while to finally figure out that the guy
was asking for one hundred and twenty pesos to cover the fare. I
then went up the stairs and knocked on the door. A ten-year-old boy
opened it, smiled, and let me in, just like that.

It was a simple deep box of concrete with a painting of the Virgin
Mary on one greenish wall. My companion, a Colombian named Al-
varo Lara, was right there working at the table. He said, "Sit down,
be with you in a minute," hardly knowing I was there.

And that's about how it went for the next two weeks.

That very first night, when I was barely unpacked in our little
eight-by-ten *pieza*—furnished room, meaning two beds and a closet
rod nailed at an angle into the plaster of one corner—he said, "Let's
go, baptismal interviews," although I caught only a portion of each
word. Enough to get the drift. He went out and down the stairs,
seemingly oblivious to the yelling and taunts that accompanied our
every step, his jaw firm, his eyes straight ahead, moving rapidly. I
kept right up, mountain boy and all, but I really wanted to check
out the place, look around, soak it in. People were yelling stuff at us
constantly. "*Yánqui*" (Yankee), "*expoitador*" (exploiter), and "*imperialistas*" (imperialists) were all fairly clear, as was "*Go home, gringo!*"
(Go home, *gringo*), although I had no idea why I was getting that
yelled at me.

We hurried across a busy avenue—no crosswalks or stoplights,
which I wouldn't have known how to use anyway—and entered a
world I didn't know existed, and I'd read *National Geographic* for ten
years. The little houses—*casitas*—were piled one on top of another,
wall supports made of bamboo-like *guadua* and the walls themselves just split and rolled *guadua*, which let sunlight stream right
in, or sometimes the walls were concrete mud. Little kids peeked
out at us through their walls, and they were almost all very dirty,
many of the youngest bare-bottomed—with no plumbing, it was far
easier to just squat when one needed to. Amazingly ugly little mutt
dogs barked, adult men went out of their way to avoid us, kids ran
ahead and then ducked into corners to watch.

Lara drove straight ahead, never smiling, never waving. I did
both—one, because it seemed the polite thing to do and my mama

had raised me to be polite, and two, just to see what kind of reaction I would get. But mostly everyone just stared.

Garbage lay in the streets in piles. A putrid little stream meandered through the barrio. Eventually my waving paid off, however, and a small crowd of children attached itself to us, half of them coming right up and tugging on our arms, saying, "What time eezeet, meester?" And with the tugging, a number of them began petting my arms, literally. Really weird.

Lara actually began to relax a bit with the children, toying with a couple of them, then waving at a group of women rubbing clothing against stones down in the river. Many of the people appeared to be pure African, but just as many were mixed breed this and that. No one really looked Indian, a phenotype that I had expected.

Then we arrived at the house Lara was seeking. Two of the kids entered before us, yelling excitedly, "*Mami! Los élderes!*"

The Elders of Israel had arrived.

A fortyish woman came into the little house from out back, wiping her hands on a towel. She offered each of us not her hand but her elbow, exactly as we'd been taught in the MTC: when hands are full, or wet, or dirty, or missing, they'll offer whatever's handy, usually an elbow. She said something to Lara and then started talking to me. Both of the children took my hands and just stared up at me, smiling. Another pair of little ones entered, then a teenage girl, and all conversation switched its direction toward me. I caught about every fourteenth word. One of the kids continued petting my arms, just rubbing his hands up and down, up and down, gently, like he was stroking a cat or something.

Elder Lara turned to me and said, "I have interviews to do. You just wait here and entertain the kids." And he and the *hermana* — sister — disappeared into another little room.

So for the next four hours, it seemed, I sat there with four little kids and a teenage girl whose front-button shirt was far too small to completely conceal her blossoming breasts, and I entertained. They would ask questions, then ask them again, till I started to get it.

"Where are you from?" (Which was asked repeatedly in a half-dozen ways: *De donde viene? De donde eres? De donde es? Donde viven sus padres? Donde está su hogar? Donde está su casa?*)

"Colorado. *Los Estados Unidos.*"

"What is your name?"

"Elder West." They couldn't pronounce it any closer than *waist*, but that worked for me.

And on and on and on, one or the other of the little ones return-ing every now and then to pet my arms. Pretty soon they started playing word games with me, and the eleven-year-old pulled out a picture book and started instructing. At some point during the eve-ning, I actually started comprehending much of the conversation. It just clicked in: the sounds, the inflections, the nuances. Nine years of public-school Spanish and thirteen weeks in the MTC started drop-ping into the unique Colombian slots, and I started to understand. Most of it.

Every twenty minutes or so, the person in the interview would come out and call in the next one, a whole family getting baptized except the little ones who weren't eight years old yet.

There was no man in the house, and I asked about it. The lit-tle kids giggled, the teenager blushed, and one of the middle ones said, "*El anda por hay*," which meant nothing much clearer to me than "he's out wandering around," which is exactly what it meant. It would take only a couple of weeks to realize that this was what many Colombian fathers seemed to do, usually with one arm around someone else's wife and the other around a Poker beer or an *aguar-diente* (whiskey).

Over the next few days, Elder Lara and I covered some ground on foot and in incredibly crowded busses, almost all of it extremely dirty and poor. But in large measure he sat around the house mak-ing posters and knickknacks for an upcoming event, I understood not what. So I asked him about the arm petting, why were the *niños* always rubbing our arms, and he looked at me for clarification be-cause I didn't yet know that verb. Finally he said, "Not ours. Yours. They only do that to the *gringos*." He actually used the word.

And I asked why.

And he said, "Because you're all so hairy!"

And I'd have kids petting my *bellos* for the next twenty-one months, my *bellos* actually getting thicker in the humidity and thus more petable.

At church on Sunday I was admitted formally to the Pereira chapter of one of the closest fraternities on earth: the mission-field Mormon congregation. (In Utah, they are typically nowhere near as kind and welcoming and inclusive.) In Colombia, brand new and stupid or not, the missionary is viewed almost with a rever-ence, an honor. Almost everybody in the room was taught and bap-tized by one of you, so you're special. We baptized our family after church services that day, except for the dad who was still out there wandering around. The teenage daughter wore no bra under the white full-immersion baptismal dress.

There I also met the other companionship operating in Pereira, both from the United States, and Elder Lara essentially told me good-bye. The city of Pereira then had about 300,000 inhabitants, about 299,000 more than any place I had ever lived except for thirteen weeks in Provo. For those first four days, Elder Lara and I had spent at least half of each day doing *vueltas* (errands); running down to the *farmácia* (drugstore) for glue, more paper, or a new pen; or going down to the main post office to get the mail daily for all the missionaries in our zone, Elder Lara being the zone leader. We'd come and we'd go, and I'd see all these thousands of people watching us, looking at us like we were aliens or terrorists or something, and I'd wonder, *When will we stop and talk with someone? When do I get to testify, or teach, or just stop and talk to a man about life and his kids and the purpose of living?* And Lara would just run from one Bic pen to another.

I was new enough that I had no clue what was right and wrong. Maybe this was really what a zone leader had to do. But I asked Lara anyway, "Can't we go find someone to teach?"

And so Monday morning, P-day, he took me over to the other apartment and turned me over to Elder David Hampton, two months ahead of me in the mission. Lara and Hampton's companion, Stevens, an old-timer nearing the completion of his mission, had, of course, more *vueltas* to do. We saw them again that afternoon at the 4:30 back-in-a-tie meeting, but I was afterward instructed to get some personal gear and train with Hampton for a few days. We were going to do splits.

So Elder Hampton and I pretty much ran our own companionship for the next two weeks, getting back together with Lara and Stevens and the other members of the zone only on Mondays, when we would go throw a football or make macaroni and cheese down at the meetinghouse. It took about three days for Hampton's blatant inactivity—leisurely lunches, after-lunch naps, and long, melancholy home-and-hearth chat sessions—to drive me nuts. I really wanted to get out there and dig up some business.

Which was exactly, Hampton finally confessed, what he didn't have: business. He and Elder Stevens had run out of leads, the program had run dry, and they had nothing to do. He said that in two months in Colombia he had learned that missionaries spent about

seventy-five percent of their time digging up new people. From time
to time, after lots of effort—twelve-hour days spent knocking on
doors or talking to men at bus stops or over countertops—a companionship would develop a program, have twelve or thirteen people
or families willing to listen to a formal discussion and then maybe
a second one, but sooner or later most would just fall through: not
answer the door, tell you to your face to go away, or just disappear.
    I said, "I don't think Elder Lara has much interest. All we do
is *vueltas* all day long. He never talks to anyone but the landlady."
Hampton said, "Yeah, that's what I've heard." And then he started
to cry, saying, "I came out here to really do a work, to be a valiant
servant, to harvest fields for the Lord, and all Stevens does is run to
the post office and write letters home and plan meetings and design
charts."
    And I said, "So why don't we just go out and build our own
program?"
    Hampton said, still wiping his eyes, "I'd really like to do that.
But my Spanish isn't real good."
    I lied and said, "Mine's great." So the two new kids hit the
streets of Colombia. We were scared to death. I would actually be
sick every morning, barely able to open the door and go out. But we
knocked on half the doors of Pereira that week, getting in maybe a
dozen. People would either just say, "No, I'm Catholic" and shut the
door or they'd go on and on with some commentary. Barely catching
a word, I wouldn't know whether to fish or cut bait until Hampton
would say, "*Grácias, con permiso*" and go in or "*Grácias, hasta luego*"
and turn to leave. Then I'd say, "Oh" and follow him, letting him
think I knew what was going on.
    I asked him once. "What the heck is *la silla*?" (pronounced *see-
ya*). And he said, "That means chair." So I asked him why people
were always whispering about the chair when we went by or even
talking to us about it, right in the middle of the street. Did they all
want a chair? And he said, "Oh, you mean *that silla. La cia.* CIA. The
U.S. Central Intelligence Agency."
    I said, "Okay, what about it?"
    And he said, "That's what everyone thinks we are. The poor
people, *los humildes*, they're actually scared of us. You'll see them
skedaddle off into the back streets when they see us coming, but the
college kids and people with money, a lot of them come right up and
try to bang chests with you, when they're in a group. Never when
they're alone, except maybe when they're drunk."

I asked him why, and he said, "Well, look at us! FBI haircuts, white shirts, and ties." And most of the *gringos* wore dark sunglasses because our eyes were freaking out in the sun. I owned two pair.

So my CIA buddy and I, neither of us ever having experienced anything of the secret agent lifestyle more exciting than Patrick McGoohan reruns on TV, spent twelve hours a day talking to men at bus stops, women in doorways, teenagers hanging out at the park or the local corner store. The teenagers and young adults would typically laugh and point when we walked by on the opposite side of the street, but when we crossed and came right over to them, my stomach doing loops, they'd get quiet and try to look tough, usually pushing a big boy out to the front. And we'd walk right up and offer our hands and smiles and say, "How ya doin'? We wanna talk about Jesus." And they'd say, "*Chevre, hombre*" —cool, man—"we thought you were CIA," and then we'd do the first discussion right there on the picnic tables, even asking one of them to pray when we were done, to pray about what we'd said, right there in the open Colombian air with the smell of dust and diesel and dog doo filling our lungs. And someone usually would, although the first few times it was a memorized Catholic prayer, and we'd tell the guy after amen, "*Eso es bueno, hermano*" —hey, that's pretty good—"but try it again from your heart." And we'd teach them the four steps of Mormon prayer: address your Heavenly Father, tell him thanks for what you have, ask him humbly for what you need, and close in the name of Jesus. I'd mentally see that very page of Elder Reefer's flipchart printed right there on the bark of the jacaranda tree and think, *Man, oh man, has my life changed.*

We'd share the teaching and door-approach duties until Elder Hampton found out I had all the discussions memorized word perfect while he was still working on number four, and pretty soon I was doing most of the talking and actually beginning to understand pretty well, my ear kicking in. While I talked, Hampton was always smiling, as friendly and as kind as St. Francis, not that Francis was smiling about it too.

At night we'd lie in bed and tell stories, him about how he had never decided he wanted to be a missionary until just six months before and about life in eastern Oregon and the girl and the track scholarship he left behind and me about how I'd dreamed of going on a mission since the day I joined the church but I'd had to gain a few things along the way, like a competent understanding of church doctrine, and lose a few others, like the best girl that ever walked,

but hot damn diggity here we were and I was not going to waste
my time, and he'd say, "Amen, brother" and fall asleep, about that
quick.

Then three weeks in, Lara called me up and said I'd been transferred. I was to pack my bags and catch a bus for Cuba, the little
town on the outskirts of Pereira. I was going out as the senior companion, trainer to a brand-new elder who I would take off the bus
from Cali right there the next morning, a Colombian kid who had
never even been to a missionary training center. I said, "Who else is
out there?" And he said, "You're it, you and the new guy."

So at 8:30 A.M. I hugged Elder Hampton and caught a bus for
Cuba (pronounced *KOO-bah*), the first time I had been more than
twelve feet from a companion in several weeks. I got out in front
of a magazine shop where a little bus-stop sign said FLOTA: PEREIRA,
MANIZALES, TRES ESQUINAS, and I carried my gear down a dusty dirt
street to the new address, a room in a clean house with a single
mother and two young children, all very pleasant, very polite, the
mother smiling and very solicitous: could they help with this, help
with that, could she get me something to eat? But I went up first
to the room reserved for missionaries and sat on one of the beds to
look around, a little deck off the second-floor window looking right
out over the regional airport a half-mile away. All alone. I didn't
even pick a bed, thinking the new guy had as much right as I did
to first pick. Anyway, the beds looked identical: thin straw mattress
with a navy-blue wool blanket folded at the foot. Then I went down
and had a juice: *tomate de árbol*, tree tomato, not bad when cooked
first with a little sugar thrown in to dissolve, pretty stiff when raw —
fortunately, this was cooked. I chatted with the *família* for a while,
waiting for the time when I'd have to go greet the new elder at the
bus stop.

The eleven-year-old boy, Jairo, went out and then came back
with an old nylon-string guitar, asking, "Do you play?"

And I looked at that thing. And said yeah. And I looked. And
he put it in my hands as I said, "We're not really supposed to play
on our mission," and Jairo said, "The last missionary played a little,
North American stuff." And I said, "Like what?" And he said, "*Los*
Bee Gees," and that was all it took. I said, "Gimme that thing." I
didn't know how to say *pick*, so I did it with sign language and he
got me a playing card, ten of diamonds, and I proceeded to reintro-
duce my hands to one of the finest sensations on earth, and his dear,
sweet mama stood there saying, "Whoo boy, *rokenrol!*"

And I did pick.

Just before noon, Jairo and I went down to fetch the new kid at the bus stop. Jairo obviously loved his new *gringo* friend, and I wasn't half-bad with my own little buddy. Jairo informed me that he and his mother had been housing "*los Mormones*" for nigh onto three years. Knew all about how the missionary thing worked. I said, "Are you *Santos de los Ultimos Días?*" And he said, "Oh no, but we love you guys, and my mama needs the income." I would soon learn, in fact, that missionaries never boarded with members of the church, the theory being that we could share the gospel or at least offer a good example of Christian values and comportment to those with whom we roomed.

We stood on the curb outside the magazine shop and waited for the bus, the blue vault of a perfect sky arching over us, no one calling us names, no one pointing or taunting or yelling "*Gringo* go home" or "*Yanquis afuera*" or "*Expolitadores imperialistas*." In fact, at least two men begged our *disculpe*—pardon—very humbly when they had to pass in front of us to enter the magazine shop. A teenage boy rode his Stingray bike back and forth past us on the other side of the street, but he was just inquisitive. And I thought to myself, *Here I've got my own little country town and a guitar and I can even talk to the people, four thousand miles from home,* and I looked off at the huge, green mountains above Pereira thirty miles away and started to cry just a little, and Jairo saw me and asked, "*Hombre,* what's wrong?" and I said, "Man, this is so cool," only it came out as something really pathetic like "*Este es tan bueno,*" and he smiled.

I was feeling real good. I was thinking things like *Man oh man, I made it, I'm really here and I can do this and please, Lord, just give me a good companion* right as the bus pulled up and out walked a Colombian kid with a pimply face but not two traces of fear in his eyes. He said, "Elder *Waist,* I'm Elder Luís Prieto, and I'm here to work."

So that's what we did.

29

> "Just to be sitting there meditating and praying for
> the world with another earnest young man . . . 'twere
> good enough to have been born just to die, as we all are."
> —Kerouac, *The Dharma Bums*

WHEN I TOOK ELDER PRIETO off the bus, he was eighteen years old. In the States and most of the world, you couldn't enter the mission field until you were nineteen or, for the ladies, twenty-one, but in Colombia eighteen was when you were eligible for being drafted into the army or the national police, unless you were doing bona fide ministerial service. In the minds of those who redrafted the Colombian constitution in 1957 and named the Roman Catholic Church as the official national church, that probably meant Catholic seminary. The Church of Jesus Christ of Latter-day Saints figured out the loophole before the Catholic legislators did, though, and started calling Colombian missionaries at the age of eighteen, thus keeping the pool of eligibles eligible.

Prieto's dad had been approached at a bus stop by two *gringos* in white shirts and ties three years before, the *gringos* wanting to come to his home and "share a message about Christ," and the dad had at first resisted, saying "I'm *Católico Apostólico Romano*," until the short *gringo* who looked about fourteen and whose Spanish was so poor he barely conversant had said something like, "Mister, the Lord loves you and he wants you to know that your family can be together forever. Can we just have twenty minutes?"

And *Señor* Prieto just stood there, his bus coming and going, just stood there because something felt really weird, not the words but some feeling, and then he said, "What do you mean?" And the young *gringo* had said, "My sister died last year, car wreck" —his tears started to roll—"but my *família*, we know we'll be together forever, because that's the plan of our loving Father in Heaven" —

bondadoso Padre Celestial—"for his children." And then he said, "I know it, sir, I know it with all my heart." And the older missionary, the one who actually looked his age, said, "Just twenty minutes?" And *Hermano* Prieto had walked them to his home right then and there, saying, "I was just going downtown for some shoes, I actually work out of my home." And then he told them that his wife's little sister, Elder Prieto's Aunt Lilia, had died of cancer two months before at sixteen years old, and Mrs. Prieto was finding no comfort in her heart or her faith. And young Luís, an acne-burdened fifteen-year-old who lived to play soccer (*fútbol*), had come into the house sweating and seen his mom and dad crying, two *gringos* in white shirts and ties right there in the front room talking to them about the resurrection of spirit and body, loved ones reuniting in bonds that would continue forever and ever, and his dad had said, "Sit down, son, and hear the most beautiful thing you've ever heard," and then he asked the short *gringo* to tell it again, seemingly having no clue how bad the kid's Spanish was.

By the third time the *gringos* visited, young Luís had actually read some of the stuff the missionaries left with them, in particular the account in the Book of Mormon of when the resurrected Christ appeared on the American continent, probably right there in the Andes, if the painting in the book was accurate. And he said that one of the guys in the painting, the old prophet holding a walking staff, kept staring right at him wherever he moved the book, and he could swear the guy was talking to him, although his mouth never moved, saying, "This is true. Follow it."

And the whole family had been baptized. Today Luís's father was the branch president there in Cúcuta, and his mother was saving pesos for the day she could travel to a temple and be sealed to her sister and to her husband and children.

Prieto loved Mormon missionaries. He could hardly believe he was one now. The only missionary training center and temple in South America at that time were in Sao Paulo, Brazil, and most of the Colombians had never been there. The mission would send them all in waves a few months later, but when he got off the bus in Cuba, Elder Prieto had no formal training and only three days of practice with the missionary discussions. He studied hard every morning and again at night, with me role-playing the investigator. It fell pretty much on my shoulders to do all the teaching in the streets and homes, but he was right there to help with the conversation, and he did his fair share of door approaches and street contacting.

• • •

We covered every inch of that town, maybe five thousand people, and soon everybody knew who we were. There had been missionaries there before us, but for a couple of years they had mostly been guys who had been out for twenty-one or twenty-two months, their bags already packed and their hearts elsewhere. "Trunky" or "Out to pasture" is what the rest of us learned to call them, and little Cuba had been seen as pasturage. I didn't ever want that said of me or anyone even thinking it, especially being so new in the country. The companionship before Prieto and me had been so useless that the mission president had moved them both out at the same time, almost unheard of. Prieto and I showed up with absolute zero knowledge of any existing program or contacts or works in progress. So we did everything we could think of, talked to anything that moved, taught discussions in doorways and at bus stops. Prieto memorized the first two discussions in less than a week.

One day we saw a guy get off the bus — very few had cars — carrying a guitar, and I beat him to his gate, opening the conversation with a simple query about his errand and mentioning that I played. He invited us in and introduced us to his two brothers, the three of them all professional musicians. Prieto asked for a song, and Los Hermanos Torres belted out a couple of *merengues* right there in the *sala*. Then the first guy, Enrique, handed me his guitar and said, "Play us something *estadounidense*," meaning from the States.

So I did one of the last ones I'd written, "All the Love in the World," barely thinking of Annie, just *Is this against mission rules?* And they clapped and patted me on the back and said, "*Mas*," so I popped out a couple of others, a little rusty on lyrics but they didn't have a clue that *dah da dah* and *huppa huppa bing bang* weren't some really profound phrases.

They didn't want religion, though, and we didn't want to lose the whole thing, so we just became friends, dropping by now and then for a little pickin' — I got my mother to mail me a Jim Dunlop nylon .46 that I carried in my little white handbook — and light chat. The eternal family thing didn't go over real big with three determined bachelors, Enrique saying, "*Madre de dios*, I have to live with these guys twenty-four hours a day now, and they drive me nuts, hah hah hah," and Jorge jovially dissing the whole chastity/fidelity concept, saying, "*Hombre*, why do you think we became musicians?"

So we picked, we laughed, we shared a few sodas — *gaseosas* — and we kept looking. The sodas were always *a clima*, room temperature, because refrigeration was about as common as clean water. Which is exactly why we drank pop for two years: that and alcoholic beverages were the only purified water available. And everyone knows the deal on Mormons and alcoholic beverages.

One Friday evening we held a big family home evening in the town square. Elder Prieto and I and a couple of the church members carried nearly sixty folding chairs and a table the quarter-mile from the chapel — a rented house — to the square and set them up. Then a load of cups and soda pop and cookies from the *panadería* (bread store, one on every corner) for refreshments. While Prieto stayed and watched the stuff — accompanied, of course, by a local member — I went back to the house with the branch president for our filmstrip projector and a couple of filmstrips that we were going to show on the wall of the Jota Gomez store if the electricity didn't go out on us.

We had distributed three or four hundred flyers around town on Thursday and Friday, inviting one and all to a presentation on families and Christ. Eight o'clock came and went, and only one old man was sitting in the chairs, right up front. We finally had about thirty kids and teenagers, one crippled man, and one old lady show up, so we ran the *filminas*, and the electricity went out only twice. Afterward the old lady tried giving me some Jehovah Witness literature and wanted to argue, while little kids hung at my legs and stared at me, one kid petting my arms. Elder Prieto chatted with both of the fathers and managed to get a brochure into the hands of the old guy who'd been there on time and actually set up an appointment with him for later that week.

Tuesday morning after P-day, we were back on the street, canvassing the neighborhood where we'd passed out the movie flyers. But no one was buying. We walked and we walked, right into Wednesday and then Thursday, getting nary a nibble. Late Thursday a young housewife let us in, and we'd had half a discussion when her father — or father-in-law, more likely — walked in and stood in the doorway, his arms folded, for ten minutes. I tried to direct an equal amount of energy his way, but eventually when I asked him a question he said, "Listen here, young man, this is Colombia, and you can't just waltz in here and preach your North American values to us. We're *Católico Apostólico Romano* born and bred, and the blood of the martyrs like Simón Bolivar — " And Prieto jumped in and said, "Wait, I'm Colombian!" But the old man essentially ignored that and just kept rolling along, *gringo* this and *gringo* that and *yánqui* exploitation of his people, taking their hard-earned money and stealing their canal back in '03, and I said, "Whoa, hang on there." And I stood up and closed my flipchart and said, "*Hermano*" — we called everybody that once they let us in — "I have never yet mentioned *los Estados Unidos*, and I never will, because that's not why I'm here in Colombia. I represent the Lord Jesus Christ as an ordained minister of the gospel. I have come four thousand miles, leaving my home and my parents and everything I've ever known and loved, paying my own way out of my own pocket, not earning a dime, eating the same food everybody else eats, living in a tiny room, and walking dusty streets twelve hours a day with one purpose and one purpose only, and that is to share the message of Jesus Christ, the resurrected Lord and Savior who has spoken once again to prophets on the earth and reestablished his church so that we can be saved." And I was out of words, so I just quit by saying, "I'm a missionary, *hermano*."

And he just stood there for a moment with his eyes open kinda wide and then walked over to me and held out his hand, his anger completely melted. He said, very sincerely, "I'm honored to know you, *joven*" (young man). "I'm not interested, but God bless you in your work."

And we left.

Outside, Elder Prieto said my Spanish had been flawless, much better than the day before. I said, "Welcome to the work of the Lord. Miracles happen."

That night we found the man from the family home evening movie, the guy who arrived early and took a brochure. The address he had given us was real, and he was actually home as appointed. His home was one tiny room in a concrete bunker of many rooms, each occupied by a different family, all sharing one bathroom, one kitchen, and one *lavadero*, the stone clothes-washing thing, like a *mano y metate* for cotton instead of corn, located in the central courtyard. He welcomed us to his room and introduced us very quietly to his wife and two children, who all took a place on the bed and waited for our teaching. Mr. Morales excused himself very politely, but only to go borrow a couple of chairs from neighboring rooms for Elder Prieto and me to sit down. He came back and took a seat next to his wife on the bed, the brochure Prieto had given him held fondly in his hand. Their entire household was right there: two beds, two boxes with old clothing and worn-out shoes, some toiletry items. And a picture of Jesus on the wall. Period.

His wife, *Señora* Morales, said *Señor* Morales had told them all about our movie, the life-before-we-lived-on-earth part, and the future with our families, after we died. Mr. Morales looked to be in his sixties, yet the children were perhaps five and eight and the missus late thirties, and I wondered if the old man's health was on their minds.

Then old *Señor* Morales said very quietly, "*Hermanos*, we would be pleased to hear your message now. Will you please teach us?" And I was almost speechless, thinking I had never had someone ask me to please start teaching. So I stuttered around for a bit, saying glad to be here and all that, but then just opened up and said, "I want to tell you that the Lord loves you and wants you to be happy. He has a plan to let you be together forever as a family," and I started to choke up, feeling an enormous, overwhelming emotion for these people, and I had to hand the flipchart to Elder Prieto, the first time he'd ever started the discussion. He looked at me for only a second and then jumped right in, the entire visit going flawlessly.

The next day at noon, while Prieto and I were having a bowl of *sancocho* back at the ranch—boiled *yuca*, cilantro, and chicken broth—the branch president knocked on the door and said, "There's a Hugo Morales down at the chapel with his family, just standing on the sidewalk in the sun. He wants to know if *los hermanos* can come teach them some more about eternal life."

I said, "How'd he find you?" because no one lived at the chapel and it was closed except for church meetings. And *Presidente* Quiceno said, "I went down to get the broom and sweep my kitchen, and there they were. I asked them what I could do for them. I didn't think you wanted him to know where you live—you know, maybe he wanted to case the joint . . ."

And I looked at Prieto, thinking, *A sixty-year-old man with two kids and a woman*? But having learned in just two Sundays that *Presidente* Quiceno was just this way, real hyper and tense about everything, I just said, "We're on our way."

So Prieto and I swallowed our vittles and hoofed it on back to the chapel with Quiceno, and there was the family, standing there in the sun, smiling. In fact, the little eight-year-old girl ran right up to take my hand, then started petting my arm. *Hermano* Morales removed his hat and gave a little bow, and then begged our forgiveness for bothering us this way, but they were just unable to control the need to have more of our *instrucciones*.

So we taught them in the chapel, which was just a house in the middle of the block rented by the church, a sign over its doorway, the rooms filled with folding metal chairs instead of couches and beds and tables and such. And we baptized them that next weekend, having to go clear back into Pereira to where there was a real LDS chapel with a baptismal font. They would have gone earlier, probably that second afternoon, but it took Prieto and me a while to figure out why they wouldn't commit to reading the literature we left them, a prerequisite for baptism. *Presidente* Quiceno would say, "They're no good — look, they're not committed, move along," and Prieto said, "I don't think any of them know how to read." That turned out to be exactly the case, and they had been too embarrassed to bring it up.

And then it took a little longer still before I figured out why they wouldn't commit to be baptized in Pereira. *Hermano* Morales said, "I would love to be baptized, Elder, but can't we do it here in Cuba?" Prieto thought the guy was scared of busses, but I left a ten-peso note on his bed one visit, and he found us the next day and said, "The Lord has blessed us, *hermanos*. Some money just appeared in our room." I asked him how much money, and he said, "Ten pesos, nine for the bus ride to our baptism and one for our tithing." So I walked him right over to *Presidente* Quiceno's place and gave Quiceno the eye: *Find me another one like this one, jéfe, just try.*

One week after that, I ordained him a priest in the Aaronic priesthood, and he started blessing the emblems of the sacrament every Sunday, as Quiceno's right-hand man.

30

> "They say of an amputee that he remembers his leg.
> Well, I remember this girl. I am not whole without her."
> —John Steinbeck, *Sweet Thursday*

ONE AFTERNOON FOUR WEEKS IN, I was trying to scrape the bar-code label off a twelve-ounce can of cashews my mother had just mailed me, and Elder Prieto asked me what the label was. Well, *bar code* wasn't exactly in my Spanish lexicon at that point, but the entire concept of running an electronic wand over a bunch of lines and having it tell the cash register and the inventory control software and the department manager the entire biography of that particular widget was just too much for Prieto, and he begged me to let him keep the label. We removed it with alcohol and a razor blade, and he sent it home to his folks in his next letter.

That night I introduced him to La Isla, an incredibly poor neighborhood on the river, one of those neighborhoods where house number one takes its cooking, drinking, and laundry water right out of the river and then throws it back when done with it, and houses number two, three, and four hundred sixty-nine do the same thing, one after another. The *agua panela*, the commonly offered cane-sugar drink, in those sorts of barrios was always a little thicker and greener than when served in the city, although the water was typically carrying amoebas and tapeworm larvae in either locale. Simple Rocky Mountain giardia would have been a reasonable step up.

We had heard about the ubiquitous *agua panela* back in the MTC, and we were well aware that it would be a little tough to drink sometimes. But we were also warned what it would feel like to be sitting there four feet away from Mr. and Mrs. Gomez, the couple sharing a milk crate or a box while you and your companion were given the only two chairs in the ten-by-twelve house, sitting there prepared to teach them something new about the God of love and peace and miracles, *Señora* Gomez or maybe the thirteen-year-old daughter who didn't even have teeth offering you a cup of their absolute best, warmed up with love, maybe the last they had in the house, and you saying, "I'm sorry, lady, but do you have something a little more sterile?"

So what you do, if you're any good at all or want to be, saying to yourself *I'm a servant of God and these are his children*, is you put out your damn hand and say, "Thank you very much, *señora*, I'd love a cup." And you drink it with a smile, worry about amoebas on your own time.

It was in neighborhoods like that where the people, even grown men, slunk back into doorways when you came by, absolutely sure you were the CIA and there to bust some heads or take someone out or to steal their women or their canal again or do whatever the CIA did in those days. Now and then a group of *jovenes* (teenagers) would yell at you from a street corner and then run when you looked at them, but mostly the people were just scared. Except for the ones who had met *los élderes* before, had a few discussions in their home maybe, some of them even baptized sometime in the past, most of such no longer active in the church because they couldn't afford the two-peso bus ride each way to the meetinghouse on Sunday.

Anyway, we were walking La Isla and that was what happened: Some sixteen-year-old boy came right up to us, his buddies hanging back laughing, and said, "*Élderes*, come to our home!"

And so we did.

Soon his mama emerged from the next room, took my hand, said, "Oh, *hermano*," sat me down on a stool, and began to crank out some story at about one hundred thirty-eight miles per hour. I knew the speed because I caught only about one in every one hundred thirty-eight words.

The lady went on and on for perhaps forty minutes, sometimes laughing, other times crying or merely reflective. She directed almost her entire speech—I was going to say *conversation*—at me, thinking, I suppose, that this American would really know. From time to time I would comment "*Bueno, bueno*" or "*Que bién, hermana!*" at which she would laugh or cry and speed it up. I would steal a glance at my companion now and then, but there he sat, miles away, his eyes wide, his mouth open, offering neither help nor hope to me. Finally we were able to wind it up and make an exit.

"*Gracias, hermano, gracias*," she sobbed, squeezing my hand. "*Que dios le bendiga*." God bless you.

As we entered the street I turned to Elder Prieto, still wide-eyed, and asked him how he was and where the heck he had been all my life.

"What was that all about?" I asked.

"What was it about?" he exclaimed. "What didn't you understand?"

"Well, from about '*Hola, hermanos*' to somewhere close to '*Que dios le bendiga.*'"

Elder Prieto stopped instantly, staring me in the face, and then he grabbed my shoulder and hurried me around the corner.

"*Que va, hermano!*" he exclaimed. "For the last half-hour that lady has been telling you how her husband left her for a younger woman, one who had teeth, and about her younger brother Chucho who they just found last night all hacked to pieces down by Tres Esquinas, and whose own father, her father, came home early this morning in a drunken stupor with blood all over his machete. You didn't get all that?"

Get that? One of the few things I barely understood was the part about Chucho, which I understood to be *chucha*, a small rodent and which, Prieto explained later, also meant body odor. What I had thought I understood was something about a hunting party looking for rodents so they could hack them up and leave them for the dogs. Pretty gross, I thought, but I didn't want to offend her, so I just responded "*Que bién, hermana. Bueno, bueno.*"

Now I felt like dog meat.

Elder Prieto finished staring at me and turned toward the river. Then he started laughing out loud, almost uncontrollably. "Hunting party! Oh, this is going to be fun!"

I was pleased that he found something to laugh about, but I chose not to talk about it anymore. And we didn't return to La Isla for a few days.

Three days later I got two surprises, one I'd been warned about but the other straight out of the blue. The first was the Andes Foxtrot, Montezuma's revenge. *Gambú.* Diarrhea. Big time. I couldn't seem to find the shut-off switch, and our days and hours were less than regular, so to speak.

The second was a letter from Annie saying she'd just received her mission call to Quebec. Not that we'd been in touch for a while or close in more than a year, but I didn't even know she was thinking about a mission. But now I figured that the disparate mission experiences—her in French Canada and me in South America—would be so unique as to pry the last of our fingers apart forever. She said desert survival had been the best thing she'd ever done, and I couldn't help but think of the cabin on the front of the mountain and how much I had loved her. She had submitted her mission papers just before boarding the bus for Moab and then walked, crawled, scrambled—whatever it took—to go three hundred miles across the desert and canyons with thirty other young people, split into groups of four or five and twice living on three potatoes, four carrots, and two gallons of water—the entire group—for five, six days; having to help, heave, lift, learn, cry, and pray together, kids actually coming in the last day, the final leg of eighteen miles, on their bloody hands and knees because their footwear was gone and blowing in chunks somewhere out there in the desert and they couldn't stand up anyway. Thirty kids coming out of the desert saying, I lived! And by the next morning saying, I made it, I can do anything!

Annie's folks had received her call in the mail a week before the survivalists exited the mirage just east of Escalante. They were going nuts but had to wait seven days until she called them from Provo to say, "I'm alive," and they opened it and read it to her over the phone. And so now she was going on a mission.

I was sitting on my little bed in Cuba at lunchtime, Elder Prieto taking a quick nap, when I opened and read her letter. Here I was waiting for a nice, mild, generic mail from the States—*Hi, Elder, how ya doin'* ditty—and she smacks me upside the head with *I'm gone, I'm leaving, I'm starting a whole brand-new life, and you're not in it nor even close anymore, adios.*

I went out on the veranda, the little three-by-five deck off our room, and stared out at the distant mountains and the regional airport, right there under our noses, maybe a half-mile away. I sat and I looked and I listened to the engines roar and the planes take flight and I stared and I couldn't concentrate on anything Colombian and I just sat. Prieto didn't wake up on his own until after three o'clock in the afternoon, and he scolded me for not waking him. What the heck was I doing?

I wasn't feeling real well, I told him, and just needed to settle my stomach. Well, he had no reason to disbelieve that, having run to the corner store twice yesterday for toilet paper, and so he just opened his books and started to study, almost ready to pass off discussion number five.

The distance between Annie and me was suddenly suffocating in its amplitude. Our relationship was years old and light years away. Once upon a time we had been so close, so perfectly matched, which put a Dan Fogelberg tune in my head, Muzak to my meandering. We were companions, lovers, Best Friends, capital B and F. As close as we could get without that paper certificate she had once asked me about, tested me on. And dammitalltohell maybe we should have gotten it. We had changed our lives simultaneously in the exact same direction even though we were three hundred miles apart. And I wondered: Should we have gotten married? Should we have just skipped the missionary service and started our lives together?

I sat there on my Colombian veranda, and the tears welled up in my eyes and the bile in my throat. I wanted to walk the woods on Paradise Mountain so badly I couldn't stand it. I wanted to walk the ridge to Mount Kolob or run up to Eagle's Nest with my hair flying off my back. Or pitch headlong into the lodgepole maze leading to the cabin on the front of the mountain. I wanted to go back.

I missed Annie, the pony-tailed daisy girl or the pantyhose-and-polyester Mormon acolyte — I loved them both, I missed them both. I missed everything. And then I just sat there and let it roll, hot, silent tears running down all over my face until I had to dash for the bathroom and then running in there a lot more.

I was sick for the next two days, or at least I claimed to be, the toilet-paper supply witness enough that all was not well in Burbank. I lay in bed, sleeping, dreaming, just staring at the rough adobe wall ten inches in front of my face. Prieto passed off discussion five to me and then six the next day, his sharp mind kicking right in.

Friday morning I decided I'd better act like I was alive and maybe even still interested, and so we went out, heading over to the Moraleses' for a boost, but no one was home, so we ambled toward the Quicenos', Prieto boldly making a few first contacts as we went, me standing right next to him looking devotional but thinking mainly: *I guess Annie'll just be a fond memory of childhood. I wish her luck.*

Prieto was making me proud with a college-aged guy at the bus stop when a young man about twenty-five hobbled by on crippled legs. He slowed down as he approached us, and I got reinterested in Prieto's discussion, thinking, *Great, another beggar,* but then he just went on by. In fact, he looked somewhat familiar, but I couldn't put a place on it, so I just concluded *beggar.* Colombia has beggars everywhere, at that time including about a million and a half home-less children—*gamines*—living in dugouts in ditch banks and un-der bridges and in squalid garbage-dump camps that'd make John Steinbeck think he'd walked right into the squatters' camps of the Great Depression or maybe even taken three steps backward.

That was just the kids. Among the adults, I don't think anybody cared enough to make the count, but there was at least one beggar on every block I ever walked in Colombia, and I don't mean guys that hop off the bus wearing Nikes and then change into their bum suit for a day, acting poor around Temple Square back in Salt Lake City and in every other American city. I mean guys who haven't seen a clean piece of food in four years or an actual toilet ever, guys whose mama fed them cheap whiskey in their baby bottle because that was all that was around and whose uncle sexually molested them from the time they were ten months old. Guys who'd lost one or both legs under a railroad car, rolling around drunk in a night stupor and then rolling around on a little platform with casters for the rest of their life, like a skateboard that they propel with their hands, holding wood blocks. Or who'd lost one or two arms to a machete-wielding thief when they were twelve. Half of the adult beggars had probably been *gamines* since they were five or six. Au-thentic misery.

Still, we had been instructed in the MTC not to give to the beg-gars, one instructor saying a lot of them weren't legit and the other saying, "You'll go broke in a week—there are too many."

But then I noticed my own personal cripple stopping a few houses down the block and just sitting on the curb, waiting for Pri-eto and me to wrap it up. Prieto was really into his parley—this guy claimed he had studied for the Catholic priesthood and they were going back and forth, while I lost focus and just stared at the crip-ple on the curb, something saying, *This guy ain't wearing Nikes, and he ain't faking it.* Pretty soon the bus came by and the almost-priest said, "I'm *Católico Apostólico Romano* born and bred, so good day," and he split, the diesel smoke choking us as the bus driver gunned it and all the people on the bus laughing at the two missionaries stay-ing behind in the smoke. We had actually been heading west, and Prieto looked like he wanted to continue that way, but I just nodded toward the cripple and over we went. As we neared him, he stood up, cleared his throat, and extended his hand.

"*Buenos días, señores,*" he said quietly, and he actually bowed a little bit. He introduced himself as Martín Uribe, at our service—*a sus órdenes*—and started to attempt some sincere inquiry into our successes this fine day. I couldn't sense in any way that he was faking it. But then he got visibly coy and explained that he had just been offered his first real job out of the coffee fields as a dishwasher in a little restaurant over in Tres Esquinas. He had a wife and two little boys to feed and a little room near the square. We knew Hugo Morales, right?

And I remembered, *Oh, yeah, the other guy at the movie on the wall.*

He told us he had no clothes for his new job except those he was wearing. Could he beg of us, *hermanos bondadosos*, just a pair of pants or some old shoes, perhaps a T-shirt? He could pay us back soon with his first paycheck. He didn't want pesos; he wanted a pair of pants.

Prieto just looked at me, and I could tell it was a look of *Okay, you're the senior companion, the one who knows. What do we do?*

So I just looked back at the guy, his grimy pants and a worn-out T-shirt, wasted boots gleaned from two different pair, neither with laces. I recognized that the three of us were all about the same size.

"Come and see us in one hour," I said. "We'll be returning for lunch to our house, that blue one on the corner. I'm sure we can find something."

He hesitated, then offered his hand again, bowed, said, *"Muy amable, hermanos cristianos"*—very kind of you, Christian brothers—and waddled away.

Prieto was still just looking at me, all fire and flame and confidence gone from his eyes now, just looking at me thinking: *What do we do now, big brother? I'm new at this.*

Prieto and I had long since discussed this beggar thing, and I had explained to him what had been explained to me in the MTC. "Your money is sacred," one instructor had told us. "It's for the work of the Lord. You can't be throwing a peso to every beggar who comes along."

My money, as a matter of fact, came in thirds from my parents, neither Mormons nor Christians; from the members of the Silver Creek Branch; and maybe a third from my own savings and the wampum gained through the sale of my VW. Prieto's money, like most of our Latino companions, was contributed through tithing dollars by members of the church around the world.

I had often wondered about the counsel in the MTC, in light of several scriptures, but ultimately I had decided to litmus-test this crippled guy, see if he would really show up in one hour as I'd suggested.

So we wandered around somewhat aimlessly, the face of the cripple and the face of Annie fading back and forth in my mind, and we turned onto our street an hour and ten minutes later. There sat Martín Uribe, just waiting quietly on the curb opposite our house, his head bowed, drawing in the dirt with a stick. He glanced up briefly as we disappeared into the house. In our room, still silent, I regarded a pair of navy slacks I had just purchased from the tailor down the alley. I tried to imagine some fault with the workmanship that would render them donation quality, but in fact they were quite nice. And I remembered something Ray Goode had once told me: "Give your best to the work of the Lord." So I folded them up.

Prieto was picking out a few pairs of socks and a shirt, probably authentically worried about his ability to replace them at some point, having no idea how big the church's tithing fund was or how long it would hold out. I picked out a couple of ties and a pair of shoes, practically new, that had nevertheless proven a poor pair for walking twelve hours a day. I looked at Prieto, and he had added another white shirt.

"I have too many anyway," he said.

We walked downstairs and out to the sidewalk. Our friend had moved over to our side of the street and was just standing by the utility pole shuffling his mismatched, worn-out boots.

"*Hermano,*" I called. "*Tenga.*" I held the bag of clothes out to him. He shuffled quickly toward me, his eyes on fire, and he held out both hands.

"*Para mi, hermano? Tantas gracias,*" he whispered, his mouth open in surprise.

He took the bag and held it up to his chest as if trying on everything all at once. All I could say was, "Good luck with your new job." We shook hands and called each other brother again. I was really going to let it go at that for now, wanting the gesture of helping to stand alone, unattached, no strings, but he was the one who said, "Will you come visit my home sometime? Teach my family about Jesus?"

And then I couldn't hold the tears.

Just before he waved again and waddled off, Prieto handed him a five-peso bread (*pan de cinco*) he'd carried out in a napkin. Again the guy thanked us and turned to go. Prieto and I just stood there, Prieto looking at me more than at the guy. Then looking at me completely. His face was a mystery; he looked stunned almost, like a kid who had just seen a vision. And he said to me, "That really felt right, didn't it."

I didn't know how to say darn tootin', so I just said, "Yes, *hermanito*, I think we're learning what it really means to be an ambassador of the Lord Jesus Christ," both of us three years in the church, both of us just kids, on the dusty streets of a little town so far away from my home and homeland and family and friends that I could barely remember what any of them looked like.

The next morning, six A.M., when I was already up and reading *Jesús el Cristo*, I got the call: my first companion, Elder Lara, had phoned the mission president in the middle of the night from a phone booth in Ibague, one hundred and fifty miles from Pereira, saying, "I can't take it anymore. I've caught a bus for home," leaving his mission with only five months to go before an honorable release. Leaving his companion sleeping soundly in the next bed.

So I was being transferred back into Pereira, this time as the district leader over eight guys.

Ten days later, with Prieto and his new companion in town for the service, I would preside over the baptisms of Luz Mary and Martín Uribe, the latter dressed smartly in a very nice white shirt, practically new, and a J.C. Penney tie.

31

PRIETO'S DAD, the Cúcuta branch president, had enjoyed the privilege of starting his own son's mission paperwork, so absolutely thrilled his first-born son was to be an ordained servant of the Lord Jesus Christ that he had told everyone in town. Many of them had said, "Well, that's a good way to get out of military service," and *Presidente* Prieto had contended vehemently that the blessed *república* recognized the sacred right of a young man to go and serve the Lord!

Which was a bummer, in a way, because the *república* really could have used my next companion.

Leonardo Aillón was eighteen going on twelve when I got him. He had actually been out a couple of weeks, during which he about drove Elder Hampton nuts. Hampton said, "He just sits in the corner and makes this horrible sucking sound through his teeth. Scared to do anything else." And I had told Hampton, as his district leader, that I thought he was being a little too critical, letting tiny things bug him too much. "Relax," I told him.

Then I got Aillón, who did little more than hide in the corner and make this horrible sucking sound through his teeth, driving me nuts! He was certainly not an idiot. He had entered the National University in Bogotá when he was sixteen years old and got straight A's in biology and mathematics.

Anyway, like Prieto and practically every Colombian elder I would meet over the next two years, he was a recent convert, supported on his mission by the church's worldwide tithing funds, the great bulk of which was generated in the United States, the place where ten percent of one's income was more money than most Colombians made in a year. Aillón had joined the church two years earlier with only his mother. A little brother, seven, would likely come along next, getting baptized at eight in keeping with Latter-day Saint doctrine. A father didn't exist. In fact, he did, but no one in the family claimed to know where. He had often come home in a drunken stupor and beaten Leonardo and his mother, and even the little one. One day Aillón's mother had let a couple of young, good-looking North American missionaries into the house, found the teachings much to her liking and comfort, and asked them to come back, confessing to sixteen-year-old Leonardo afterward, "I felt something inside me when they taught me about José Smith seeing God and Jesus, what about you?" And Leonardo had said, "I wasn't really listening, Mom, but if you want me to I will next time."

In the meantime, Leonardo picked up the pamphlets the North Americans had left and read them over and over again, saying, "Mama, this stuff on the Word of Wisdom, what these Mormons call their health code, could really be good for Papa, teach him that his body is like a temple for the spirit, learn to overcome his alcoholism." A neighbor lady three doors down told Papa one night while they were in the sack together, "You know you're wife is entertaining *los Mormones*?" And *Señor* Aillón, Husband of the Week, came home and beat Leonardo's mom until she was unconscious, breaking one of her cheekbones with his fist, Leonardo getting in the middle of it, trying to protect his mama from the animal and getting beat into the other corner, beat until it didn't even hurt anymore.

The old man had then fallen asleep on the couch — rough day at the office — and Leonardo and his mom and brother had disappeared into the night. She got the kids installed at a distant relative's before checking herself into a hospital. Then Mama started having dreams in the hospital while under sedative to get her face rebuilt, dreams of *Abuelita*, her grandmother long since dead, appearing to her and saying, "This stuff about José Smith? It's true, *mí hija*, don't let it go." And then she told Leonardo in the morning when he came: "Go find those *hermanos* in the white shirts, tell them what has happened, and ask them to pray for us." Aillón went back to the barrio in full daylight and walked around dressed in bruises for three hours looking for the missionaries, who he finally found having a couple of warm *gaseosas* and a *pan de cinco* at a corner store not four blocks from the old house. The younger of the two — the shorter one who looked a lot like me, according to Aillón — actually dropped his pop bottle to the floor when Leonardo walked up to them looking like he'd been rolled by a truck.

The missionaries had accompanied Leonardo, scared to death, to the house, saying, "Let's gather what we can — your mom's going to need it." Leonardo said, "*Hermanos*, my dad could still be home," and the really big missionary — a guy who had left a scholarship playing *futból Americano* at a university in California, said, "*Ojalá que sí!*" And he got his wish, finding Señor Aillón lying right there on the floor of the house, coming awake only because the big boy lifted him right up, pressed him into the wall with his feet twenty inches off the ground, and then, using words we hadn't learned at the MTC, told him he'd come back and break his *pendejo* arms and then his neck if the rotten scum-sucking *cabrón* ever touched the *señora* again. Then he just held him there for a half-minute while he probably debated doing it anyway, Leonardo and the smaller missionary watching for several seconds and then moving off to quickly collect some things. They left with three armfuls, mostly just clothing and a couple of family photos, the dad by then just sitting on the floor next to the wall throwing up and wondering *What the hell?*

And so I cut Aillón a break.

For eight weeks all I had eaten was big green bananas (*plátano*), *yuca* (a tuber, kind of like potatoes only quite fibrous), white rice, and a stiff chunk of meat — what kind of beast I wasn't sure — three times a day. Now and then a bowl of *mondongo* (like the Mexican *menudo*), tripe replacing beef as the meat (?) of choice (?). Plantain could be fixed a couple of ways, either boiled in soup with the *yuca* or sliced and deep-fried in lard, but the diet was incredibly boring and probably fattening. But then there were the tapeworms and amoebas, which meant getting fat was only theoretical anyway.

Additionally, I was supposed to follow these instructions: Do not drink water unless boiled and never drink milk, since most of the dairies added raw water to the processed milk, which was not common in any case. Keep your mouth closed in the cold shower — hot? what's hot water? — or you'll rinse your teeth in amoeba juice. All of this was in the handbook or at least in the common street wisdom of the mission. And almost impossible to live by. You entered a home as a guest in Colombia, as in most of Latin America, and you would immediately be offered something to eat or drink, rarely refrigerated, rarely clean, but the best they had and likely prepared with more care than what they just gave their kids.

Back in Pereira, Aillón and I moved into a room in a nice apartment on the ground level of an eight-story building. Our *doña*, or landlady, lived there with her two adult kids, all from Argentina, *la familia* Ruíz. And *Doña* Ruíz knew how to cook. For my first and last time in Colombia, I met meals I actually enjoyed eating, in particular a dish she called *perico*, which was the same word used for someone with dishwater-blonde hair, kind of like goulash: eggs scrambled with onion, peppers, shredded chicken, and peas.

One time she waxed Colombian, however, and fixed cow tongue. When she served dinner that night, it was disguised in a batter mixture and fried in slices, but I had seen it in her refrigerator that morning. I used to sell one or two a year at Paradise Finer Foods. A little chewy, ironically, but tastier than *plátano*.

Our *pieza* was tiny, Aillón describing it as a place where "*no cabe ni la menor duda*" (the slightest doubt wouldn't fit), but it was clean and the neighborhood felt safe, mostly people with college degrees and good jobs, such as architects and business owners and professors at the University of Risaralda. Here in the big city, however, the safe neighborhood was entirely too small. Two hundred yards from our *pieza*, we hit the *avenida* and the world changed. From that point on, for twelve hours a day, we faced an incessant onslaught of taunting, catcalls, flying projectiles—from old men, young men, teenagers, little snot-nosed kids. Women. Kids would throw rocks, then run away laughing. Or they would turn around in their bus seat and just stare at us, twenty inches away, like we were inorganic specimens from another universe, just looking right at us, their eyes wide, flinching in total surprise when I'd say something like "Boo" or lean in close and stare back at them. Bizarre.

College-aged youth, when in groups, would come right up to us and curse us and threaten us and, always, spit out, "*Yanqui* go home!" I would tell them my companion wasn't a Yankee, trying to explain that *La Iglesia de Jesucristo de los Santos de los Últimos Días* wasn't a *gringo* church but a worldwide one, and that got me about as far as the second curse: "*Gringos* go home."

To which Elder Aillón, of course, would say nothing, doing his absolute best just to stand at my side without fainting from fear.

But living with Colombian companions was doing wonders for my Spanish, which became apparent every time we ran into a two-*gringo* companionship or at district meetings, where the Colombian elders talked to each other or to me and the North Americans all talked amongst themselves.

From time to time my confidence would get shaken, like the times I would knock on a door and, after I'd introduced us in

Spanish, the lady of the house would say, "I'm sorry, young man, but I don't speak English." So I'd turn to Aillón, who would just shrug his shoulders and smile. Of course, he understood me just fine, as did the folks back at the apartment; the people at church, all very accustomed to being around North Americans; and most people on the street. At such times I would assume it was simply a refusal to hear us out or a plain and simple mental block: *This guy has a white face; he must be* estadounidense; *clearly I won't understand him because clearly I don't speak English,* the last part actually making it out and over the lips.

So one time I tested a lady just to see if she was bluffing. She was responding, "*Si, hermano, si*" to everything I said, whether it was a question or not. So I asked her in Spanish, "Do you think we should hang the pope?"

"*Si, hermano.*"

"Would you like a thousand pesos?"

"*Si, hermano.*"

"Does your husband often beat you with a banana leaf in the middle of the street?"

"*Si, hermano.*"

At this point my companion was standing there with his mouth and eyes wide open, staring at me in disbelief. Now, the poor lady may have been answering every question honestly, but when I told her we would be back that very evening with the President of the United States and a flame thrower, she said, "*Si, hermano.*"

So we left. I didn't want to blow her gourd just in case she understood something all of a sudden. And perhaps she had her own flame thrower.

We spent about a fourth of our life, it seemed, on the city busses, usually real crowded and often with no seat for us, some tough guy or fat woman just sitting there taking up both lanes and staring straight ahead. Most of the missionaries got to where we could ride a bus over hill and dell, potholes, corners—you name it—without holding onto the overhead rail. Just ride it like a surfboard, perceiving beforehand where to shift weight, which toe or thigh muscles to relax or flex, what way to lean. It became a game, a contest, Mormon missionaries standing there reading their Bible, thirty-six-degree angle—Look, Ma, no hands—while everyone else on the bus went *whoaaaa*. And slid around.

Problem was, Elder Aillón could fall asleep while standing

straight up, which was fine as long as the bus was crowded, packing him upright. I was never sure he wasn't just resting his eyes or something, until one day a whole group of people got off the bus at one stop, and it happened to be the same group that was holding him up. As soon as they moved, his hand dropped from the bar and down he came, straight into my arms.

And then there was the problem of warm bus seats. As the story went, there was a nun who got pregnant a few years back, the culprit, of course, being a warm bus seat, sitting down too quickly before all the previous passenger's germs had a chance to either exit with him or just go back to sleep. I asked Aillón his opinion of the theory once, and he just laughed. But one day I was poking him in the ribs to wake him up, because the bus seat right under where I was standing reading my Bible was about to be vacated. Knowing that the best way to grab a bus seat was to jump right in while all the locals waited for it to cool down — *Stupid gringo!* — I jumped right in and motioned to him. He kind of glanced around and then slid into the space next to me on the aisle, his legs only half bent. I stared at him suspiciously for about half a minute until he caught my eye.

"Something wrong with the seat?" I asked.

Glancing around again, he gave me a sheepish *I've-been-caught* grin and eased himself down with an enormous sigh.

And he never got pregnant.

Speaking of busses, I think Elder Aillón stocked every bus in Risaralda province with an umbrella. He'd buy one, forget it, buy another one, forget it. Always on the bus, never at someone's house where we could walk back, knock on the door, and say, "Sorry, ma'am, but just before you kicked us out my companion left his umbrella on your couch."

And umbrellas were essential equipment, as it rained every day at 1:12 P.M. Okay, maybe 12:49 one day and 1:36 the next, but *every* day, all the fountains of the great deep bursting forth upon our heads, big honkin' rain coming down in sheets and buckets and streams from the heavens. But then it would quit for two weeks, just up and dry out, the streets getting dusty, the heat bearing down. They called that two weeks *verano*, summer; then the fountains would open up again and the heavens would pour. That would be *invierno*: winter. It was impossible to predict, thus the umbrellas.

As with my very first companionship, however, the position I assumed in Pereira had no program — no one currently being taught, no leads, no addresses. I knew from five weeks in Cuba that it wouldn't be easy, but neither was it impossible. A blank appointment book for more than a couple of days was an inexplicable mystery. So during our days Aillón and I would cover a section of the city, eventually covering it all, as it was all in my district, visiting the entire roster of church members, about six hundred and eighty of them in the Los Alpes Branch. Some of them we already knew from Sunday meetings, but some of them, though still on the rolls, hadn't thrown their shadow across the threshold of a Mormon meetinghouse in years, not even remembering the basics of the faith. With the former, we would give a spiritual thought and then just talk to them about their neighbors or extended family, finally getting to someone who sounded like a potential contact for us, and we would say to the member, "Brother Buitrago, would you introduce us to this guy? We think he sounds like a really good man, one who would respond to the gospel message."

We knew that the best candidates, statistically, were close friends and family of church members. We knew further that the best candidates among friends and family were the ones with a hole in their life—recent separation or death of a loved one, loss of a job—or at the threshold of a major change—marriage, leaving for college or the military, something like that.

But not always. Sometimes it was just pure and simply someone looking for Truth, a seeker, someone willing to admit he or she didn't have all the answers but would be really grateful to have a few. Sometimes this person was already within the circle of influence of some good Latter-day Saint and just didn't know where to look, what to ask.

While we worked the membership rolls, bringing in a few strays along the way, which was very gratifying, we would also just work the streets: approaching people in parks, at their places of business, in their doorways, asking them if we could come share a message about Christ and families with them in their home.

Sometimes I got so scared I felt like puking, going right up to grown men, women, college youth, and teenagers, most of them ready to push you away or call you a piss ant to your face and spit at your feet. I was twenty years a mountain boy who whistled into the wind and kept up with running deer in dense woods and hugged trees and felt reciprocal emotion coming back from them, barely competent with either a clutch or a crosswalk, but I had a work to do as an ordained minister of the gospel, and I decided to do it. We taught discussions over the counter at auto parts stores or sitting on park benches, feeling challenged by mission rules that required the teaching of at least three discussions a day, with sixty hours per week of in-the-street proselyting.

And then I found the hospital. No baptisms, but a lot of discussions. I think it worked for two reasons: One, we truly shared a message of hope to the weary and downtrodden; two, they couldn't get away. Captive audience. Pick your patients right, and they didn't even try. We had to sneak into the building most of the time, however, because the hospitals were Catholic and we were heathens. We got chased around by a few Mothers Superior along the way.

We always tried to concentrate on men, fathers. We could have baptized hundreds of little kids and their mothers, but church leaders encouraged the finding of families, not splinter groups like me. However, the reality was that most Colombian men were not living at home, never sober, or already dead, either from pitiful diet and health and sixteen-hour days in the coffee fields or from liquor and the cruel bite of some other AWOL father's machete.

A lot of missionaries, including most of my district in Pereira, spent their entire day tracting, which meant knocking on doors. While easy enough to do — a plain and simple anonymous no every minute for twelve hours a day — it was mostly a waste of time. And meeting with church members, I didn't have to get told to go to hell every forty-eight seconds. Very hard on the self-esteem.

I was privileged to receive regular letters from home, both from my parents and from friends in the Silver Creek Branch, which sometime that fall got made into a ward, with Ray Goode as its first bishop. Bishop Goode wrote me about his monthly visits to my folks. They would talk about money, what the ward had raised that month for their missionary and what remained to be raised, my folks always writing him a check and bringing out the cookies. Then Ray would always say, "Here, let me show you what kinds of things Elder West is doing down there," and teach a lesson on Joseph Smith or tithing or the Word of Wisdom or something, my parents going, "Yeah, yeah, Ray, just take the check."

He was a gem.

I had thought and desired that I would be serving among the indigenous peoples of the Americas, but in fact Colombia has few pure Indians, who mostly live in Peru and Ecuador and Bolivia. In Colombia lived mostly those of *sangre mezclada*, mixed blood, and they all had titles: the Caucasian-Indians were *mestizos*, the African-Indians *zambrano* or *zambo*, the African-Caucasians *mulato*. Lots of African blood, the conquering Spaniards having employed the slave trade pretty heavily along the Caribbean and Pacific coasts. They encountered the Chíbcha, the indigenous Colombians, in the high Andes and from them learned the story of the Golden Man, El Dorado, but they would secure little else, the Chíbcha moving quickly into ever-higher country or south into Ecuador or into the great *llanos*, the eastern plains that lean toward the Orinoco and the Amazon.

So I had little chance to tell anyone, "This *Libro de Mormón* is a record of your own people, a record of the prophets in *América Latina*," although our claim that Jesus himself had visited the American continent after his resurrection went over pretty well, his declaration to the people that they were as important and worthy of salvation as those in Jerusalem, and that he would visit other peoples as well, and that other scriptures, other records would be kept by them and would one day be held in the same esteem as the record written in Judea.

I learned about fleas and cockroaches. Old pros like our zone leaders taught us to keep the legs of the beds in small cans, such as tuna cans, full of kerosene. A cockroach's easiest access to your bed was up the legs, so if he attempted it up and over a can of kerosene, he went for a long swim. The major problem with this, in addition to the constant aroma of raw kerosene, was that some of these *cucarachas* were big enough to span the entire tuna can, so it merely slowed them down. When they were that big, though, you could hear them coming.

The leaders of the church may not have known this, but kids who served their missions in Colombia and Bolivia and Nigeria and the Philippines learned a unique way of saying their prayers: kneeling down on top of the mattress with their tail ends in the air, another cockroach avoidance technique. At first I felt kind of kinky doing it that way, so I attempted the normal floor procedure with a blanket draped over my legs. But cockroaches are smarter than they look, and I found myself hopping onto the bed as the buggers squirmed their way under the blanket and up my hairy calves.

•••

Aillón had one heck of a memory, I could say that for him. He began passing off the discussions rapidly, although for quite a while I
couldn't get him to teach during a visit. When I finally did, I wondered if I'd made a mistake. Seven o'clock one night, in a real home
with a father and everything, Aillón was on his maiden voyage, just
approaching one of the most serious and solemn moments in all of
the missionary lessons, a moment so solemn not even Aillón would
be caught sucking his teeth. When we taught, we would occasionally turn to a photo or diagram in our flipchart. Elder Aillón had
developed the uncanny technique, at home in our room, of saying
"Bleep" each time the text indicated a change of the flipchart picture, as if he were one of those old training filmstrips.

So at 7:16 P.M. in the first discussion where God the Father and
Jesus Christ first appear to Joseph Smith, the heavens opened and
God himself descended to earth with a *bleep*, shattering the eve-
ning.

The family looked at me, I looked at Aillón, and he smiled shyly at all of us, shrugged his shoulders, and went on. I could have
wrung his bleeping neck.

32

> "What are we to do? Pray to be kind,
> wait to be patient, try to be fine."
> —Kerouac, *Visions of Gerard*

IN EARLY OCTOBER, my companion in the MTC, Elder Ruff, got moved into my district as a co-companion out in Dos Quebradas, a little town just north of Pereira. Near the end of the month, we "bumped" our missions, or hit six months in the mission field. You bump at six, hump at twelve (halfway), slump at eighteen, and finally, at two years out, you dump. So my companionship and his met in Pereira at noon for ice cream—or the granular substance that passed for it down there—and had a good time for a couple of hours.

Ruff had been doing a little bumping of his own, thirteen stitches in his head and his right hand in a cast from breaking three fingers on a guy's head in Cartago, his first assignment. Not his companion's head, fortunately—one of the five guys who had jumped him and Elder Peña right out of the afternoon blue, jumped 'em holding lengths of two-by-four and one of them a brick. And as little bitty five-foot-nothing Elder Peña took off running for who knows where, Ruff had whooped it up on these dudes, taking the brick in the back and then on the head, then grabbing one of the two-by-fours and swinging it wildly through the blood in his eyes, knocking the living *caca* out of these boys until four of them fled screaming and the fifth kept fighting, Ruff finally turning the kid's jaw into crackerjack dust. And messing his hand up pretty good.

Peña came back when the coast was clear and performed first aid on both of them. He was an M.D. just beginning a modest practice when Mormon missionaries knocked on his door back in Túnja. He joined the church and struggled with the choices before him for a couple of years before deciding he really wanted to be a missionary, really wanted to show the Lord his faith and his gratitude for allowing him a way to climb out of the economic poverty of his childhood. And so he sent in his mission papers, suspended his practice, and came. In Cartago he was serving as the branch president, and he would finish his mission eight months later in that same role, then return and start his medical practice all over right there among the people who already loved him.

Ruff's new companion in Dos Quebradas, a big, fat Colombian named Cubillos, said, "Yeah, Ruff did a lot for the church in Cartago," laughing, and Ruff said, "Well, what was I supposed to do, *bobo*, just let them beat us up?" They showed a lot of tension in the companionship, three days into it, and Aillón said to Ruff and me, "Why don't you guys just finish the night out, and we meet back at the chapel at nine?"

So Ruff and I went to my apartment just to chat for a couple of hours, R and R, and then we headed off to my nightly appointments, Aillón and Cubillos probably doing about the same twelve miles north. Ruff said, "What's the big deal with a fight? Some of the companionships down in Cali go to movies and some even have girlfriends—what about you?" I said, "C'mon, man, are you nuts?" And he said, "That's what I thought you'd say." Then he told me he was barely hanging on, ready to just call the president and go home—or forget the president, just find the airport and a Master-Card. He was hating the people, hating the work, his head just not in it, wondering why he'd come. He could be playing quarterback on a college team, had two offers ten months ago. Also, his companions were jerks, including Cubillos, who was a fat pig who never washed. I admitted, "Yeah, he's kind of different."

For instance, Cubillos had purchased or begged or maybe chased down and harvested his own slab of cowhide, the hair still on it, to make a slipcover for his flipchart, the most disgusting teaching aid I'd ever seen. Then, at our first district meeting three weeks before, the guy giving the prayer started out, "*Nuestro Padre Celestial*" —Our Father in Heaven—and Cubillos said, out loud, "*A ver?*" —Yes?— and laughed to himself through the whole prayer.

I concurred with Ruff that companions could be a real challenge and told him about Aillón bleeping his way through half a discussion a week before, but some could be real gems, like Prieto and maybe even Aillón and Cubillos some day. Ruff said, "But Cubillos has been out twenty-one months!" And I said, "Well, that's good news for both of you. Just hang on."

So we went to my appointments that night. The first one wasn't home. Plain and simply forgot the appointment or decided we weren't worth the time. At the second place, I saw the dad hop up out of his chair and scoot off into the back of the place as we approached the front gate. We knocked, and in half a minute a kid answered the door, a boy eight or nine years old who had something to say before we could even open our mouths and say howdy-do, buckaroo. He said, "*Papá me manda a decir que no está.*" Daddy sent me out to tell you that he's not here.

It was a very common occurrence, so common that Ruff was ready to go with his own canned response: "You mean that guy we just saw stand up and walk toward the back of the house? The fat guy with the Poker beer in his hand?" (That last part varied according to the visit, but not much.)

And the kid, as usual, ran that around his brain, trying to figure out who was tricking whom, and finally just responded honestly, saying "*Sí.*"

Finally, on the third appointment we found somebody home and waiting for us, a single lady about fifty-five named Alma Rúbio whose mother had died a couple of weeks before, leaving her all alone and lonely too. I told Ruff ahead of time, "If this lady's home, be as good as you can be. She's got fifty-five years of Catholicism in her head, so her questions get a little bizarre, but she really wants to know." This was my third visit with her, and when she saw Ruff she inquired about "*el negro,*" Aillón, who was very dark-skinned. But she greeted Ruff politely, a bit taken back by his noncommand of the language, although Ruff was never embarrassed about it anywhere—he'd just come right out and speak at ya in train-wreck Spanish. Understanding him was your problem.

Anyway, I got right into the commandments discussion, telling her about the law of tithing, the law of chastity, and the Word of Wisdom health code. She never flinched at tithing, just saying, "I have always contributed to the Lord's work." She actually laughed at the requirements of the law of chastity, saying, "*Diós mío,* I haven't been with a man in twenty years, and it wasn't worth it when I was." Ruff busted into a gut laugh and told me in English, "I love her!"

But it was when Ruff did the Word of Wisdom concept that I knew we had something going with her: she was converting. The only thing she said was, "So I have to forsake my little *tinto*"—coffee—"each day?" And Ruff said, "Yes, *hermana,* you gotta pitch the little bag of *tinto*. Let the neighbors have it." She said, "Done," and we all shared a little laugh.

Then she turned to me and said, "*Hermano*, tell me again about where my little Julio is," her eyes starting to flood over. I told Ruff quietly how her little Julio had died of typhoid or something when he was ten years old, about twenty years before, and I gave him the nod to dig right back into the *Plan de Salvación*, what the Book of Mormon calls "the Great Plan of Happiness," but she saw the look and said, "No, *hermano*, I mean you" — pointing right at my face — "I want you to tell me again what you told me last week, about seeing Jesus, and the saints, and my mother. And my little Julio."

So Ruff handed me the flipchart, but I was getting to where I didn't like using the thing anymore, preferring that the people — the ones I knew were going somewhere — look me right in the eyes. I loved this part. I loved this with all my soul: testifying to a humble listener that I *knew* these things were true, that the Atonement of Jesus Christ prepared the way for us to all return to his presence. If we lived the commandments and did our part.

And she was crying freely now and said, "*Hermanito*, I really love what you say, my whole soul wants to believe it, but how can I know?" And so I told her again about prayer, about real heart-to-heart talking to her Heavenly Father, not the memorized written-in-a-book stuff but the words that groaned their way up right out of the soul. I told her of my own first experience with prayer, wanting to know with my whole being, no preconceptions, no chalkboard to erase, nothing in the way, having already quit or abandoned everything I understood to be a spiritual block between me and God, and the answer coming pure and sweet and fully winged for flight.

And she said, "Oh, *hermanito*, I really want to know," and she fell right down on her knees with me and Elder Ruff a second behind her, and she said this beautiful prayer out of her heart. And then we hugged her and went away, big tough boy Ruff with tears in his eyes.

I always tried to wrap up the good ones like that, just like Elder Reefer had done with me — get out of there while they were still warm and leave them to their own thoughts or knees or whatever.

With a block's worth of quiet walking under our belt, Ruff said, "You still seeing pages in front of your eyes? Reading scriptures off the wall?"

I said, "No, man, the discussions are just kind of automatic now. I know what to say, I know what comes next. I've heard most of the retorts and questions, and I've pretty much figured out how to answer them."

Then he said, "Were you telling her the truth about your first prayer?"

And I stopped and looked at him. The streets were quiet except for the distant sound of cantina music. And I said, "Yeah, that really happened."

He said, "I can't do what you just did, man. I've never taught like that in my life. I've never felt what I just felt."

I looked at him several moments and then said, "What did you feel?" That was one of the questions we asked our investigators.

And he said, "Man, I felt like everything you said was true."

"Of course it was. I wouldn't tell her lies."

"That's not what I mean. What I mean is the religion. What we're doing here. Maybe it's real."

I looked at him a bit longer. "You and Sister Rúbio are at the same exact place, aren't you."

And Ruff said, "I'm gonna pray like you said."

The next day Elder Aillón and I returned to the house of the lady who I'd offered to charbroil with a flame thrower. Aillón was petrified when I asked him to make the door approach this time—after all, the lady had at least been very polite to us. He actually faded in color, then moved stiffly up to the door and stared at it. I moved up next to him, knocked on the door, and stepped back out of the way. He continued to stare at the door so intently that I wondered if he'd actually notice if the woman opened it. She did, and he did, drop-shifting into the greeting without a hitch: pure, perfect Colombian Spanish, considered by many academics the purest in the world.

The old lady said, "I'm sorry, *hermanitos*, but like I told you before, I speak no English. *Buenos días.*" Then she closed the door.

I had to squeeze my legs together to keep from embarrassing myself. Poor Elder Aillón just stood there deflated, his nose pressed into the door.

And stood there.

I walked back out to the street to laugh, and he eventually joined me, walking right past me blowing sparks out the bottoms of his shoes. He said, "Elder, that's the last time I ever chicken out in a doorway."

And it was.

One week later in a district meeting, Elder Ruff stood up and told us all a joke, his Spanish still the most pitiful I'd heard in Colombia.

Lucky for all of us, much of the joke could be done with hand gestures.

Here was the joke: One lunch time when a certain missionary hit six months out, he found a fly floating in his soup—certainly not the first—and excused himself quickly from the table, shoving his bowl away as he ran. At twelve months the same elder again found a fly in his soup—hopefully a different fly, although Ruff didn't say. This time he cringed, then daintily plucked the beast from his broth and continued eating. At eighteen months, this same hardened soul found yet another fly in his soup—oh, that it happened only once every six months! This time he hardly noticed the bug and, stirring it in, proceeded to the last drop—er, chunk. Now finally at twenty-four months out, we saw this same matured and experienced young man plucking flies from the windowsill or swatting them with practiced skill in midair and tossing them by the handfuls into his hearty bowl of stew.

Everybody liked the joke, even the Colombians. In fact, Cubillos was practically rolling out of his chair. He got up and hugged Ruff, slapping him on the back, and the two just stood there smiling with each's arm around the other guy's shoulder, body language saying, *This is my comp, man, and we're a team.* I could see that the two had found their stride somehow, probably through humor. Ruff looked happy, he really did.

33

"If there can't be love among men, let there
be love at least between men and God."
—Kerouac, *Desolation Angels*

ONE DAY COMING OUT of the downtown post office, where we had to
fetch mail for the whole district once a week, I decided to wander
us through the *féria* that was happening there in the central town
square. Usually it was a kind of farmer's market, open-air fruit
stands and such, but this week was unusual: it was an artists' market, with painters and potters and musicians and glassblowers all
over the place. Aillón was actually mumbling something about
wasting time when out of the blue I heard someone calling, "Elder,
elder!"

Two young men, maybe nineteen or twenty, were waving us
over to their stand. My first thought, very brief, was that they were
church members, maybe even returned missionaries, but they both
had long hair—I'm talking ponytail-length—and were wearing hon-
est-to-Jerry-Garcia tie-dyed shirts. The shorter one, who we would
soon learn was named Thomás, came right over and gave us both a
hug.

Harley and Thomás. Thomás wasn't his real name, however. He
had picked it some years back in honor of the biblical apostle who
finally came around. These were real-live hippies, Colombian-born.
Thomás said he and Harley had run into missionaries like us all
over the Andes and had even listened to four or five of the discussions in Quito one time. Loved the José Smith story. But they were
on the road, making a living, not quite ready to settle down and get
mellow (*tranquilo*).

Most of the people in Colombia, including most of our own
missionaries, wouldn't even talk to the hippies, thinking they were
from another planet or a waste of time: *drogadictos*. I still felt like

one of those hippies in a lot of ways, and I had joined the church in seven days while right smack in the middle of them.

We looked over their stuff, Big Sur beads and macramé, really similar to what Bob and Larry had taken to Missouri but most of it with a South American twist. I bought a little bracelet to maybe send home to my sister. But mostly we talked: life, love, the path of honor, and the gentle way. Thomás had read the *Tao Te Ching* and the Book of Mormon both, but Che Guevarra had kind of surfaced as his real hero. Cultural icon. Political savior.

Then Thomás made me the gift of a tiny ceramic tube painted with little orchids, the Colombian national bloom. Sealed on one end, hollow, with a little cork stopper. I said, "What do I use this for?"

He looked at Harley and laughed. "Some like to use them to carry a little marijuana, just enough for one joint" — *cosita* — "hung around your neck, but one elder down in Putumayo bought one for his *aceito sagrado*" — sacred oil, the stuff we used to give priesthood blessings — "and all *los élderes* wanted one after that. So I make you the gift, American man of God."

He said, "Please, accept my gift, brother to brother." And so I did, and we shook hands and then gave each other an *abrazo*. Then I said, "Can we come back down and teach you some time?" I really felt a soft spot in my heart for these gentle peaceniks. I was thinking of Cris and Justin and Cricket. And Annie, the only one who ever came along with me.

But we never saw them again. By the next morning the *féria* had moved on, somewhere to the north. I saved that little flask, wrapped it up safe in a handkerchief and kept it in my suitcase, clean and empty.

Whether or not it was the very satisfying little encounter with the two hippies, something finally clicked in Elder Aillón. That next day I walked out of our corner *panadería* with a *pan de cinco* and a tamarind soda, and there he stood trying to get an appointment with a couple of nuns. He didn't get it, but it was the thought that counted.

Which is kind of what happened all over the mission: kids from Plain City, Utah, and Burley, Idaho, who had heard it all their lives, yeah yeah yeah, started catching fire about five weeks in, saying, *Man, this is real, and I can't waste any more time.*

Some of them, at least.

We had our flakes, Latino and *Norteamericano* kids who slept in, took naps at lunch, and wrapped it up about dinnertime. But very few. Some became excellent teachers, some didn't. Some of the northern boys mastered the Spanish, some never did. (Some of us, like Morrison and me, actually read the Spanish dictionary like we'd done with the English one as kids.) Some of the North Americans seemed almost immune to the constant taunting, laughing in our faces, spitting at our feet or in our hair when we walked under a bridge. Some of us about went nuts and maybe did in a few ways.

The chicks didn't help.

Clothing for the typical working man in Colombia was a pair of polyester or cotton pants and a T-shirt or button down, the ensemble matching only in the sense that they defied the laws of fashion and color coordination equally. Guys would wear things like a lime-green shirt with an orange tie to their business meeting. But the women — well, the women nearly all wore stuff that was low cut and stretched by very capable bosoms and shapely fannies. Many had a way of walking with their chin up, their whole topography extended, that drove us nuts. Some older women did the same, although they often tended to put on significant poundage with the addition of each child. But the topography was still there. A lot of belly, a lot of skin. Very smooth, clear, unblemished skin.

And flirtatious.

Not only did everyone think we were U.S. CIA agents but the girls all thought we wanted to jump in the sack. One afternoon we pulled up — on foot, of course — to Marlene Ramirez's little house, an older widowed church member we visited often when we were in need of a cold *milo* (like malted milk) and a *buñuelo* (like a cheese donut) or three. Marlene was not there, and who should greet us out the front window but this young thing in practically nothing but a handkerchief and shorts. She was what they called an *enchilada* in Colombia, for scrumptious, I'm sure. She just kind of hung out the window and assured us that if there was ever anything — and she emphasized *anything* — she could do for us, just stop by. She leaned over so far that I could describe the lint in her navel, but I'd have to skip some other very prominent points, so I'll just skip it altogether. Needless to say, I explained to her that our visit wasn't anything critical; we were just stopping by for some quick refreshment. That didn't produce the response I was seeking at all. Finally, I just told her we had an appointment down the road, and we skipped off into idiocy.

One day we were riding the bus up to the chapel to show a film-strip or two to a group from the Chamber of Commerce. Between my feet was my trusty old travel bag loaded with my filmstrip projector, my state-of-the-art stereo cassette recorder, a nice Spanish Bible, and a couple of great Alpina-brand Swiss chocolate bars, with almonds and everything.

At least it *had* been between my feet. Just as I turned around, the back door of the bus closed and I saw some guy running away with my stuff. Four guys in the back of the bus were all smiling at me.

I yelled at the driver, grabbed my companion, and we jumped off the bus and started chasing the guy. It was raining cats and dogs, and this guy was a block ahead of us, down the arroyo and back up the other side, which by now was running muck. We slid down after him, scrambled up and out, and the guy was gone. Nowhere in sight.

A hundred and sixty bucks worth of made-in-Japan, bought-in-the-States equipment. Impossible to replace in Colombia, except for the Bible and the candy bars. I wasn't the first missionary to get robbed, of course, but it was *my* first time to get robbed. I could only hope that the guy who stole it would read the Bible, if he could read at all. At least I didn't have the bag over my shoulder; an arm would have been hard to replace.

Certain people would have us back again and again, everything going well until one day, *poof*, so sorry, don't come back again. And that was that. We rarely knew why. One lady, Señora Velasquez, had us over twice before we knew she had a husband. One day he just came in the house and walked through, ignoring us. I asked her who, what, and where, and she said, "Husband, usually not here, *andando por hay*" — just hanging around somewhere. Common hangouts for Colombian men included the corner bar or the nearest neighbor lady's bed.

Anyway, on visit three Mr. Velasquez just kind of hung around in another room, although I invited him out as cheerfully as I could. Sister V. shook her finger at me, like *Don't do that, not him*, and so I took my seat and proceeded. At some point he wandered out back, and Sister V. explained that he really had trouble with someone teaching a religion other than Roman Catholic. It was an enormous issue in Colombia. Most had no interest in discussing verses, or comparing doctrine, or even in opening their Bible and reading along. I'd told the first half-dozen folks or so that we'd even use their own Bible, but I quit that after the first half-dozen folks or so said, "Oh no, *el cura*" — the padre, the priest — "won't let us read the scriptures on our own. He does that for us." So the Bibles were all just lying there on the table or the desk or the apple crate gathering dust, opened for the angels to read them, not the people.

What the Colombians did know was that we weren't the cultural religion, the national religion, the one that everybody in the world believed in but us, stupid *gringo* kids. We had frocked priests yell at us on the street, calling us devils and liars and "*Yanqui explotadores.*"

And then we had the Sister Velasquezes of the nation.

On visit three, she opened up to us and said, "Why don't you guys ever talk about Mary, the Blessed Virgin. Don't you believe in *La Virgin Santísima?*"

I verified that we did, and I read her a couple of verses from the Book of Mormon to prove it, but then I explained that Mary was not intended to be the center of Christian worship — rather, her son was. I said, "Mary was special, a nobler woman was never made — that's our honest theology. But she is not the Savior. Jesus Christ wrought the atonement, he is the Son of God, he is the Savior of the World."

And Mr. V. came in from the back patio and said, "That's kind of how I've always seen it."

And he took a seat next to his wife.

We started the discussions all over again, and *Hermano* V. made every one for the next two weeks. Elder Aillón taught the Word of Wisdom, and *Hermano* V. quit drinking liquor and both of them quit coffee. I taught the law of chastity, and a week later he promised me — because I cornered him privately in the kitchen and asked — that he was sleeping with no one but his wife. When I challenged them to be baptized, Sister V. said, "I'd be so happy" but the *hermano* just said, "Hmm" and looked at his feet.

We'd had a General Authority of the church, Elder Klamm, a guy who'd been called to give up the rest of his life and serve full time anywhere in the world until the day he died, come to Colombia and tell us all that this was Latin America, the land of the Book of Mormon, so we should challenge the people to be baptized on the second or third visit. If they said no, we should drop 'em, move along, there was another guy down the street waiting to hear and accept. That's exactly what I had done, and that's pretty much how I worked: one week, two weeks, a third if they were really trying, and then I moved along.

So anyway, one night really late, when Aillón and I were wondering if we'd miss the last bus back to our apartment and have to walk four miles of dark Colombian streets, I challenged *Hermano* V. again: "Show the Lord you love him, and get baptized this Saturday." And Sister V. said right in front of him, "He can't quit smoking." And the *hermano* said, "Yeah, I've tried real hard, tried chewing gum, sucking sugar cane, keeping a *guanábana* seed in my mouth all day long," really sincere and really depressed.

Aillón started in on some sort of counsel, the usual stuff about prayer and fasting for strength and whatnot, and my mind, losing clarity after fourteen hours in the street and the equatorial sun, locked onto a thought about a backyard swimming pool back in Paradise. I could smell the water, the chlorine mixing with the scent of pine.

I had grown up scared to death of swimming, even though floating eight hours on a log down the Colorado River into Utah one time seemed different somehow. I'd enrolled in lessons once as a ten-year-old but never even got through bubble-ups. Petrified.

But in the weeks just before my mission, I had finally learned how to swim. A lady down in King's Valley was offering private swimming lessons in her home pool and somehow, at twenty, I was suddenly no longer petrified of water. So after four weeks and thirty-two bucks, Michelle Kirkpatrick taught me how to swim, awarding me a certificate as an advanced beginner. Along the way we became close friends.

Michelle was about ten years older than I was, married, with two little boys. She and her husband, John, were reformed hippies too, so to speak, so we had a lot of cross-sectional chats. I often dropped by just to visit on Saturday afternoons coming home from my meat-cutting job at Paradise Finer Foods, and by the end of the summer I'd been to their house three or four times for dinner. The first time had been a barbecue. Still a strict vegetarian, I ate potato salad and a couple of buns. Michelle was so embarrassed, saying, "I thought Mormons ate meat!" And I said, "Well, most of them do" and apologized for not telling her earlier; I had quite simply forgotten to ever bring it up.

Michelle and I always talked religion a lot, however. She, but not John, was very interested in my Mormonism and was eager to follow up on such interest. I had toned down my early zealousness quite a bit, no less committed to spreading the word but increasingly gun-shy after having lost, alienated, or angered people left and right, several of them joining the church under their own mental power but then checking out with great big chips on their shoulders. Michelle was what she termed a lapsed Christian Scientist, and I was of course somewhat able to relate to where she'd been and what she'd once believed in.

But mainly, right after Annie and I went to heck, I was just needing to talk to someone, and Annie was not quite the discussion I wanted to have with my mom.

One day I pulled up at Michelle's house, and the place looked deserted, which was weird. But I knocked anyway, and a stranger opened the door, just a crack. A woman asked me who I was and what I wanted. I told her I was just a swimming student there to say hi to Michelle.

"Just a minute," she said. And she closed the door. Mere moments later it opened quickly, and I was whisked into the house without another word.

On her way up the split-entry stairs, she said, "We thought maybe it was John or one of his friends." The house was dark at midday, the blinds drawn tight at every window.

And then I saw Michelle. She appeared at the top of the stairs, wrapped in a blanket, her eyes red and swimming but a smile playing on her lips. From the top of the landing when I was still only halfway up, the other woman grilled me: Have you been with John? Do you know where he is? Do you know what he's done?

No, no, and no. "What's happening?"

Michelle stepped forward, held out one hand for me to take, and said, "Oh, Kit." Real mournful.

Good old John had up and split with another woman, two nights before. He announced the relationship as he was packing.

The sentinel was the sister, who stepped off a Greyhound from Southern California at U.S. Highway 285, milepost 229—Shaffer's Garage—at four A.M. that very morning. She'd come to comfort. To console. To beat the sucker over the head with a frying pan if he even parked the car.

And now everybody was sick. The sister brought the flu with her.

Michelle embraced me, telling her sister, "This is a friend we can trust. He'd never be involved—he's a Mormon." But I stood there dumb, and Michelle started blubbering again, and the sister, Beth, still looked like she wanted something to hit. I just let them vent, trying to look supportive and concerned and hurt and helpful, but

in fact I had nothing to say worth opening my mouth over. After all,
I was the stupid twenty-year-old doofus who let the best woman on
the planet go home crying six days before.

It was a sight.

Finally I said, "Where's Brandon?" The three-year-old.

Michelle said that Brandon, who always entertained himself
swimming circles around me in the pool when I was doing bubble-
ups, was sick too. Back in the crib. His little baby brother Ryan was
on Momma's bed with a little cousin who had also come on the bus.
Both sick.

It was a situation, so to speak.

They encouraged me to sit, and we just talked. Michelle wanted
to know about Annie, and then she cried about that, and I looked at
Michelle and at the sister and thought of John and Annie and said
to myself, *Is there only misery everywhere?*

And then the sister came right out and said, "So you're a Mormon. How can you help?"

I said, "Help?"

"I've known a couple of Mormons, people of faith. What can
you do?"

I knew exactly what she was getting at, but I was scared to
death. The two women just looked at me, staring into my soul, Michelle probably thinking, *You're the guy who told me how special your
religion is. Prove it.*

My heart said, *You're right — my religion's special,* and I really felt
that, a heat rushing into my guts like a warm wind. I almost choked,
it was rushing in so strong and hot and rapidly. And I, to use the
language of the Apostle Paul, girt up my loins — I might have even
stood up — and said, "Michelle, I hold what is called the priesthood
of God, the same power held by the ancient apostles, a power that
can grant blessings of healing, comfort, even miracles." I said that
if she was of a mind, being a Christian Scientist and all, I would be
honored to give her a blessing — something I had never done before
in my life.

Michelle said, "I'd be very grateful, Kit." That quick.

So I went to her chair, anointed her head with the sacred oil I
carried in a tiny steel flask on my keychain, and sought for the will
of heaven.

It was abundant that day.

As I closed the prayer, Beth scooted her chair right up next to us
and asked if she could be next. So I blessed her as well. When I had

finished, Michelle went off for twenty seconds and then came back carrying Brandon, barely rousing from sleep.

"Does he need to be awake?" she asked me, and I said no, having no clue, really. I just anointed his head and blessed away, listening really hard for the feeling I knew would come and then saying word after word just as it came into my mind. Then Beth brought out Ryan and her boy and sat them down in the two chairs and said, "Now be real still, boys. This man is a pastor. He's going to make you well, say a prayer over you." The little boys looked up at me and then bowed their heads, Mama blubbering to beat the band.

And that's exactly what I did that day: exercised the power of God in a household of faith. I left quickly, scared to death about some of the things I'd said, real big promises, but Michelle called me the next day and said everybody was well.

Exactly like I'd said.

I was twenty years old, barely an advanced beginner.

I busted right out of that memory with "*Hermano* Velasquez, the Lord can heal you," just blurting it right out in the middle of Aillón's attempt—and it was a valiant one—to challenge *Señor* Velasquez to greater faith, harder effort, deeper prayer, a bit more sacrifice.

And *Hermana* V. said, "*Diga, hermano.*" Speak. Tell us.

Aillón looked at me. The Velasquezes looked at me. The Sacred Heart of Jesus hanging on the wall looked at me, and I knew the eyes of heaven were staring down as well. I scrambled back into the cave of my soul and looked around, and that was all I could see: Jesus was ready to heal this man. He had done great things, made enormous strides on his own, gone maybe as far as he could go on his own. I heard a voice—it sounded like Ray Goode—saying, "Elder of Israel, stand and show forth the power of God."

So I did. I stood up, not being real clear at all where the other three were in their conversation. But I called my companion to take his place next to me, and I asked *Hermano* V. if he had faith in the power of Jesus Christ, his power to change, renew, heal. He looked at me for several moments, then at his wife, who was already seeing a new man there in her kitchen chair, and then said, "I do, *hermano.*"

So we blessed him. I didn't have to do any scanning of the heavens at all in my mind, because I already knew exactly what I was supposed to say. And then we hugged them both and took our leave.

It was past ten-thirty, and mission rules were pretty strict about being back in our apartments by nine-thirty and in bed by now. Having no interest at all in taking our chances on four miles of darkened Colombian streets that were a serious risk at midday, I prayed in my heart for a cab, and one appeared, and we got in and went home, keying the lock at 11:08.

I lay still in my bed with my eyes open for a long time that night, just staring at the plain plaster ceiling. Aillón snored. Cockroaches skittered about under the bed. And I lay staring at the ceiling, thinking about what I'd just told Mr. Sanford Velasquez, a fifty-year-old man who'd been drinking and smoking and carousing with women for thirty-five of them. I had told him, really just voicing words that had been dictated in my head, that he would never smoke again, that his desires for drink and his "former ways" would fade away like dew before the morning sun, and that his commitment to Jesus Christ would make him an entirely new man.

And I thought of me. I thought of former ways, former days, or as Joe Walsh put it, "days gone by." But mostly I wondered, *What about me? Am I healed? Am I clean?*

And finally I fell asleep on that, and a fitful night it was.

Next day I got a letter from Quebec, Canada. Sister Annie Hawk, following eight weeks in the MTC, was on the ground, ready to be a missionary, although she was very concerned about her ability to speak in French, the training never having quite taken hold yet. The letter was very circumspect, closing very cautiously: *Your friend in Christ, Sister Hawk.* But not before she wrote, *Think of where we've been, what we've learned, and how far we've come! How grateful we should be to the Savior.*

But all I could think of was where we'd been, what we'd done, she and I, and now the taunts in the street, the bricks thrown from windows and the spit from passing bus windows. I thought, *Okay, maybe I'm getting exactly what I deserve,* seeing only the bad.

But it got worse.

34

"Suppose we suddenly wake up and see
that what we thought to be this and that
ain't this and that at all?"
—Kerouac, *The Dharma Bums*

A NEW ELDER IN MY DISTRICT would become a most unlikely friend in
the most unlikely of ways. Ernesto "Rocky" Mianno was a big Ital-
ian-American kid from the Bronx, a place I had never heard of, in
New York City, a place I had. He had been a star high-school football player and then a quarterback at Ricks College, the church's junior college up in Rexburg, Idaho, that would later become Brigham
Young University—Idaho.

This guy was built like a junior Schwarzenegger. According to
his companion, Elder McCarthy, he jumped rope and lifted weights
for thirty minutes every morning and for a couple of hours on P-
day. He had never seen a mountain until his mom drove him across
country to Rexburg, never walked a mountain trail, never stuck his
tail in the air and plunged his lips straight into the crystal pool of
a mountain stream. We had absolutely nothing in common but our
commitment to be good missionaries and our common ability to
sound just like a soaped-down version of Cheech and Chong, me
from their record albums, him from life experience.

Growing up in what sounded to me like a really big, really in-
tense rendering of Roy, Utah, he had never adopted any of Elder
Ruff's interests in gang fights, vandalism, and raising hell. In fact he
and Ruff, both in my district now, could find very little to talk about,
whereas he and I went on and on and on, one particular perspective
being our shared image of a personal religious faith that didn't get
passed along to us in a nice little package tied up with ribbon and a
kiss from Grandma. Elder Mianno's folks, leading little Rocky and
his sister by the hands, had stopped by the Mormon pavilion at the

World's Fair in Flushing-Queens in 1964, mostly to let the kiddies look at the big statue of the golden man blowing a trumpet, and then filled out a card saying sure, come on by. They listened to the missionaries and joined the church a few months later, against the extended family's wishes.

The Mianno family was *Católico Apostólico Romano* straight from the old country, and the unthinkable exodus to Mormonism had been seen as a hemorrhage that for some time threatened to kill their place in the family. But little Ernest John was such a good kid, everybody's favorite nephew, a trusted neighborhood kid, and his mother's pride and joy.

And within a few years on the football field, he did kick butt. It was that prowess that eventually put him over the top with the extended family.

One afternoon in November, as we were preparing for an open house—"Come Meet the Mormons"—at the meetinghouse in Los Alpes, suddenly the glass foyer doors slammed closed and then popped back open, and an enormous gust of wind roared through the place. Elder Mianno said, "What the hey, look at that," and I turned to watch the sidewalk roll toward us in waves, up and down, up and down, right up to the building. And then the building did it. Really big waves, throwing me and Mianno and Aillón into the opposite wall. Windows started to shatter, doors to pop right out of their frames.

We all ran outside right through the door frame, and suddenly Mianno and I were looking at each other from the crests of opposite ground waves. When my wave was up, I could see what was happening in the world beyond: cars crashing into walls, buildings coming down in swirls of dust, people jumping from third- and fourth-floor windows or open walls.

People were screaming everywhere, including us pretty soon. And then it stopped, Mianno on his knees looking the opposite direction from me, saying, "Oh man, oh man, oh man."

Twenty-seven high-rise buildings came down during that one, a 7.8 on the Richter scale, and about thirty-five hundred huts and houses just in Pereira, the epicenter. We spent the next three days loading rubble into the backs of Jeeps, dodging broken gas mains, covering our mouths with our handkerchiefs whenever somebody carted out a body. People wandered around in a daze, and looting was as common as dust, gangs of youth even breaking the windows of shops that hadn't broken in the quake, taking TVs and radios and toaster ovens by the cartful. Electricity was down, water lines were busted, raw sewage was flowing in the streets.

People were setting up cardboard lean-tos in the parks and in the streets, and we helped hundreds of them, six guys in CIA shirts and ties saying, "Brother, are you and yours okay?"

With no phone service, as district leader I had to check on my boys somehow, so Aillón and I thumbed rides all over the Risaralda province. My district was twenty miles wide, from Cuba to Dos Quebradas, where Ruff lived. In fact, Cubillos and Ruff pulled up to our apartment building the next morning in a taxi. They'd been down at the *panadería* having a *pan* and a Postobón soda for dinner when the entire roof of their apartment fell straight down as the walls opened out, crushing everything in sight. The lady of the house, *Doña* Mariela, had barely escaped being flattened by standing in a doorway. But she was now in the hospital from a heart attack or something.

We helped clean up Colombia for a week afterward, white shirts and ties firmly in place. I wrote my folks the weekly letter, not knowing they wouldn't get it for nearly five weeks, not knowing they were about to go nuts after watching the evening news broadcast about a killer earthquake in Colombia, 7.8 on the Richter and epicentered thirty miles straight below the last place they had heard from their kid, four hundred people dead.

After several days of waiting for a phone call or letter, my parents asked Ray Goode to please call Salt Lake and see what was known. He did, of course, and the Missionary Department told him that all missionaries in Colombia were safe and accounted for and that they'd had the Public Communications Department put it out on a press release, after all. And Ray said, "Well, that does a lot of good in Colorado. Channel seven has never heard of the Mormon church."

Even when it wasn't earthquaking, the mail to and from Colombia traveled very slowly. I had never placed a phone call, of course, because that was against mission rules. Not against all church-mission rules, just against the ones in Cali, Colombia. Mission president's prerogative. And I never broke the rules.

When I finally heard from home, my parents were chewing on rocks—what kind of an organization was this anyway, not to let a kid call home to tell his Mama and Daddy he's still alive? But by then I was in bed again with amoebic dysentery, nine pounds lighter than when I'd entered the country not quite five months before.

And then we had another earthquake, just like the last one. I would have troubles with nausea for another ten years every time I felt a big truck go by on the street.

My first Christmas in Colombia, I got a T-shirt from my companion, a bar of fancy soap from the landlady, and a letter from Sister Hawk in Quebec. Nothing from home, although I figured it had gotten hung up in the transit process. One Elder Wilcox had received his second shoe in the mail — you never mailed them together, due to theft — five months after the first, although they had been postmarked in Torrance, California, on the same day.

I was surprised by all of it. But something about Annie's letter — *Oh, don't you just LOVE your mission!?* — bugged me. A lot. I was really struggling to love Colombia. Perhaps it was the photograph she sent of P-daying around the Quebec woods on snowshoes. I'd spent my last four P-days tossing bricks into the backs of trucks while people yelled "Go home, *gringos*" when we weren't looking.

I often wondered what it would have been like to be an American G.I. walking the dusty streets of Korea or Vietnam. I told myself that at least they were carrying guns and wearing helmets, with a dozen comrades around them, armed to the teeth. Getting paid to be tough guys, whereas I was a preacher, supposed to be preaching kindness, patience, brotherly love. Which is really who I was inside, anyway.

But the taunts, the spit at my feet, the rocks and bricks thrown through the air, the incessant accusations of "imperialist whore," "Yankee exploiter," cultural polluter of the minds and hearts of the humble and poor, made me think again and again about what it must have been like to be a soldier fighting a foreign war, where people weren't spitting at you but shooting large bullets; where one's job was to shoot people, to blow them up or get shot and blown up yourself; and never in a war that we started, just one where we were trying to end it or keep some lunatic like Hitler or Hussein from rolling over the earth. I started feeling the stirrings of what I could only label *patriotism*.

Weird.

Nothing had ever prepared me for being the bad guy. I had never dreamed that so many people hated America or despised Americans — even its preachers, good Lord — and I couldn't help but take it personally. I kept reminding myself what Christmas was really all about; it was my whole mission purpose, after all. But that day, my first Christmas on the equator, the bells of the season tolled for no one. I was just a lonely American kid a long way from mom, home, and apple pie. I'd even have settled for a Chevrolet commercial on TV.

And then transfers came again: Aillón, Ruff, and Mianno stayed right where they were, and I headed south sixty miles to open the new year in the little mountain village of Sevilla, the coffee capital of Colombia.

Elder Aillón shook my hand as I got on the bus. Then he hugged me. He looked me in the eye and said, "Elder *Waist*, with you I learned how to be a missionary."

And I hoped that was true. I had shown him everything I knew. Which wasn't much.

35

"[Everything] is eternally flowing from use to use, beauty
to yet higher beauty; and we soon cease to lament waste
and death . . . and faithfully watch and wait the reappear-
ance of everything that melts and fades and dies about us,
feeling sure that its next appearance will be better and
more beautiful than the last."
—John Muir, *My First Summer in the Sierra*

SEVILLA WAS A MOUNTAIN TOWN, and I was almost instantly in love.
Quiet, no, but lots of character.

Monday mornings the cowboys would ride past the windows
of our house, a place on a corner with an actual hacienda-type open-
roofed courtyard in the middle. When I heard the horses the first
time, clickety-clack on the cobblestone, I went to the window to
watch six guys mounted up on fine steeds, with hats, chaps and
everything, riding right down the street. But in the place of lassos,
they carried long machetes. Before them, en masse, thousands of
townsmen and boys were flooding into the hillsides to spend twelve
hours peeling the bright red coffee beans from the bushes that covered the hills as far as I could see. A good portion of them would
probably peel the bright red coca berries that grew right next to
them. Banana trees grew all over, their eight-foot leaves bending
down to caress the low-growing coffee bushes.

On Friday nights the cowboys, the coffee crew *jefes*, would ride
back into town to get drunk, shooting their guns in the air, hooting
and hollering. Just like the streets of Laredo, I suppose. Horsemen
in the streets all over town, hundreds of them. They liked the principal routes, so we just kept to the side streets or got off the streets
altogether by late evening.

And in the meantime, small-town friendliness—praise the
Lord—showed its best face in Sevilla, especially in the *farmácias*

for some reason, I suppose because these were the places where beauty was supposed to bloom. Every time we entered a corner drug store — they are always on corners in Latin America — all seven clerks, always pretty young ladies, would spring to the counter like bunny rabbits.

"*A la órden?*" — May I help you? — they would all sing in chorus.

"*Gracias*, no," we would answer. "We're just in for razor blades." Back in the big city, I suppose, we could have gotten a personal tour of the features and benefits of each brand. In Sevilla there was only one brand, so we would just pay for our blades at the counter, take one long look at the features there without any benefit, and take our leave. Of course, we would buy only one week's worth of blades at a time.

See ya next week, girls.

My companion, Julio Gonzalez, was a real looker. The women would look at him, and he would smile back sweetly and frequently turn back for a little chat. I taught more discussions to teenage girls and young ladies in that town than I did anywhere else in Colombia — all added up. We had a monthly contract to eat lunch with a member family halfway across town. Good food, as the sister was trained well after feeding missionaries for nearly five years, and really cute daughters. Elder Gonzalez often made me nervous, flirting just a little too freely with the fifteen-year-old, Liliana. I honestly think the main reason something serious never happened there was because Liliana knew the rules as well as the missionaries did, and she would cut it off, pull away to do homework about the time Gonzalez' jets were about to go into turbo. I felt sorry in advance for the missionaries a couple years down the road, though.

As mentioned before, the common everyday woman in Colombia wasn't prone to wearing an abundance of clothing, some of that being cultural, some to be blamed on the thermometer. But even when covered, they liked it really tight. The Latina figure tended toward full-bodied in any case, and coupled with sleeveless shirts, open bellies, and low necklines, it was a wonder any one of us ever finished our missions.

And flirtatious? I wouldn't have a girl stick her hands right down my pants or actually out and out pop the wanna-go-to-bed question for several months still — and those would be two different girls, by the way — but the looks, the leanings, the pressings up on the bus—oh man, oh man, oh man. And something about that smooth, well-toasted skin, those deep-brown, puppy-dog eyes, that long, glossy, pitch-black hair, those full, rosy lips . . .

Thus the encouragement learned in the MTC for times such as these: "Sing a hymn, Elder." Turn away, focus on something else.

We'd come out of our room on the south side of the courtyard in the morning, and the twenty-six-year-old daughter of the woman to whom we paid our rent would be sitting right there eight feet away with no shirt on, nursing her baby. Really big nursing mechanisms. In fact, no kidding, that was usually right when the baby had to burp, so she'd pull her off and throw her up and over a shoulder, mechanism number one staring us right in the face. Humongous nursing mechanisms.

And Gonzalez would say, out loud, "*Cante un hymno,* Elder!"

The nursing thing wasn't normal, however, either the practice or the positioning. Most women in Colombia—and all over the Third World—had been taught by a generation of U.S. health workers and real pretty full-color literature that bottle-feeding was better, so they'd fill up the bottles with *agua panela*—sugar water—or *gringo* formula stretched out for economics with nice, clean water out of the tap or the adjacent stream. The very few who did nurse, typically the ones with a bit of money and education, usually did so discreetly.

Our gal Nora was unique. But superbly capable.

More common were the "Travoltas."

These were the adult men and women who were barely "staying alive" by collecting the peelings, shreds, and remains from the streets under the *galerías*—outdoor fruit markets—at night. Wherever it had been, whatever it had seen, they ate it right there where they found it. Their hair was so matted with the grease and dirt of years that it slapped against their shoulders as they walked, as stiff as cork board. Their skin was blackened with the same kind of stuff, which often peeled off in chunks as they moved along. I followed them on the street and watched pieces fall. Typically they were quite crazy, the effects of malnutrition and cocaine, according to the doctor we met one day making his rounds.

In fact, Pompilio Varón found us.

The guy pulled up to us in a Land Cruiser, not a common sight in Colombia.

"Hey, *Élderes, como les va?*" Real friendly-like and smiling. We soon learned that he'd been reared right here in Sevilla but was now living and practicing medicine in the big city of Cali, a hundred miles to the south. He was a counselor in the stake presidency down there, a regional church leader of some rank. One Saturday a month, he came back up to the old homestead and treated the country people — *los campesinos* — for free, as many as he could round up in one day.

He rented out a simple room in a boarding house as his office, and he drove around in the hills handing out his business card and — because most *campesinos* couldn't read — telling people where they could find him and when. He had located himself in a very conspicuous place: right next to the electric-appliance store where, according to signs in every window, Colombia's first broadcast of a color television program would air in exactly three weeks: a boxing match.

So from time to time, when we could, we would join *Presidente* Varón for a few hours on his excursions around town and into the hills, bringing the Mormon gospel message to folks who had never even seen a toothbrush, let alone a North American or a Land Rover. They couldn't read, and they would probably never make it to church services, but I took it as my personal task to let the gospel go to the hills. It seemed the least I could do for the mountains of Colombia.

One afternoon we were sipping *gaseosas* with *Presidente* Varón in his office, and he told us about growing up right there, actually up in the hills above Sevilla, picking coffee beans from the time he was seven years old, picking right alongside his father. That's what everybody did thirty years ago, he told us: you either owned a coffee *finca* or you labored on one, for thirteen or fourteen hours a day in the sun, even the kids because no one really cared about school back then. He'd move from bush to bush, always right there with his father, and his father would say, "Pompi, as you grow up I hope you can find a better way." And then his father insisted, when Pompi was eleven, that he enroll in school, get the little blue uniform, and let the *monjas* — the nuns — make something of his life, get out of these cursed fields with their snakes and stinging ants and finger-gnawing bugs almost the size of Pompi's little fist. And so he did, and then he qualified for medical school, and after he had entered that field he came back and bought a small coffee *finca*, fifteen hectares, and gave the workers shorter days, better wages, and free medical care.

And then he became a Mormon, and his rank-and-file leader, a mission president previous to mine, told him to sell his coffee farm because it wasn't an appropriate way for a Latter-day Saint to make a living, although he was really just feeding half the town and keeping them healthy—he made his living as a doctor down in the big city. I thought of a guy back in the States, a bishop who was the director of public relations for a major beer company, and I thought of a stake president's counselor who was the assistant director of gaming for a casino in Las Vegas, and I asked, "So what'd you do?"

He looked at me like I was stupid. He sold the coffee farm, of course.

So I was sitting there wondering how a guy with a Wharton M.B.A. and three cars, a boat, and a motorhome couldn't find a different job in the States, when someone knocked on the door. Elder Gonzalez opened it to find a *campesino* couple carrying a baby boy who did not appear to be doing very well. His eyes were waxy, his little fists were clenching, and his belly was convulsing. Dr. Varón barely took a look.

"He's suffocating," he said in surprise, and he grabbed the baby from the mother, laid him down on his table, opened his mouth, and arched up his neck. The action relieved something slightly, and the boy began gasping for breaths. He actually opened his eyes then and turned his little head to look right at me.

Varón said, "He is choking on tapeworms" and turned for his bag. And I did the weirdest thing I had done yet on my mission: I asked the mother if I could hold him. She assented, and I lifted him up, keeping his passageway in this partially open position. I cradled him in my arms and just stared in his eyes, and he stared back, right into me.

Varón said, "Why did you bring him here? He should be in the hospital right now."

The parents just stood there quietly, the man, looking fifty if a day, holding his leather hat in his hands, rolling it around slowly by the brim, he and the missus both just standing there being scolded, no power to contest, no answer worth giving.

Varón hit them again. "He should have been in the hospital days ago."

He came over with his light, directed me in my holding, and looked the boy over closely. It was then that I could see every couple of seconds or so a flat, white, wiggling thing tickle the back of his throat. Varón said they were up his nose and in his ears too, but I was beyond wanting to see. I just looked into his eyes. I thought I should feel like vomiting or crying at least, but I just asked the couple how old he was. About twenty-seven months.

Varón turned off his light, looked up at the man, and said, "You've got to get him to the hospital."

And the *campesino* couple just stood there, the man rolling his dirty hat around, looking at the floor.

"We have brought him to you, Doctor."

"I can't treat him here! He has worms. *Ascaris. Solitaria.* Killing him."

Finally the man said, "We cannot go to the hospital, doctor. We have no money."

Dr. Varón took a couple of deep breaths. He knew very well where the man was coming from; these were his people, and this was his country.

"He is beyond my care, my friend. He needs a hospital quickly. He is dying right now."

I watched as the father looked up finally, meeting Dr. Varón's eyes, but then I turned my own away, looking straight down into the face of the little boy, his eyes glassy, his fists and tiny limbs still jerking in spasm. *Oh God,* I prayed, *not here, not me, and not right now.*

And I heard the man say that they could not go to the hospital. If Varón could not help them, they would just take the little one home to say good-bye. I looked up at Varón and then at the old man, my stare pleading, *What now?* I couldn't believe this dumb farmhand was just going to walk off into the hills with his kid. The mama stood there looking at me, then at her baby, then at me. And I thought, *Am I supposed to do something? Should I stand up and call upon my God and direct the powers of heaven to heal this boy?*

But I couldn't. It just wouldn't come.

I heard Dr. Varón say, "I'll speak to the hospital, but you go now. Go, go, go!"

The couple just stood there as I held the baby, not offering him up or anything. And I continued to wonder, *Am I supposed to do something?* So I did.

I stood up and handed the baby to his mama and said, "Let's go. I'm grabbing a taxi." I went down the stairs and into the street, looking mostly at the blue sky, thinking, *The same big blue heaven over Colombia as over Colorado, and I have to be here,* just staring up at the sky until I heard my companion say, "*Suban*" — get in — not two feet away from me, and I looked to see that he had already hailed a cab and was shoving the couple into the car, the woman cradling her baby boy.

And Gonzalez said, "How much to take them to the hospital? Their baby is dying." Then he put out his hand to me, needing my wallet, as he never carried anything, not even his ID papers. I handed him what I had and said, "Keep the change, and go man go," and the *taxista* hit it and split, throwing dust right into our faces.

And then finally I cried.

Presidente Varón came down the stairs saying, "I got the hospital. Dr. Cifuentes. He'll take care of 'em." And then, "*Ascaris. Solitaria. Hombre*, that's bad stuff."

I'd remember those words when I got diagnosed with the same stuff one month later.

36

> "All living beings, whether it's just a little cat or
> squirrel or whatever, all are going to heaven
> straight into God's snowy arms, so never hurt
> anything and if you see anybody hurt anything
> stop them as best you can."
> —Kerouac, *On the Origins of a Generation*

I SPENT MOST OF February in bed or on the floor, the bed when I could get there, the floor when I couldn't. Usually the floor of the bathroom. In the time it took me to lose twenty-one pounds, I got three letters from home and a Christmas package sent the third of December, containing a beautiful Colorado aspen tree T-shirt, three-dozen homemade chocolate chip and peanut butter cookies, and my harmonica. I would lie in bed and blow some tunes, then run to the john and blow some cookies, then lie on the floor and sing the blues.

Day after day after day.

I received a letter from Ray Goode and two from Annie in Quebec sent a week apart. She told me about knocking on doors six hours a day through moose-leather mittens, the young French Canadian gals up there answering the knock wearing nothing but panties, maybe, and the sister missionaries off the streets by four in the afternoon because that's when flesh started to freeze, even when covered by four layers of wool and Annie's Mountain-O goose-down vest.

And I'd think: *Tapeworms or ice? Tapeworms or ice?*

And take ice, any day.

In one stretch over two days, when I was still able to sit up but unable to walk very far, I went through the Spanish hymnbook and sang one verse of every hymn—even the ones I had to sight-read and learn on the spot—into a tape recorder and then gave the tape to President Gomez so that he or whoever was directing the music each Sunday would be able to learn every hymn. The way it eventually worked, he'd pick a hymn Saturday night and cue it up on the tape recorder, then everyone would sing along with Elder *Waist* the next day in meetings.

I laid around a lot thinking about that baby with the tapeworms, who Dr. Varón told Gonzalez two weeks later they hadn't saved. I'd think, *Is it just poverty? And if so, why the poverty?* To all appearances, the land was like a peat-moss playground. I saw fence posts of *guadua*, pine, or mahogany stuck in the ground with wire wrapped around their waists and necks, sprouting leaves out the top. Fence posts saying, *Nice plot o' ground, thanks a lot,* and growing again, I kid you not.

Or was it, like the "enlightened" college students always told us, the curse of religion? The national religion essentially taught: "The Lord placed me here to be poor and ignorant, and that's his will, and it's all I'll ever be. His hand is upon me, I cannot be smart or have money or drink water without those weird red floaty bugs in it. I was made to suffer." Which was—chalk one up for the college kids—kind of a suck-o type of religion.

But then the same kids, the college crowd and their parents, cursed us to our faces, saying we had come to destroy their blessed religion, *la santa fé.* The religion that got poured over them only in Latin and told them the word of the Lord was not meant to be understood by the peasants, the common folk, the ignorant masses. Their priests charged them money to get married, money to get baptized, and they baptized infants at that, infants who had no sins to be remitted in the first place or money with which to be forgiven.

And here we came dressed in relatively common clothing—not a purple robe found in the whole of Salt Lake Central Casting—thousands of miles from our homes, earning no salary, to a foreign land, speaking a foreign tongue, risking and suffering disease and sickness and living as celibate as the priests. Getting bricks thrown at our heads. But teaching a different religion entirely: read, study, find out for yourself, then go and make something of your life.

Yet we got yelled at for being just another church, come to denigrate the people, to hold them down, to keep them in bondage. As one know-it-all eighteen-year-old told me in Pereira, this Jesus we were preaching was the "cause of all the suffering in the world," and he had "started it all" two thousand years ago.

I thought to myself: *This isn't what he started. This is the work of humans.*

But we weren't there to debunk Catholicism. In the first place, Colombian Catholicism was totally different from Québécoise Catholicism, for example, so most of it was just cultural anyway. And in the second, that just wasn't the Mormon way. Oh, sure, some of us had started out that way, coming out of the MTC with seven readings of the Book of Mormon under our belt and a fetish for stuff written by Elder Bruce R. McConkie. We had come out swinging around our big Mormon axe and had some second-year Catholic seminary student kick our butt in a scripture bash in the streets of Dos Quebradas — Elder Ruff watching — or had some sweet, pure soul with Bambi-brown eyes and flaxen hair on her way to heaven with or without us burst into tears and say, "Ministers of the gospel, and you talk to my grandfather like that?"

And walked away, the door slapping us in the butt as we went, saying, "Oops." Which had also happened in Pereira.

Once a day I'd shuffle the block from our house to the hospital to drop my drawers for Dr. Cifuentes and three or four nurses so one of them could plant a needle in my bum cheeks — left today, right tomorrow — and the others could watch, usually the nurses.

Elder Gonzalez spent his days out doing the missionary thing with Chucho, the branch president's twelve-year-old son, and twice a day he would bring me morsels of food from the Romeros' house, since I was too weak to get there and not hungry anyway, and I'd lay there for the hour he was gone every day thinking, *Man, I hope he's keeping his hands off Liliana.* Sister Romero came by herself several times to bring a plate of food. During one stretch of nine days, I did not eat a single piece of food but continued to evacuate the innards of my soul, wondering what the possible hell on earth was still coming out back there, actually peering in the bowl to see if it looked like brain matter or intestines, whatever those might have looked like.

One night about twenty-six days into my journey through hell, I thought I was either going to die or kill myself. My guts were on the verge of exploding all over the bedroom walls. I stuck my finger down my throat repeatedly, tickling the little thing back there that's supposed to let you gag something up, just wiggling away like I was finger-painting a pretzel.

Elder Gonzalez was off at the Romeros' for dinner and dessert too it seemed, as the clock in our room read 8:38 P.M. The folks of the house were off to mass or La Leche League or something, and I was all alone and getting desperate. I tried reaching the mission president by phone in Cali—our place hosted one of the few phones in town—but the only number the operator in Cali could find was to the mission office. And it was closed for the night.

Lying on the floor by my bed, I attempted to kneel and do a real-live honest humble prayer, but I couldn't get to my knees, so I just called out loud through my tears as I left the room by pulling myself on my stomach, pushing through our tall, wooden saloon doors with my head, and crawled toward the kitchen for a knife. I was cogent enough to remember how a farmer could stick a cow when she ate too much green alfalfa, puncture her gut to release the pressure. I was going for that knife, even though I knew cows had more stomachs than I did.

Elder Gonzalez found me about six feet from the kitchen counter, awash in cold sweat and passed out even colder. I woke up as he drug me by the heels, my head bouncing, back to my bed. He was blubbering like a baby, saying, "*Hombre, hombre,* God, don't die on me now," and then he saw I was awake and said, "Brother, I'm going to bless you with the priesthood." I didn't have the strength to ask him if he was worthy to exercise the power of God, since he'd been off till who knows what hour with Liliana Romero, but I did wonder why we never asked for blessings for ourselves, thinking of Ray Goode back in Silver Creek telling me one time, "Yeah, we men are always handing it out, but we never ask for ourselves, weird."

So Elder Gonzalez blessed me.

The next day I was hungry, the same day a six-pound can of peanut butter showed up from Paradise Mountain, U.S. postage forty-four dollars, worth every dime. I introduced half of Sevilla to *mantequella de maní,* and they said, "This stuff is food? You can eat it?" And I said, "This is the food of the gods, *hombre,* manna from heaven, the solace to all my suffering, the substance of things hoped for but never seen until today."

Branch *presidente* Pedro Gomez made a poor living fixing radios and televisions out of the front window of his house. Oh, it was a standard living in Colombia, but a pitiful standard nonetheless. He played guitar and sang a bit on the side, making a few extra

pesos on Friday and Saturday nights. One Saturday afternoon at the
church building, the upper floor of a house we rented, we held a tal-
ent show. I played and sang a couple of tunes, an instrumental with
a lot of flat picking, and a love song I'd written for Annie the week
we started falling apart:

> *If the world were to go and sell me*
> *All the love it has to give –*
> *Darling, you know*
> *That I would give it all to you.*
>
> *And if the mountains*
> *And the starlit skies were mine,*
> *Even the sunlight*
> *And the warmest summer rain*
>
> *I would never sleep*
> *Until I found a way*
> *To wrap the world up*
> *And put it in your name.*
>
> CHORUS
> *Darling, I love you*
> *Can't you feel the pain?*
> *The heartache I feel,*
> *When alone I call your name.*
> *All the love in the world –*
> *Can I really find the way?*
> *Love isn't really love*
> *Until you give yourself away.*
>
> *I would walk around the world*
> *And sail across the seas*
> *Just to find you happiness*
> *And to set your spirit free.*
>
> *The sands of time may follow me –*
> *The face of death may greet,*
> *But I would live to find you happiness*
> *And set it at your feet.*

But now I see that you're not looking
For the riches I can bring –
All the gold, the stars, the sunlight –
When all you really wanted was me.

CHORUS
Darling, I love you –
You know I feel your pain,
The pain that you feel
When alone you call my name.
All the love in the world –
Have I really found the way?
My love isn't really love
Until I give myself away.

Nobody had been baptized in Sevilla for a year and a half. Not a soul. Members of the church, all converts, said, "No, this is it – we're it, all you're going to find. Second Coming might as well happen tomorrow, we're all here." But then Pompilio Varón gave us an address and said, "I trust you guys – go visit my niece, Gloria Pino." So we did, and within two weeks we had baptized her and her three children, the whole branch going, "Man alive, maybe there's a few more out there." Happens all the time.

The baptismal font in Sevilla was a beautiful natural pool at the base of a waterfall located a forty-minute walk into the hills above town. The entire branch accompanied us, thirty-seven people plus about a dozen investigators, fifty people in dresses and ties snaking their way up the long trail through the coca woods. We took along vittles for a fine Colombian picnic, Sister Berta Franco bringing a tin pail full of big, steamed cornmeal-and-chicken tamales wrapped in banana leaves, by far the best food I'd had in nearly a year. While the kids and President Gomez played in the pool afterward, Gonzalez splashing them from the edge – missionaries are not allowed to swim for two years – I lay in the sun on an open slope and just watched the sky and the clouds and stared off into the forest. Loving it, saying, "Man, this is so good."

And then we baptized again. And again. Three picnic excursions back up to the waterfall.

We got to go to Pereira to talk about it. Actually, it was a three-zone conference, all thirty-eight missionaries in about a two-hour radius meeting together to be taught by the zone leaders before going out for ice cream or fried chicken, something *gringo*, even the Colombians saying, "Man oh man, that's good," although there was always the uncomfortable pairing up of *gringos* with *gringos* and Colombians with Colombians once the social thing began. One of the principal topics of conversation was the taking of the U.S. embassy in Bogotá the week before by a violent paramilitary group named M-19 for April nineteenth, a very popular date in the day planners of terrorists. The news reports all pointed out that two of the terrorists, sisters, were "*Mormones*" but neglected to mention that the other twenty-six were Catholic, the same kind of reporting that still happens in the United States. Now our LDS college students all over the country were getting beat up, assaulted, accused of running M-19 as a front for the CIA.

I didn't want anything to do with the conversation — the Colombian elders were starting to vent about North American politics and intervention and *imperialismo* and all — so I grabbed a final chicken thigh and went out to the sidewalk. A couple of North Americans joined me. Elder Mianno, now serving up in Manizales, said, "Man, your English stinks!" The other elders would laugh at me, saying things like, "Hey Elder West, can't you *hablar* the old hometown *lengua* anymore?" And one of the zone leaders, a guy actually named Robert "Rusty" Rainwater, said, "How long's it been since you spoke English?" And I could honestly answer him that, except for one desperate prayer a few weeks back, it had been about four months.

"Even your prayers?" he asked.

"Yeah, except for the one just before I died."

Then I had to explain that, the guys laughing again because I didn't know half the words in English so I did it in both languages, in and out, like knitting a sweater with two colors of yarn.

Gonzalez and I didn't get on the road again until nearly 8:30 P.M., figuring it was about two hours to Sevilla and then we could hop in bed at just about white missionary handbook time.

But it didn't quite go that way.

37

"I sing to the stars, remembering previous lifetimes
when I was a prisoner in dungeons, and now
I'm in the open air."
—Kerouac, *Desolation Angels*

WE CAUGHT THE *FLOTA*, the long-distance highway bus, out of Pereira, bouncing out past Cuba to Tres Esquinas and down into the valley of the Cauca River at Cartago, where Ruff had had his head busted open. But in Cartago we made an unscheduled layover when the bus wouldn't restart after stopping for two passengers. I just stayed in the bus while nearly everyone else took a break in the street or in the cantina across the street. I stared out the window thinking, *So this is what's next — I'm gonna die in Carthage* — Cartago — *just like the Prophet Joseph Smith.*

After practically rebuilding the engine right there under a street light, the driver got back on and turned 'er over, practically shutting the door and rolling before everyone made it back on. In fact, maybe we left a few in the bar. We rolled south again, and Elder Gonzalez and I got our call just before midnight: junction coming up, highway to Bogotá. The bus driver pulled to the side of the two-lane highway and let us out on the shoulder. Then he pulled away, blowing dust and diesel into our faces.

We stood looking around for a few moments, Elder Gonzalez still climbing out of a slumber, and tried to get our bearings. His illuminated watch — I didn't wear one — said it was about twenty minutes past midnight. There was only the one other road, another two-laner splitting right off the valley highway, no exit ramp or nuthin', just peeling off and pointing straight east toward the *cordillera* — mountain range — whose dark outline stood in contrast to the sky. Maybe forty miles. Maybe eighty. At least we assumed it was east — it eventually went to Bogotá, after all — but my scanning of the heavens for the Big Dipper, the pointing stars, and Polaris, the North Star, was producing no proof. The sky was packed with stars, however, so I figured at first that I just wasn't picking it out as easily as I always could at home. It was as good as any southern Utah night sky I had ever experienced, the dry desert air always revealing a lot more than mountain air. And at that my mind reeled back to a night once spent under pinyon pines on the far end of the Mogollon Rim in eastern Arizona and the song that I wrote there, sitting on a rock up above the dirt road that wound south out of Alpine.

Away in the night sky over Tucson
The settling sun rests its head tonight.
The full, rising moon greets me head-on.
There won't be many stars to see tonight.

Somewhere in the mountains north of the border,
Just me and my six-string playing a tune.
All quiet and still like a boat on the ocean,
Quite a trio: just me, the earth, and the moon.

Elder Gonzalez drew me back out when he said, "*Mire.*" (Look.)

Just north of us and across the highway was a large building with gas pumps out front. As we moved toward it, walking just as slow as we pleased across the vacant midnight highway, we saw the large sign overhead proclaiming this PARADOR ROJO, literally the Red Stopping Place, and by starlight—no moon in sight—we could see that the roof of the place was indeed made of red clay *tejas*, or tiles. No light from within, of course. The place was closed.

We wandered up, pressed our faces into the wrought-iron *rejas* covering every window, and tried to look inside. To my left Gonzalez said, "*Que cosa*," and I said, "What?" and he said, "The bus schedule, taped right here to the door. The last *flota* to Bogotá went by at eleven-eighteen."

Long gone.

I looked back at the highways, both of them. Nothing was moving on either one in either direction, at least nothing motorized. Probably plenty of other things moving.

"*Qué hacemeos?*" Elder Gonzalez asked me, as if I would know.

But in fact I did. I smiled and showed him my thumb, saying, "*Cojemos así.*" I had no idea what the word for hitchhike was, although I'd done a bit of it back in Pereira after the earthquake, getting out to check on my outliers.

Gonzalez helped me out here. He said, "Hitchhike?" And I said, "Whoa, you know some English!" And he said, "Huh? That was Spanish"—just like *clooch* (clutch) and *windshield* (windshield) and *panquek* (pancake), probably the same word in every language. I said, "Yeah, sure, what else we gonna do?" And he said, "*Con quién?*" With whom? But we wandered over to the Bogotá highway and took up position about a hundred meters away from the valley highway.

And stood there.

In a few minutes, Elder Gonzalez started taking off his tie, but I told him to leave it on. Out here in the middle of the night valley, we'd need all the good-guy karma we could come up with. So he pulled it tight again, and we stared up at the stars.

The feeling of being alone, more or less, and in the middle of nowhere was one of the sweetest feelings I had felt in—well, in almost a year. I walked off the highway shoulder, leaving Elder Gonzalez standing there looking at me, and just kind of oozed back into the sorghum field at the road's edge.

"What're you doing?" Gonzalez asked.

"Taking a leak." *Haciendo orines.* But as soon as I finished that, I moved farther into the tall sorghum, a cornlike plant with long racemes of seed at the top end, like a great big old curly dock back home on Paradise Mountain. Acres and acres of it.

I stood there looking at the stars, listening to the sigh of the breeze and the chirp of crickets—or whatever they were—and my mind just took off without me.

I thought back to my post-Annie trip over to Capitol Reef, the last trip I ever took with Uriah. I had just pulled to the side of the road halfway into the park, turned off the car, and stared off into the red-blue desert panorama for twenty minutes, the cool spring wind rolling past my face. When Uriah nudged me, I let him out, and he just slumped down by the car in the shade.

The more I sat and stewed, the more it all bubbled over. I had been so stupid, or if not stupid then cruel. Or maybe not cruel but—ah, I didn't know. I had no idea what all had gone wrong. I had wanted the girl, I had wanted the marriage. But I had wanted the mission too. I really wanted to go serve the Lord of my redemption, be an ambassador for Christ. I couldn't have both and didn't really believe I could have the mission—I had no money, and no one had told me about the options — so I'd decided that getting married was the best course my life could take. So then I'd pushed the issue, actually trying to force Annie toward that conclusion.

I had just wanted to scream, the rising mental foam and froth and outrage melting the ice of my isolation and giving me license to yell out loud, and so I did. I told the windshield how I had thought Annie would say yes, how I had prayed and struggled for months, and the answer seemed to be "Marry the girl." Then I actually got out of the car and bitched at my right rear fender for a full ten minutes about how the answer had been wrong, clearly, and how was I supposed to know that someone else could help pay for my mission? I'd never been on one! Then a car went by, the driver probably thinking, *Man, he's really pissed, yelling at his car. I better not stop even if he's in trouble.*

But then I thought of something Kerouac had said somewhere, probably in *Dharma Bums*, that prayer was the only decent activity left in the world, and so I decided to do that. Thinking myself unworthy to go sit on an actual boulder made by God, however, I opened the passenger door and sat down on the seat, Uriah urging himself over toward my legs, and I hung my head and prayed, my heart going mellow, my head saying, *Now shut up and just* BE HERE NOW.

Thoreau's gospel according to this moment.

Elder Gonzalez called, "There's a car coming. What do I do?"

And I said, with half a mind to run the other way, "Just stick your thumb in the air, *hombre!*" And he did, straight up over his head, and the car went zoom, the lone driver probably scared to pick up a couple of CIA agents on a lonely stretch of highway in the middle of nowhere. The guy actually swerved into the far lane, as if Brother Julio were gonna reach out and snag him by the door handle.

So I laughed at both of them and then came up out of the sorghum and gave Gonzalez private lessons, showed him the stance, the casual, cool *Yeah-I'm-standing-here-with-my-thumb-out-lazily-at-my-side-but-really-I don't-care-I'm-just-crossing-South-flippin'-America* stance. And I actually yelled out, "I'm crossing South America!" in English. The sorghum and the snakes in the weeds went, *Man, this guy's nuts — give him space.*

And Gonzalez said, "C'mon, man, don't leave me up here alone."

So I stood there with him, the highway black and silent again, and looked back on my life and then put my own little tune to Kerouac's refrain: "I sing to the stars, remembering previous lifetimes when I was a prisoner in dungeons, and now I'm in the open air." Absolutely getting high on the starlight symphony playing overhead.

I looked off to the north, where Annie was probably wrapped to the nose in four feet of goose-down quilts, and realized I was staring right at the Big Dipper, sitting right down on the northern horizon, looking like it was about to take a scoop right out of Cartago or, four thousand miles farther north, Colorado. I turned and looked back at Elder Gonzalez, who was just standing there staring straight up at the stars, probably on his own journey, only about four months from wrapping up this thing and going home to Bogotá. Going home in honor, a servant of God who had spent two years—seven hundred and thirty days—not doing his own pleasure (to quote Isaiah 58). When I asked him flat out a couple of weeks earlier about Liliana Romero, he said, "*Que va hombre!* I'm just trying to stay sane. I'll come back and see her later."

So I tilted my head back too, but I closed my eyes and finished my song.

> *Here and there people may wander —*
> *What they find is always what they choose.*
> *Looking for gold or treasure in heaven,*
> *Any way you ride, life has its dues.*
>
> *Sometimes life can be a risky venture,*
> *We never do know what we'll lose.*
> *But everything that we need is within us,*
> *Whatever we need we can use.*
>
> *Just keep on thinking about that person*
> *That you really want to be,*
> *And someday you will look back on these words*
> *And realize that you are he.*
>
> *Sometime in this way, do you ever feel lonely?*
> *Sometimes all alone, are you blue?*
> *The road up ahead can be the same old story —*
> *The ending is all up to you.*

I opened my eyes and followed the pointing stars on the Big Dipper right down almost to the ground, the North Star sitting there smiling at me about one inch off the northern horizon. The weirdest sight.

And suddenly I felt twin shivers run through my entire body. One was a shiver of thrill, the full realization that I was in a foreign land, speaking a foreign language with skill, and doing my own part in what was surely one of the most selfless labors on the planet. But the other was a shiver of fear, a haunting fear that I was not doing enough, or that I was doing it with my hand still on the plow, looking back, always looking back, wondering what might have been. . . .

And then I heard another car.

A little Renault 4S came off the valley highway and angled toward us. We were standing far enough from the highway to be safe in case he was a maniac and yet out far enough to be clearly visible in his headlights. The perfect position of a practiced international hitchhiker.

The car went right on by. But then the taillights flared, and the car skidded to a stop. And waited. I could tell it was a Renault 4S because there were only two makes of car, it seemed, in the entire country: Renault 4S's and 1946 Willys Jeeps. Gonzalez and I had once sat on a rooftop over the street in Sevilla and counted one hundred and forty-six Jeeps in thirty minutes.

We started to trot up the road toward the car, but then the driver threw it in reverse and came back toward us. We met halfway.

A lady rolled down her window. "*Venga.*" Come on. "*A donde van?*"

"Sevilla," I answered. We got in, joining just a male driver and what appeared to be the missus, forty-ish. Nice looking. Safe looking.

"*Mormones,* huh?" the man said, then pulled out and sped along at top speed, about fifty miles per hour, straddling the yellow line and talking about six hundred and thirty words per minute. From time to time we slipped in a word edgewise and then just huddled back into the tiny rear seat, warming in the mental satiation that we had a ride all the way to Sevilla. Twenty or twenty-five miles later, just as we were approaching the edge of the valley and the long climb up the *cordillera* to Sevilla, we had to pull far into our own lane as a Willys loaded with men sped by in the opposite direction. They yelled viciously as they roared past us, and we could see clearly the glint of several automatic weapons as they waved them in the night sky.

"*Locos*," spoke the man, much quieter now. "Probably the local *guerilleros* out for some fun." In those days the paramilitary insurgents were still running the country. Pablo Escobar up in Medellín was still working two jobs—one, stealing gravestones right out of the cemeteries, sanding off the inscriptions, and reselling them as new; and two, starting up the world's largest cocaine cartel. He wouldn't run the country for another five years or so.

But then we saw another jeep approaching, same speed, same crazy driving, and a half-dozen guys standing up in the back hanging on to the rollbar. But as this one approached, our headlights caught something falling out the back, something the size of a human body.

The jeep whizzed passed us, its occupants once again yelling taunts and curses and waving automatic weapons in the air. And then we spotted the object of their celebration. The lump that had come to a rest in the middle of the highway was definitely a human body. Our driver rolled to a full stop in the opposite lane. It was the body of a man, steam pumping out of a dozen puncture holes, bullet holes. He was rolled up strangely from the toss out of the Willys, nude except for his undershorts, and half-peeled from his roll down the highway.

My stomach lurched into my throat, and my breathing almost made me cough. Elder Gonzalez just covered his eyes with his hand and turned away. As we watched, the steam vents lessened their pumping, the steam easing back to mere ooze. As our driver released the clutch and pulled away, the lady spoke: "*Que pesar.*" What a pity.

And off we zoomed, me thinking, *Man, I'm gonna go nuts or something.*

38

"I . . . came not with excellency of speech
or of wisdom, declaring unto you the testimony
of God. . . . I was with you in weakness,
and in fear, and in much trembling."
—1 Corinthians 2:1, 3

I HIT ONE YEAR in the mission field swearing to myself, my journal, and my God that I was done being homesick, that the Outlaws and Annie and Paradise Mountain and even Highway 50 going west over Monarch Pass would just have to get along without me. Colombia was one hell of a mess, and I had work to do. A work I believed with all my heart and soul could do the job.

And then we got a call from the mission office: transfers again, and I was going to Medellín. I actually said to the mission president's assistant, Elder Porter, "You mean Gonzalez. He's the one's been here eight months already." And Porter said, "No, I mean you. Gonzalez is staying right where he is." So I packed my bags and made the rounds, everyone at the Gomezes' crying, the little kids hanging on my leg, then the same thing at Francos' and Delgados' and Pinos' and Romeros', Julio and I having baptized a third of them. People all over town, saying good-bye to the *gringo* who loved them and even shared his resurrection peanut butter, saying, "*Waist,* you're a good man, *que le vaya muy bién.*" I think there were around sixty people at the bus stop when I left—the whole branch, plus most of our investigators and a couple of shopkeepers with whom I had made friends. I'd been in Sevilla four months to the day. Elder Gonzalez eventually stayed there ten and never went over the line with Liliana Romero.

So I caught a bus for the biggest city in the mission—nine hours away, two and a half million people, the drug cartel homeland—thinking thoughts like Ed Abbey's "another day, another dolor," ho hum, just another day in the life of a traveling preacher, *I've seen it all, just try to surprise me.* And the bus broke down halfway to Caicedonia, ho hum, no surprise at all, so I missed the elder I was supposed to ride north with from Pereira and just sat there reading letters and cards and notes that people in Sevilla had handed me as I got on the bus. I had a little bag of *cucas* to nibble on at midnight, cookies I had become quite fond of, even sending a Pringles can full of them home to my folks one time before I learned that the great butterscotch flavor came from coffee, the second ingredient after flour. And quit eating them.

When we pulled into Medellín at six A.M., two and a half million people spread out all over the map, skyscrapers and everything, I pressed my face right up to the window and thought, *Oh Lord, I'm gonna die from suffocation or getting trampled or something.*

Where I ended up was a sector of the city known as Calasanz, serving as district leader again, in the same neighborhood where cocaine kingpin Pablo Escobar and most of his lieutenants lived, homes with garages, beveled glass on the doors, front parlors with chandeliers hanging over their baby grands. Domesticated animals that actually looked like dogs instead of the dog-rodent hybrids I'd seen everywhere else. Actual lawns, curbs, and gutters. People wore ties and drove cars and went to work in offices.

And we couldn't get in a single door.

I started out with a four-month guy who actually knew his way around town, but within two weeks he was moved and I got a brand-new Colombian elder right off the bus. Rodrigo Ramirez was another eighteen-year-old and, like Aillón, a guy I thought I was going to kill. Only with Aillón, I got over it as he grew up. Rodrigo Ramirez never grew up while I knew him. He couldn't get up in the morning, took three-hour naps at lunch, complained about everything, even in his own country.

The whole world was different in Medellín. Capital of the state, or *departamento*, of Antióquia, it was the Catholic cradle of Colombia, and the LDS Church was barely limping along, with four branches — no wards — scattered around the huge metropolis. Many of the residents in our area were into, uh, exports. Their wives would have little shoe shops or dress shops down on the *avenida* where they would stock maybe twelve pairs of shoes, three or four leather purses, and one cash register, for laundering the money. Made it look legit, however unlikely.

First day there, one of these shoe-store trophy-wife *dueñas* sitting on a chair filing her nails and crossing her legs just as we came in, revealing a whole bunch of really nice thigh, asked me where I was from—she thought Mormons were all *gringos*. First I corrected her, letting her know that The Church of Jesus Christ of Latter-day Saints was a worldwide church, with members and leaders in hundreds of nations, but then I confessed: "Yes, I happen to be North American. Why do you ask?

"Because your Spanish is flawless." *Pura paisa.*

I thought of saying the same for her legs, but in fact much of the requisite vocabulary was not in my flawless lexicon, so I just said thank you and asked her if she'd like to know what we were teaching. And she said no, but if I had any lady friends who needed a nice pair of shoes, she would be *a la órden*. And then she uncrossed her leg and lifted over the other one, staring me straight in the eyes all the while.

And that's about as far as I got with anything for weeks: surface interest, mostly in the *gringo* part—most didn't have a single comment for my companion once they knew he was *rolo*, and he had none for them. A bit of cleavage, a lot of leg. Women really flaunting their stuff, especially the monied ones.

My first three weeks in Medellín, I didn't teach a single discussion, and the local church members helped us not a bit. We'd mail our weekly *informe* to the mission president with our stats: hours spent seeking investigators, fifty-nine, sixty-five, sixty-two; hours spent visiting members seeking referrals, eight to twelve; complete discussions taught, nada zip zilch zero.

I had a blank book for more than a month.

People wanted to argue a lot, especially the college students and especially about the U.S. hostage situation going on in Iran or about the situation with Russia or about *la cocaina*. Guys would ask me my opinion of *Colombiano oro* – the best pot in the world—but I confessed no knowledge of it, and I'd tell them honestly that I'd never even seen *la cocaine*. If they continued to ask about pot, I'd just avoid the question by saying, "We don't do that—we have a health code," and they'd say, "*Qué va hombre*, all North Americans use *la droga*," and I'd say, "No, man," serious now and completely honest, "we all *don't*."

I was on a split with one of the assistants to the mission president, the A.P.s, when I got offered my first joint. We'd been together all day, visiting members, talking in the streets, knocking on a hundred doors, and I hadn't gotten within fifty yards of giving a missionary discussion. Elder Porter couldn't believe it, having never worked in Medellín. So about eight P.M. he and I came around a corner right into a group of college students, sitting on a wall and mingling across the sidewalk. *Their* sidewalk. I ambled to the left, hoping to go out and around invisibly, but Porter—an A.P. and all, trying to be the example of a brave teacher—walked right up and put out his hand to one of them.

"*Hola, me llamo* Elder Porter. *Cómo le va?*"

And a big guy on the wall said, "We're doing fine, *gringo*. Who let you into my country?" And then he took a really deep toke on the finest-smelling reefer I'd ever smelled and passed it on.

Nine guys stared us down, and the dude on the wall actually hopped down and came right over to bump chests with Porter, who was about the same size, exhaling in his face. The circle closed around us. Porter, always smiling, cleared the air with his hand politely and said, "Juan Valdez let us in personally," referring to the guy in the American coffee commercials on TV.

The Colombians all looked at each other, no one knowing Juan Valdez from Uncle Sam or the Bionic Woman but willing to let the guy approve us if he thought so, and the guy from the wall said, "To do what?"

Which was perfect, because then Porter just jumped right into a typical variation on the first-contact approach: "We're here to talk about Jesus, *hermano*, about *la Biblia*." And off we went, half of them griping about religion and half saying *la santa fé* was the only way and asking what we taught about the Bible and stuff like that. Porter threw most of it to me eventually, and pretty soon we were having a decent conversation, if not just a tad *mellower* than the usual. It was so weird, the whole country person by person hating you one moment and laughing with you the next or saying "*Oye chico*, try this stuff, man, pure *Colombiano* right out of the dryer."

I acted like *Just a minute man—gotta finish this thought* and told them about Joseph Smith's First Vision and the coming forth of the Book of Mormon, bearing into it with all my soul, thinking, *Well, if they're gonna kill me, I'm gonna go out testifying*, and the guy from the wall said, "Listen to this trip, *hombres*, and he's not even high," and so someone else offered me the joint. He just stood there in the street waiting for me to take a hit, with everybody looking, including Porter, wondering what I was going to do. And so I taught them the Word of Wisdom, the Mormon health code, the body being the temple of the spirit and all that.

The big guy from the wall, the guy who'd come down to bump breasts with Porter, turned to the guy bogarting the joint and said, "Put it out."

And the guy said, "*Como?*"

The wall guy said, "I respect these guys, man. They're preachers. Honor the valiant American man of God, and *apague la cosa.*" Snuff the joint.

We went back to the apartment that night counting two discussions and an appointment to meet with a few of the guys again in a few days, right there in the park behind the wall.

I started spending a lot of time with the one other North American in my district, a hilarious Californian named Scott Murphy, because Rodrigo was about to drive me to crime. Murphy and I actually talked about him as Rodrigo and not Elder Ramirez, because it seemed so unlikely that he was a real missionary, a holder of God's higher priesthood. This tendency seemed strong in the Medellín zone—*gringos* with *gringos*, Colombians with Colombians. Or when the handful of Ecuadorian elders were in a given area, *gringos* with *gringos* or Ecuadorians, Colombians with Colombians. Many of the Colombians just couldn't seem to get along with anyone but Colombians.

Murphy's companion, Ludwig Parra, was as anti-American as any Colombian I'd ever met. I'd ask him why, and he'd smile and say, "Because it's so easy, *hombre,*" as if I was supposed to understand something from that. But I understood nothing, so I pushed it. I pushed it with all the Colombian elders who felt such rancor for the United States of America, probably half of whom would move there within the next ten years.

The educated people—college students, bankers, the architect and his live-in girlfriend in Pereira who we taught three good discussions before he showed us his art studio with nude sketches and paintings of her all over the place—ranted and raved about CIA intervention in Chile and the U.S. presence in Panama and the fact that we stole their canal back in oh-three—that's *nineteen* oh-three—and on and on. The poorer classes, the uneducated ones, had no idea. They had just learned to yell what everyone else was yelling. And I'd think, So why spit on me? I didn't steal your stupid canal—whatever that was about—or finance the coup in Santiago or invent the gross national product. I didn't even know what the gross national product was, but I did know I hadn't done it. Nor had my folks.

It was the Ludwig Parras of the mission and even some of our Colombian church leaders—every one of them converts to the faith—who when pressed came right out and said it just didn't seem right and proper that one nation should have so much— someone in Washington was clearly cheating. The church leaders, mellowed with time and integrated into the ecclesiastical and administrative training machine that the church effectuates all over the world for its lay clergy, would articulate it gently, saying, "It's okay, *hermano*, we'll get by. We know God loves us too." And in fact most of them would tell us how their lives had improved in every way, including financial, since joining the church—after all, they weren't spending their money on booze or women or gambling anymore. They got a shave and a haircut and a better job; the Mormon concept of eternal progression put something inside them that said, *Hey, I can do more with my life than just pick coffee beans.* Also, they'd tell us that they felt confident it wasn't us—the Mormons—who were doing what all the other *estadounidense* were doing anyway, whatever it was that the rest of the North Americans were doing to keep them all in the pit of misery and woe.

However, the Ludwig Parras would just come right out and say it: All North Americans were imperialistic wolves, cheating in business, oppressing in politics, stealing resources, manipulating Latin America's armies and presidents, seducing their women, poisoning their crops, shooting their prairie dogs, and on and on and on. They'd say, "Why else would life in this beautiful country suck so much and hurt so badly?"

And I'd look around and say, "You're right, the place is beautiful"—and it was; it looked like Hawaii without the gross national product—and life there *was* often pitiful, unfortunate, heartbreaking. I was the one who'd held that little boy in my arms while he choked to death on tapeworms. But I didn't import the tapeworms, and neither did my family.

But about the whole nation-state political picture, I knew absolutely nothing. We were just nineteen-year-old or twenty-year-old kids. Most of us had never been to college yet. For those two years, we were asked to not even read the newspapers or listen to the news. And our parents were asked to not fill our heads with it. We had one purpose, one mission, the same expressed by the Apostle Paul: We were committed for two years to know nothing among the people but Jesus Christ, and him crucified.

So Parra and the people would push, and I'd get pissed, and I'd wonder and fret and examine my soul and just end up saying, "I'm sorry, man, I have no idea how it all happened." And everyone—*everyone*—owned a San Francisco Forty-Niners or Pittsburgh Steelers or George Washington University T-shirt and wanted to come to the States so bad, including Rodrigo and Parra, Rodrigo thinking Colorado was real close to China.

So Murphy and I split together as often as I could justify it, to keep each other sane. Or giddily insane. One time Murphy looked up in the sky and said, "Well, looky here," and he headed toward the door of the nicest house I had ever seen in Colombia—it would have been a nice home in the States. Murphy explained to me that the big thing sticking up in the air off this guy's house was a ham radio antenna. (I wouldn't have known a radio antenna from a hydroelectric plant.) So we went up "just to chat."

The guy let us in, real friendly, and we used his radio. We talked to people in Fort Worth, New York City, Florida. A dude in New York did what he called "phone patches" and told us we could make a collect call to our folks. He'd get us as close as possible so the phone call would be cheaper. I was ready to leave—calling home was not in the little white handbook—but then we got clear to Leavenworth, Kansas, and Scotty had him place a collect call to his uncle in Ogden. ("I can truthfully tell President I have never called home," he told me.) By then I couldn't resist—for fifteen months I hadn't spoken to my parents, not even when I died in the Colombian earthquake. After Scotty's turn, suddenly I was hearing my phone ring on Paradise Mountain!

Nobody was home.

39

"The way for you to live in this place is to stay out of it."
— Wallace Stegner, Angle of Repose

I REMEMBERED DAILY — and endeavored to keep daily — my vow to keep my head in Colombia, but I still woke up sick to my stomach every morning, thinking about the mean streets I was about to face. I'd sit in the roofless bathroom of our *pieza* in La Floresta and meditate on the detail of the banana-tree branch that arched over the wall, thinking, *Here's something real, something natural, something that doesn't want to kill me.* And then I'd go inside and put on my tie.

A couple weeks into Medellín, I got set apart as the elders quorum president in the local branch and then as the second counselor in the branch presidency, all while being the missionary district leader too.

Although six-foot blonds with blue eyes were not uncommon in Medellín and in the state of Antióquia in general, our branch president was a black fella, *un negro* named Jorge Buitrago. He and his wife had joined the church years before the church's twelfth president, Spencer W. Kimball, had announced the revelation in 1978 that granted the priesthood to all worthy male members over the age of twelve. Within weeks of that announcement, the mission president ordained Buitrago as an elder, and he was set apart as the branch president only a few weeks later. All of this had happened just two years before I arrived in the area. Buitrago's daughters, beautiful teenagers who drew lots of visits from the missionaries, had pretty much grown up *Mormones* in a church that most Colombians viewed as a racist *gringo* enterprise. They had few friends outside the branch.

I would pester the president and his family regularly for the name of someone we could visit and teach a discussion or two, and they continually turned us down, saying, "No one wants to hear." Finally, the oldest daughter, Ilse, gave us the name of a guy, a work associate of her father, but she said, "Don't use our name." I whipped out a scripture in Romans—"For I am not ashamed of the gospel of Christ"—and she said, "We're not ashamed of anything, but just don't use our name." This meant we'd really just be doing another cold contact with no reference, no foot in the door, no friend of a friend or anything.

But we visited the guy, went to his house one evening, and he answered the door and blew us to bits before we even had a chance to say *hola pachuco*. He called us a bunch of dirty names and then lit in on Jorge Buitrago, who hadn't even been mentioned, saying, "You tell that Jorge Buitrago we're not so stupid as to join some *gringo Yánqui* capitalist whorehouse church. We're a religious family, *Romano Apostólico Católico!*" And he slammed the door.

It wasn't until three months later that we finally taught and baptized a man and his wife, the first baptisms in that area for months. Hector Anacona had worked for eleven years as a tour guide over in the prehistoric ruins of San Augustín National Park. Hosting tourists from all over the world, he had picked up a conversational ability in six or seven different languages, so we started off with that interest. But on the second visit ol' Rodrigo started chatting with the wife, Diela, about the Book of Mormon, explaining to her that the book was a record of their own people, the indigenous peoples of South America, such as the Chíbcha. Overhearing them, Hector cut me off and said, "Say that again," looking right at Ramirez. And Elder Ramirez repeated his statement, adding, "Those same people you tell the tourists about over in San Augustín."

And that was that.

Hector and Diela started to read. We started to teach, Ramirez actually grabbing the flipchart and asking to start each time. And I finally started thinking of him as Elder Ramirez.

On the first P-day of July I got a letter from Julio Gonzales, postmarked Sevilla. (I had long since made it my M.O. to collect and read mail only on P-day—too much to mess with your head otherwise.) *Adiós, amigo, I'm on my way home in honor, mission accomplished*, Gonzales wrote, adding that little Maria Elena Pino, age eleven, who we'd baptized together, still cried every time someone mentioned my name, which was often. I was Sevilla's all-time-favorite elder, he said, but he was running a close second. Ten months in one little town. He said he'd go home to Bogotá and see what the world held for him there, but he'd probably come back to visit Sevilla, maybe take Liliano Romero out on a date or two.

I also received a cassette tape from Annie Hawk. Half of it was in French just for fun, then she told me that she had just attended the baptism of her first convert. I had converted nearly twenty at that point, nowhere near the number I had been led to believe would be normal in South America but a lot more than one. Yet Annie was aglow with it all, and I could hear it in her voice. I heard lots of things in her voice, although she didn't really articulate the rest of it. It was just my imagination, I knew, but it was as if I heard her telling me what a beautiful cabin I had prepared for her, how she loved it when I brushed her long blonde hair—which was now cut short and permed—and how she loved that view out over Lion's Head and Mount Rosalie.

I took the tape recorder into the bathroom and listened to Annie's tape again, not that Elder Ramirez could understand any of it but just because I had to be alone. I confirmed that she had, in fact, said none of the above. But the tone of her speaking, the gentle sound of her voice . . . I hadn't held a girl's hand in more than a year and hadn't been kissed by anyone but my mother in forever. The hardest part was that I had known that touch, that fire, the sweet warmth of her lips, the curve of her back, the caress of her hand on my face.

I went out and told Elder Ramirez that I wanted to change the day's plans. The guys in the zone, as usual, all wanted to go play American football in a park somewhere, then eat ice cream at Mimo's, then hang around and talk, Colombians with Colombians, *gringos* with *gringos* or Ecuatorianos. But I asked Ramirez if he wanted to go climb a mountain instead, and he said sure. So I called Murphy, and he said, "Get real, man. That sounds like more work. I want ice cream." So I called Elder Jolley, and he said, "You bet." Jolley was a real big boy from Snoqualmie, Washington, hands the size of baseball mitts but a real teddy bear.

So the four of us—Jolley's companion was everybody's favorite Colombian, Lucas Cifuentes—packed a big lunch, found some water jugs, caught a cab, and hiked a pretty good summit above Medellín, passing through beautiful forest that included some sort of five-needle pine trees, reaching probably nine thousand feet in four hours. Wild raspberries along the trail, a mountain stream, an authentic Swiss chalet on what appeared to be a logging road. Jolley and I were in heaven, and the two Colombians thought it was the prettiest place they'd ever been.

But instead of trunking me out—the missionary term for packing your mental bags, ready to go home—our excursion got my head right where I needed it to be: right in the middle of western Medellín, Colombia. That night I was back in the saddle, knocking on doors, talking to every person who moved and getting nowhere, but feeling fine about it. Doing my job the best I knew how. If there was anything between Annie and me, I'd find out when I was supposed to.

Midweek, the new assistants to the president showed up. Lo and behold, one of them was Brad Morrison, his hand in a cast from breaking it on some guy's face in a soccer field in Cali the week before.

I said, "What'd the guy do?" And Morrison said, "Same thing everyone else does, anti-American crap, calling all Mormons sons of whores, Yankee exploiters, capitalist pigs." And I said, "So why bust him up?" I'd felt the same impulse fifteen zillion times, but so far I'd been able to show forth the faith and forbearance of a missionary, a servant of God, wondering how long I could keep it in before I exploded one day.

"I just exploded one day," Morrison said. "This same guy did it every morning when we left our apartment, just stood there and yelled across the soccer field, fifty yards away, top of his lungs."

"You just went over to him and beat him up?" I wondered what that felt like, hitting a guy in the face. Or getting hit in the face.

"No, we went over to try and be reasonable with the guy and his two friends, but he was drunk or stoned or something, nine-thirty in the morning, and he spit right in my face. So I told him that *operativos* of the CIA would not be treated this way, and I pounded him."

When I asked Morrison about the other two guys, he said, "Against the CIA? No way, man. They split."

Morrison and I worked together that morning, and he knew all about Medellín because he'd started there. At one point he said, "You know, we've been out almost sixteen months. How ya doin'?" And I said, "Okay. I thought I finally knew what I was doing, but it doesn't seem to mean much in Medellín. No one to teach."

"What about the Anaconas? President's pretty pleased with that."

I said that was good to hear, since I hadn't exchanged more than a hundred words with the mission president on my entire mission.

"That's the way he works," Morrison said. "You hear from him if you mess up." And he told me about guys from all over the mission who got pulled into Cali just so the president could keep closer tabs on them. Guys who got caught going to movies, sometimes just the elders on a Wednesday afternoon but a couple of times the elders in Tuluá with *dates!* A couple of others, including Elder Pfeiffer from my MTC group, caught a bus and headed out to Buenaventura on the Pacific coast, an area not even within mission boundaries because if a *gringo* showed his face in the Chocó jungle he could get it removed above the shoulders by the locals. Reassigned to the mission office district, Pfeiffer was lucky he was still on a mission. And alive.

During the afternoon and evening, I worked with the other assistant, Nelson Fierro. Thirteen hours that day, and only one discussion, more or less. A lady on a bus asked us to please come by her place at three P.M. because she really wanted to hear the word of God. So Fierro and I showed up, and the lady introduced us to her pastor and her Green Dragon, the missionary term for the Jehovah's Witness version of the Bible with half the verses missing. I was trying to do my shtick and have a nice spiritual lesson, and she started hitting us with all kinds of off-the-other-wall stuff, stuff not even related to what we were talking about, and the pastor kept egging her on, saying, "Ask him about this" or that or the next thing, out of left field.

At first we answered her questions one by one, but she never heard an answer, just jumped into the next one, *wham, wham, wham!* She never heard a word I said, and her every comment was derogatory, vicious, combative. I refused to fight back, just kept trying to tell our story. Finally I told her that what she wanted to do so badly just wasn't the way Mormon missionaries did it; we didn't fight, we would not argue, contention was not of Christ. If she wanted to hear us out and then tell us to go to hell in a hot handbasket, great, that was her choice, but she wasn't even letting us talk.

Finally I said, "Lady, you can look up *our* answers in your own Bible, if those particular verses don't happen to be missing." She wanted none of it. So I just bore them my testimony of the Lord Jesus Christ as Savior and of the Restoration of authority and knowledge through the Prophet Joseph Smith, and we left.

She followed us out, yelling and spitting and all lathered up that we wouldn't stay and have a nice little war. She seemed baffled that we would leave.

Fierro told me that I was perfect, which I should have known would get me in trouble.

• • •

In the middle of August, we baptized again, the members of the branch starting to go *Whoa, what is this,* and then again a week later.

On the street with Murphy again one Monday evening, we went back to the ham-radio guy and tried another call. We got a guy in San Antonio, Texas, who made the phone patch. My dad answered the phone, talked a few seconds, then handed me to Mom. She was all blubbering, jumping on one leg. I wished her a happy birthday, talked for four or five minutes, then told her I had to go and I'd see her in eight months. Nowadays missionaries can call home twice a year, on Mother's Day and Christmas. Actually, I think the rules allowed it then too, but it was pretty much up to the individual mission presidents. And mine was a disciplined banker — enough said.

So I broke the rules the same week I got a call from Elder Morrison back in Cali telling me I was going south to Palmira. My companion would be Rocky Mianno. And together we would be zone leaders.

40

"If God be for us, who can be against us?"
—Romans 8:31

ROCKY MIANNO HAD BEEN a zone leader in Palmira for a month, long enough to know his way around the town of a hundred thousand and to understand how much was expected of a zone leader. Except for the president's assistants, no full-time missionaries held more stature in the mission. Often they were the guys who had knocked more doors, walked more streets, fielded more questions, and taught more discussions than anyone else. Sometimes they were just good motivators or good teachers or captains or coaches.

Me? I hadn't a clue.

One of our missionaries was the mission president's daughter. Typically, young ladies can begin serving a mission when they turn twenty-one, as Annie Hawk had done, but the Church allowed those whose fathers were mission presidents to serve in their father's mission anytime after they turn nineteen. That was what Maryann Bills was doing, and Elder Mianno and I welcomed her to the trenches, her name tag straight and discussions fully memorized. We were often asked to accompany Sister Bills and her native companion, Elder Fierro's widowed mother from Bogotá, to any appointments after six P.M. that they just couldn't avoid. Other than that, they were supposed to suspend their proselytizing activities after the dinner hour.

All in all, sister missionaries could be a real problem. For one, you looked at them and remembered the good girls back home. And these were typically *really* good girls—the ones committed enough to the gospel that they would put everything else in their life on hold and throw their names in the hat, willing to go anywhere, speak any language, face any risk for eighteen months, right alongside the Elders of Israel who had been told that they were going since they were three, who had sung songs written about them—such as "Elders of Israel"—who had an entire machine dedicated to aiding their decision and lighting their way. But the sisters, like converts, just looked in the mirror day after day for months, maybe years, and one morning with the world flying by outside said, *I want to do this. I just want to go. I want to go find my life by losing it in the service of God.*

Annie had told me not a few times in our years together, the years before our Mormondom, that she had actually considered becoming a nun—not that she wanted to be Catholic, but she admired what they did, their selfless service, their sacrificing of self in the service of something higher. Sister Teresa was her role model in life.

Sister missionaries made me want to shout hooray, hug 'em, and cry all at the same moment. Hug 'em for obvious reasons, and cry when I worried about their risk as targets for predatory activity. But somehow, in my experience, nothing ever happened to the sisters who I guarded after dark, even though most potential predators had no idea how big or tough the elders watching from the other side of the park were.

Mianno, for instance.

Mianno grew up in the streets of New York City, getting a daily dose of beggars and knife fights and traffic and noise and pushers on the corner along with his orange juice and megavitamins. He had a set of weights in the *pieza* and lifted every day. So I started lifting with him. And in Palmira we had bicycles, just two of them, although the size of our zone required that we either catch a bus or do something else to visit the outlying cities. Something else like hitchhike.

The Big City Boy had never hitched before, but he caught on quick, although he looked a bit intimidating on the side of the road. On one trip to Buga we got picked up by a young rich kid in a Chevy Blazer with a tape deck and great speakers, blowing Van Halen and Journey all the way. On the trip back that night we flopped on top of a load of bananas in the back of a stake-bed truck, and I told Mianno about doing this same gig, under a different sky, in the back of a garbage truck coming out of the Great Sand Dunes, and he told me, lying there under the equatorial stars, about how the thing he missed the most was the music. Then he proceeded to name a dozen bands or artists I had never heard of, including Earth, Wind and Fire, the Commodores, Barry White, the Ohio Players, Kool and the Gang, Marvin Gaye . . .

City stuff a body could dance to.

And I said, "Why would you want to dance? You can't watch the guitar player's fingers if you're doing that."

We had a place to eat breakfast and lunch in Palmira, a nice little café that gave us a great package deal and good, clean food, but at night we had to improvise. We talked the lady of the house into letting us use her two-burner electric stove, and then we started wrapping it up at nine at night so we could come in and cook some vittles and still be in bed by ten-thirty. Lots of rigatoni and cook-style pudding from the States, the spaghetti seasoning and pudding sent by my mom, arriving just before I left Medellín.

In Palmira—which is, ironically, the name of the little town of Palmyra in New York near where Joseph Smith founded the church—we had an actual brick-and-mortar meetinghouse, a full ward building. And a full ward, with a bishop and an elders quorum and a Relief Society and Tuesday-night youth activities and everything, except that the entire time I served there the bishop refused to come to church because the stake leaders were accusing him, on good evidence, of having absconded with about a thousand U.S. dollars of tithing money. So the bishop's counselor ran things for a couple of weeks, and then the first counselor in the stake presidency was asked to take the reins while still fulfilling his stake responsibilities. Twenty, thirty hours a week, all for free, and of course this Antonio Banderas–looking guy named Pedro Alarcón also had to hold down a full-time job, love his wife, help raise his kids. And keep his eyes open.

When a pair of North American sister missionaries had knocked on Pedro's door in Muzo seven years before, he let them in primarily because he really wanted to watch a couple of good-looking blonde *chicas gringas* speak Spanish. At that time, he was the national secretary general of *JUCO, la Juventud Comunista de Colombia*—in other words, the Communist Youth of Colombia. The twain refusing to mix after his baptism, he bailed the party and took the heat. His associates assumed that his acceptance of a *Yanqui* capitalist *explotador* church meant that he was going to turn in the *JUCO* membership rolls to someone in the CIA. So the party harassed him until he packed up the family one night and fled.

The Alarcóns had been successfully relocated in Palmira, clear on the other side of the Andes, for nearly five years, during which he had come to love North Americans and their church, proving himself a very able administrator and faithful shepherd.

• • •

One day not five days after I arrived in the city, some big black lady the size and shape of a Renault 4S came right up to us in the street and said, "We need to talk. Follow me." So we said sure and accompanied her to her house, in the black section of town. Many pure and nearly pure Africans lived in Colombia, descendants from the Caribbean slave trade. And for some reason they usually lived in geographic separation from the other bloods.

Elder Mianno whispered to me as we walked, "Man, I would love to baptize a black family. I been dreaming about this for fifteen months." Mianno was Italian, but he was a pure brother in the head, having dug their music, their jive, and their company for most of his life. Given the church's ban on blacks holding the priesthood when we both first joined the church, including some of the most faithful members of his branch back in Queens, this communion was like his peace offering for a doctrine that very few in the current generation had ever liked, let alone understood.

Well, he got his black family.

On our way into the neighborhood, the little kids started coming out of houses in floods and sticking to our legs like cockleburs, teenagers joining them, the little ones discovering and then petting my arms, the teenage girls giggling, glancing at us only from the side, especially at Mianno, who looked and sounded just like Sylvester Stallone's Rocky Balboa dude, after whom he had been nicknamed as a kid.

When we got to the house, another lady a few years older than the gal leading us said, "Oh my goodness, Emérita!" And she stood back against the wall in fear while Emérita sent all the kids who weren't hers or closely related home—leaving only about thirteen kids—and said, "Teach on, *chicos*. We're ready." So Elder Mianno and I taught about the most clockwork-perfect discussion of my sixteen months—I actually looked sideways at him, thinking, *So this is what it's like to have a real companion from the get-go.* And Emérita Figueroa said, "Uh huh, uh huh" to everything we said, and so we taught discussion number two and then three, and she said she had no problem with the law of chastity or tithing. "Well, I don't have much," she said, "but ten percent of nothing is only ten percent of nothing." It was yes-yes-yes to everything.

And then I said, "Emérita Figueroa, I challenge you in the name of Jesus Christ to be baptized this coming Saturday as a witness before God that you are willing to keep his commandments for the rest of your life." Elder M. looked straight forward at her, not at me, although I knew by his posture that he was thinking in his head *Oh man, he's gonna go and blow it – there goes my black family.* And the woman we would come to know as Figgy said, "Yes, *hermanos,* I would love to do that." And she started crying.

And so did Mianno. He said, "*Hermana,* you need to be sure. We want you to pray and ask *El Señor Jesucristo* for a confirmation in your soul that these things we've been telling you are true." But I already knew what she was going to say because something had already told me thirty minutes before: *This is one of the pure ones. She's ready.* What I didn't know was the answer she was going to give Mianno when he asked her why she was so sure, which made me want to hit him, thinking, *You're going to lose your black family, Big Boy – just be quiet.* And Figgy said, "Because I've seen that face in my dreams for three nights telling me he would be here soon to bring the true gospel of Jesus," her big black finger pointing right at my face.

No jive.

And so on Saturday we baptized her, her sister, three kids who were old enough, and an eighteen-year-old niece who lived with them and caught up with the discussions over the next three nights.

We soon taught and baptized several more of the Figueroa family, and by now many of the neighbors were dropping in to listen to the discussions. Every time we entered the neighborhood, two-dozen kids would come out of the woodwork squealing "*Los hermanos!*" and then hang off our arms and legs, a couple of them always petting my arms.

Figgy was going out during the day to hand out the pamphlets we supplied her, and so a number of adults usually followed us down the street as well, just to look at us and wonder. We'd call out over the crowd and invite them all in, and seven or eight kids and a couple of women would usually come. A couple of others would typically say, "*Claro, hermano, sí Díos quiere*" – sure, friend, if God is willing – and we'd call back, "God is willing, *hermana* – get in here!" (*Díos quiere, hermana, venga!*)

41

"Truly in vain is salvation hoped for from the hills,
and from the multitude of mountains: truly in
the Lord our God is the salvation of Israel."
—Jeremiah 3:23

ONE DAY WE RODE our bikes next to a guy walking down the street carrying a pretty good load of boards on his shoulder, maybe sixty or seventy pounds worth. Good boards, saw-milled. The guy was limping, and you could tell by the limp that he was rather crippled, one hip thrusting high into the air just to get the foot off the ground and down the road another step. Mianno called right out, "*Hermano*, can we help you?" And this guy, who we later learned was named Wilman Oliveros, stood there looking at us with big scared eyes, never having seen a *gringo* up close in his life. He was one of *los humildes* (the humble ones), a back-street guy who had never owned a car or a refrigerator and had never been as far away as Cali, forty-five miles. Elder Mianno explained that we were missionaries, *representantes personales del Señor Jesucristo*, and then pointed to the little racks on the backs of our bikes.

So there we went, a little crippled Colombian in a T-shirt carrying a paper bag of screws and two scrubbed North Americans in white shirts and ties rolling along with half-a-dozen ten-foot one-by-twelves clipped *sideways* onto their little wire bike racks.

He led us nearly three miles to his small *casita*, a two-room place on the outskirts of town, with a nearby bathroom shared by several families. Normal middle-class housing. His family consisted of a very shy wife and two adorable kids, eleven and eight years old.

We stacked the lumber against one wall, the wife and kids almost hiding behind another stack of lumber. He told us he made furniture and showed us several pieces, a couple steps down from Ethan Allen but strong and functional. He hand-carved the knobs.

The little missus looked at our name tags and said, "You both have the same first name. Is that normal where you come from?" Up there next to China.

We explained the ELDER title and that we were ministers of the gospel. Wilman pulled up a couple of chairs for us and said, "Please sit down."

Elder Mianno looked at me, and I could tell we were both thinking the same thing: we didn't want to push the missionary part of this visit. Mianno said, "Thank you, *hermano*, but we really just wanted to help you out today, carrying all that wood." No bait and switch thing. "Maybe we can come back tomorrow."

But the wife said, "Please sit down. I'll go make a *juguito*."

Mianno and I knew enough to protest only momentarily and then say, "*Tantas gracias, hermana – muy amable*." Wilman showed us around his shop, the two kids watching us from behind their pile of wood, eyes huge, both giggling. Pretty soon our *juguito* showed up – tree tomato, uncooked – and the missus said, "Wilman, will the brothers teach us a message about Jesus?" And Wilman said, "Yes, the *hermanos* are going to do that. *No es así?*"

And we said sure.

We taught them three discussions that week – no problems with liquor or adultery, willing to pay tithing, absolutely loved the story of Joseph Smith's First Vision, really the most important principle of all. Elder Mianno said, "West, we gonna break some baptism records this month," and I said yo, just like he always did – whether he learned it from Rocky or not I never asked.

On Sunday we fully expected to see the Oliveroses at church, but they didn't come. We went by the house afterward, and the place was vacant. Not a board or a body in sight. We knocked on a couple of neighboring doors, but no one had a clue or was talking if they did.

Absolutely smitten down, we packed it in for the day, Elder Mianno crashing out on his bed and staring at the ceiling of our little room, listening to the Commodores on a tape player. I hadn't heard music in English in more than a year, and "Three Times a Lady" was, I had to admit, a pretty good reintroduction. When the tape stopped, I was writing in my journal about how many times – again and again and again – this had happened, people saying *Yes, I love it* and then just fading away or flaking out or simply disappearing.

Mianno asked me if I had a girl back home. I said, "Yeah, I *had* one" emphasis on the *had*. And I just looked at him as if to say,

Thanks a lot for the reminder. But then I said, "What about you?" And he said, "Nah, just my dear mutha."

So we lay and talked for hours, only getting up to do noodles and pudding about 9:20 that night. It was the first time I had been trunky in months, thinking about home and my mom's hot rolls and the climbing cliffs and my guitars. And Sister Annie Hawk.

Mianno rolled up toward the wall and got quiet, so I started writing Annie a letter, eventually reaching nine pages and going so far as to ask, after chatting only about missionary stuff for seven of the pages, *What about us?*

And then I signed off and lay there with the lights out thinking, *What about us? What about trying again, in the woods this time and not in the stinking city? How about going for a big veggie burrito at that little place in Indian Hills, couple o' mugs of Red Zinger tea, a little John Prine on the muzak. Or Kottke or Fogleberg, for crying out loud!* Dreaming.

I woke up to P-day, really glad I didn't have to go out and knock or preach or seek or even look like a freakin' CIA agent for one more freakin' day, every third kid saying "What time eezit, mister?" and every other adult yelling "Go home, *gringo*" and then smiling to all his pals at what a clever damn *caca mugre payazo* he was. Just mentally and physically blitzed. Worn out.

Mianno and I spent three hours in little shops downtown looking for something casual to wear on future P-days. Actually, I sat, waited, and made fun of his absolutely maniacal drive to find just the right outfit with the twenty bucks his dear mutha had just sent him. I'd say, "Man, what you wearing already looks fine," referring to the red sweats and orange polo shirt he'd started the day wearing. And then I'd say, "Man, that looks fine, referring to whatever ensemble he was currently fingering fondly, but he'd move on, looking, looking, ever vigilant for the perfect set of duds. After two and a half hours I said, "Yo, cowboy, ya fingered every flippin' shirt and slacks in the Palmira *tejido* district. You wanna pick something out, or should we catch a bus for the Cali stores and blow off zone meeting?" He and I were the dudes running zone meeting.

And he said, "Listen, Colorado Boy, this isn't as easy as it looks. You can't just walk into the first store and find the right look."

And I said, "Ya left the flippin' house with the right look! Ya had pants on with a shirt. Done. Sheez, you even tuck in your T-shirt," that being one of the most bizarre things I'd even seen on a guy.

And he just stood there looking at me, his big Sly Stallone chest and firm square jaw that I've seen on TV a couple times since our missions, all the store clerks, the women, right there staring at him, never moving an eye.

And he said, "I look like a bum, man. And you — nothing personal — look like something out of *Buckaroo Bonzai Meets the Rat Patrol.*"

And so we went around and around right there in English about what was casual wear and what was grubby. I thought 501s were a mere half-step below Sunday best and was still not into shoes much. So Rocky looked at one of the *a la orden* clerks, an absolute doll with brown puppy-dog eyes about the size of Lake Titicaca, and said, "Can I try these on?"

And all three girls led him to a little corner changing booth, helped him in, and then stood outside waiting, helpful, ready to respond to his every need. I laughed, stood up, and stepped outside the store to await the runway strut. On the sidewalk in 501s and a generic T-shirt — no little crocodile or guy's initials or anything — I was practically invisible, anonymous. A little too blonde, but nothing that made me stand out like a corn dog at a luau. I moved up the sidewalk a bit, just mingling, then crossed the street and turned back to watch the clothing store from thirty yards away. I had not been sixty feet from my shadow in almost a year and a half. For all intents and purposes, I was absolutely, totally alone.

It was such a sweet feeling. I could walk off right then and disappear into the bowels of Colombia. I spoke the language nearly fluently; I knew the mannerisms, the *dichos*, the history, the regional colloquialisms; and I knew my way around half the country now that I'd finally gotten the Andes to run north and south in my head instead of east and west (confusing, that). I couldn't see an open road from where I stood, just dirty streets and little brown people, a million of them crawling all over the place, but I could see the mountains — running north and south — about thirty miles away. Mountains filled with snakes and gunrunners and little roadside cocaine *fabricas*.

And then someone tapped me on the shoulder. I turned to look and it was Patricia Figueroa, the thirteen-year-old, with little Yamileth and another girl I had seen in our last two neighborhood meetings up there. Meetings where I had stood and preached the restored gospel of Christ with power and clarity I had never dreamed myself capable of, dozens of people in tears, one gal in the back corner so black she was blue, wearing a red turban on her head and actually clapping when I talked of Jesus.

The girls were all smiling, and Yamileth, about age three, took my hand and just stared up at me. And then Patricia said, "When are you and Mianno going to come and teach us more about Jesus?"

And I said, "Can we come tonight?"

And then Patricia asked, "Where's *Hermano* Mianno?"

So we went over and caught him just coming out of the changing booth and moving to a mirror, every eye watching him move except my eyes, which were watching all the moving eyes. Dude was cool. *Cool,* I thought again, but I'd heard him preach. He knew what he was here for. Clothes were his link to the former reality, the one where his family lived in a place not entirely different from the one we were now in, a place where he often wondered if he'd ever get out, ever make anything of his life, ever see the world, ever feel like he was in control.

And there he stood looking at all these people, at least three of them — the little girls — thinking he was not too many steps away from God, joking with them in fluent Spanish, a language he used to hear in the streets of New York and wonder what the heck they were saying, was it about him? And then he looked at me, stars in his eyes, and said, in English, "I feel good!" and then tousled the hair of the young girls and leaned over to pick up Yamileth and toss her in the air, almost hitting the ceiling tiles, everybody giggling, the *a la orden* clerks thinking *This is no stranger – he lives here!* And then Patricia told him that *Hermano Waist* had told her that we would be over that very night to teach about Jesus, and I could see the clerks turn to look at us in an entirely new way, maybe thinking that Mianno, at least, was maybe just a few steps away from God.

And Elder M. asked the clerk with the Titicaca eyes if he could just pay for the outfit — *el equipo* — and wear it home, and the three clerks all giggled and said, "*Claro, a la orden.*"

And we went out like that, Yamileth on Mianno's shoulders and Patricia holding my hand, which was okay because she was only thirteen, and I never even remembered to look up at the mountains.

One night that week Pedro Alarcón invited Mianno and me into his little study and opened up a cloth bag full of cut and polished emeralds — he said about 350,000 pesos worth, seven thousand U.S. dollars. Pedro and his brother had worked for years in the emerald mines above Muzo, dropping the odd stone into their pocket or cuff now and then. He was embarrassed, saying, "I wouldn't do that now, of course—*soy Mormón!* But what am I supposed to do, take them back?"

Anyway, they were his ticket out of Colombia. He hadn't known how soon he'd need the ticket until the Saturday before. While he was doing his business as an assistant manager in a local appliance store, a guy came in and just looked at him. A guy he recognized, a former cohort in the communist league. Then the guy turned around and walked out, never saying a word. The next day, Pedro's nine-year-old boy was harassed by two men in an American pickup truck as he walked home from school with two friends. The men told him to "tell your daddy we need him, real bad." Pedro knew it was nearing the time he would have to take his family and disappear into the night again.

Midweek Elder Mianno and I decided we needed to do a pretty serious fast, show the Lord we were willing to get back on track, do his work and maybe more than that, as a sort of penance for the day off we took while still on the payroll, so to speak. We were about twenty-one hours into the fast when we saw Wilman Oliveros on the other side of the central plaza downtown, carrying a bag of something out of the hardware store. We rode around the plaza, and Mianno just skidded to a stop right in front of him. Wilman hugged Mianno and then me.

He said their landlord had just showed up one night, about ten minutes after Elder Mianno and I had finished a discussion, and told them to pack up and be gone by morning. No reasons, just the eviction.

Wilman and Marina, his wife, hadn't known how to contact us, never having been to the chapel yet. He said, "Please come to our house," and Mianno said, "Get on."

So we gave Wilman a ride.

In fact, his new place was much better for their needs, with a sort of garage attached to the living quarters that he could use for his furniture making. He had walked about a mile to the home of a wholesaler who bought a lot of his furniture and said, "Don Luís, I'm losing my home and shop. Could I rent a place in the back of one of your warehouses," and Don Luís had said, "I got a better idea" and even helped him move with one of his trucks to this little place not ten blocks from the *centro.*

Marina and the kids squealed when we came in, and Wilman's face lit up like a Rocky Mountain winter moon: *Look who I found!*

We finished the discussions with them that week and urged them to come to church on Sunday. Then Wilman told me the confession I had heard a thousand times, that they were just humble people who didn't have anything proper to wear to *servicios religiosos*. People often thought that this was a *gringo* church with people all wearing suits and driving really nice cars like the guys on *Dukes of Hazzard*, that and *The Incredible Hulk* being the current cultural imports of note. So I said, "*Hermanos,* you have to understand that this is a Colombian church, a Colombian congregation, Colombian people, folks living right here in the *barrio* maybe," although we'd never been in this barrio before, so probably no active members lived here.

What we did get from them — Wilman just as embarrassed as he could be about his poverty and his crippled leg — was a commitment to attend a baptismal service that Saturday, where we would baptize at least four other people from the Figueroa clan and other companionships would baptize four or five additional people.

On Saturday there they were, the whole Oliveros crew, dressed in their finest but still taking seats far at the back. One of the district leaders, Elder Paul Smiley, a stellar zone leader for seven months but now out to pasture for his last few weeks before going home, ran the meeting and gave a powerful talk, his last in Colombia. Then we had the baptisms — nine of them — waiting several times for the white clothing to be handed back out soaking wet for the next person, since there wasn't anywhere near enough baptismal clothing in the building for this many baptisms on one day. Mianno was doing our four. A couple dozen members of the ward — the first actual ward I had attended in Colombia — came to the service with us, and the chatter in the hallway was along the lines of "Can you believe it? Look at all these people in white." Every one of them was a convert, but for some weird reason everyone seemed to think they were the last converts who would ever be found.

Eventually all the newly baptized started coming back into the room for the next step: having the hands of the elders laid on their heads to be confirmed members of the church and receive "the gift of the Holy Ghost." In the States, this waiting time was when one of the members, usually a sister, played some interlude hymns on the piano. In Colombia, almost no one played the piano, but a piano still sat right there in the room, part of the standard meetinghouse supply package from Salt Lake City. So Elder Smiley stood up and looked around, watching the just-baptized members file back into the room, and then he started to cry, just hanging his head, unable to speak. Then he looked up and told the people of Colombia the great feelings of his heart, the honor of spending two years among them preaching the gospel of peace, the only thing that would bring solace to their nation or any other. His time was now almost over, and his heart was breaking with joy. And people all over the room were sobbing.

Then Elder Smiley looked around with the oddest expression on his face. "Is there someone else in this room today who would like to be baptized by the authority of the holy priesthood of God, just like these people, as a witness before God that you are willing to keep his commandments and serve your fellowman for the rest of your life?"

And just as Mianno stepped through the doorway in his dry street clothes, Wilman stood up and said, "That's me, *hermano.*" And then he walked right up to the front. Mianno looked at me like *What the hey?* and Smiley embraced Wilman, never having seen the guy before, and asked, "Who has been teaching this good brother?" And Mianno said, "He's ours." And Smiley said he would interview him for baptism.

So Elder Smiley and Wilman stepped out into the hallway for a couple of minutes, while the entire congregation just sat there stunned, no one saying anything, and then they came back in, Smiley smiling, Wilman firm-faced. As they walked past, Smiley told me, "This man's ready. We'll worry about the paperwork later."

"Your turn," Mianno said to me. So Wilman and I went into the bathroom, and I pulled one wet jumpsuit off the shower rod and Wilman pulled down another. Saying nothing, I just put an arm on his shoulder as we left the bathroom for the font.

Just as I was baptizing Wilman, I saw Mianno come back into the room with a young lady who I later found out he'd been interviewing in the hallway. One of Elder Piraquive's investigators, she'd stood up and asked to be baptized soon after Wilman and I disappeared into the bathroom. After hearing this news, I stood in the font and waited while a couple of the congregation sisters got her dressed. And then I baptized her.

Later that week we baptized Wilman's wife, Marina, and their two kids, Marisol and Jimmy, with fifty-one members of the ward in attendance on a Thursday night, along with six of our missionaries and eleven other investigators, members of the ward having suddenly started bringing friends and relatives out of the woodwork.

As a zone we came in second in baptisms in the mission that month, new zone leader Brad Morrison and a little fireball Colombian named Orlando Santos beating us by one up in Armenia.

But then something reminded me that not everyone loved us or loved what we were doing. On a Friday night Elder Mianno and I were riding away from the Oliveroses' new place when we came around a corner moving along pretty fast and had to weave ourselves right through a group of about twenty-five or thirty young adults and teenagers crowding into the street outside a corner cantina. Shouts and spitting sprayed us, and a bottle of beer swung at my head missed me only because I swerved quickly. About thirty yards beyond the still-yelling group, a little kid, maybe two years old, ran into the street right in front of me, and I hit him with the down stroke of my pedal, throwing him onto the pavement.

Lousy luck, that.

I jumped off the bike while it was still moving and went to the kid. He was scraped but mostly just screaming, very loudly. As I tried to comfort the kid, the whole group of rowdies started moving toward us.

Mianno pulled around and parked his bike between the group and me. Just sitting there on the saddle like Clint Eastwood, he told me to get up and ride — it was time to go. But I was trying to comfort the kid, and I told Mianno, "How good's it gonna look if the *gringo* just creams the baby and rides off into the sunset. Missionaries won't be able to show their faces around here for a couple years."

And Mianno said, "I'm hip, but you and me ain't gonna have faces to show in about ten seconds."

I just stood there like a stunned deer with the whole pack of wolves almost on us. I was scared to leave the kid but nearly wetting my drawers staying there — in fact, by then I was probably out of time. No way could I get on my bike and get it rolling before the first kids had me surrounded. So I did the first thing that came into my mind. I pulled my Paper Mate pen from my shirt pocket and talked to it, quickly.

Something like, "Breaker-breaker, good buddies, we need some backup here on Third and Main. The crap is hitting the fan."

In English.

And the whole group disappeared into the alleys and side streets. Quickly.

Mianno just raised his eyebrows in absolute disbelief. The

mother of the little boy ran into the street, snatched him up, called me a name, and ran back to her little doorway in the long brick wall. And off we rode.

Monday morning someone tossed a hand grenade or something at the front doors of our chapel, shattering glass for thirty feet in all directions and mangling the doorframes. No clues until Wednesday midnight, when they blew up the whole classroom wing of the building and left a note on Pedro Alarcón's door. His former colleagues in the communist league wanted to chat.

Two days later when the whole family disappeared, Mianno and I thought they'd been kidnapped or machine-gunned somewhere. But the counselor in the bishopric said, "Don't worry—they got away." And that's all I knew for another year: they got away.

And so the counselor, *Hermano* Dorronsoro, was made bishop and given oversight of the rebuilding project. And that was the last of the bombs for a few years.

One afternoon Mianno brought me a letter from Annie, saying, "This that chick in Canada? I thought she was history."

My nine-pager had never reached her yet—our questions, comments, and responses were typically about five weeks apart. So instead she wrote that Ronald Reagan had just been elected president of the free world and that she was down to her last five months and was going to work it out with heart and soul, and then she signed off: *Well, that's my love letter for the week. Je t'aime (I love you), Sister Hawk (Annie!)*

I lay around and thought about those words almost right up until I got the call from the mission office. Elder Rojas said, "Elder *Waist*, pack your bags." I was going to Armenia, replacing Elder Morrison as the companion of the little Colombian fireball, Orlando Santos.

42

"I'm tired, I'm already tired of all this, where
will I go? what do? how pass eternity?"
—Kerouac, *Desolation Angels*

WHAT YOU DID when you got transferred was spend your last day
covering the city to visit every last soul you possibly could who left
some sort of imprint on your mind and heart. Someone to whom
you poured out your heart and soul, day after day for weeks or
months, and someone you would very likely never see again in
your life. Kind of like a girlfriend, only different.

Figgy and the kids hung on me and wouldn't let go. People kept
saying, "Can't you tell them no? Tell 'em you're staying right here
forever?"

No. I couldn't tell 'em anything of the sort.

What I hadn't expected was the grand reunion in Sevilla.

Elder Rojas had told me, "Oh yeah, Sevilla is in your new zone,
it's one of your districts, and the elders there have a couple more
baptismal candidates you'll need to interview. Stop there on your
way north."

So Elder Mianno and I hugged each other farewell, he put me
on the *flota*, and I headed north. When we turned off the highway
at Parador Rojo, angling east toward the mountains, I got this big
lump in my throat and started thinking of everywhere I'd been, everybody I'd known, visions from all over Colombia dancing in my
head as I stared off at the long fields of sorghum that I'd last seen
under a full moon. Then the bus started laboring up the slope and
into seven miles of switchbacks, just like on Paradise Mountain except this was paved, kind of, and I started breathing in deeper.

When I stepped off the bus in Sevilla, twenty people were awaiting my arrival. Branch President Gomez and his family; the Pino
family we had baptized; Berta Franco, the tamale master who had

once told me about her dream that I would return someday dressed all in white (which didn't happen this trip); and the Sevilla elders. Elder Velarde, an Ecuadorian who sounded just like Walter Brennan in Spanish, certainly the funniest of all the Latino missionaries, said that no one in Sevilla would let me go. No one since Elder *Waist* had meant "*papas fritas*" (french fries) to them — those were his words. It was clear they liked their current elders just fine, but I realized that perhaps we each would have our favorite place in the mission. Mine would forever be my little mountain village of Sevilla.

I stayed two days, doing four baptismal interviews on Saturday — they all passed — and then getting asked, last minute, to give an ad-lib talk at sacrament meeting on Sunday. The meeting started with everyone singing "*Somos Los Soldados*" ("We Are All Enlisted") along with two Elder *Waists*, one live, one coming out of the little cassette recorder sitting on a bench.

After the prayers and the sacrament, I stood up and told about my latest experiences as a missionary, particularly the first meeting with Emérita Figueroa and the whole thing with Wilman Oliveros — losing him, then finding him, then his feeling the Spirit and standing up at the baptismal service, saying "Me too." I was really rolling, the Spanish perfect, the stories rich, the feeling in the air between me and the audience nearly palpable. These people didn't just remember me as the Elder *Waist* who had lived with them and loved them. President Gomez and Berta Franco both told me: *Hermano Waist, you are the visiting authority, a zone leader, the elder who ended the drought and broke open Sevilla for baptisms again.* Nine more had occurred since I'd left five and a half months earlier.

Right there in the meeting, just as I was preparing to close my talk, a nineteen-year-old guy in the back of the room stood up and said he was ready, would I please baptize him unto Jesus? I asked the elders if they had been teaching this good brother, and while they just shrugged at each other the guy himself said, "No, I saw the sign out on the street — The Church of Jesus Christ." He believed and wanted to be baptized.

So after the meeting we taught him three discussions, and the next morning, P-day Monday, I delayed my trip to Armenia and the three of us taught him the rest of the discussions. He had heard them a couple of years earlier but just wasn't interested then. But when he saw the sign on Sunday morning, something clicked, he came in, and that was that. Then I interviewed him and signed the form, and they baptized him on Thursday up at the waterfall.

But I missed that picnic. By then I was finally in Armenia with Elder Santos.

Santos was about five-foot-two, solid muscle and nerves. He looked kind of like Mianno in dark miniature. Two years earlier, he had been the tae kwon do champion of Colombia in his weight class, which was about sixty-two kilograms (one hundred thirty-five pounds). And he was as tough mentally as he was physically. We worked out hard every morning, and he taught me tae kwon do at a level way above what Cris and I had done back on the mountain, stuff with the fists, the feet, and the umbrella — which we carried daily without fail.

In title we were co-companions as zone leaders, neither of us senior or junior to the other, but Santos knew the city, and he functioned at a frappe whirr most of the time. He moved down the sidewalk, rush hour or otherwise, like a halfback running for the end zone, and I learned to move with him. We could thread the needle between any two, six, or nineteen moving bodies without slowing, flinching or misguessing a single move. For three months I moved down the sidewalks and streets of Armenia taking turns in my mind behind the wheel of that pickup back on the Big Rez in New Mexico. Many were the times I actually thought of going *vroom*, out loud.

We didn't knock on doors at all in Armenia, which was an absolute waste of time — in fact, I wouldn't knock on more than ten doors the rest of my mission. We did do a lot of street contacting, but Santos agreed with me that our best work was getting the local church members to trust us, believe in us, and invite us to speak with their friends. And we never let the members down. Oh, the friends might say *no* sooner or later, but Santos and I were good at what we did — we had fielded every objection, heard every alternative interpretation of scripture, been through every complaint, every vice, every sordid story a thousand times. Two thousand.

We got to where we could read a contact within minutes, and of course we claimed that the Holy Ghost was helping us, inspiring us. We were doing the work of God, a God who bestowed miracles, revelations, spiritual gifts. We started challenging people to be baptized on the first discussion.

One day we received a visit from a stake president down in Cali. He had actually sat in his car at the curb watching Santos and me for several hours, seeing if we appeared to be committed elders. He wrote down the name and address of a friend of thirty years, saying, "I've never given his name before because I've never felt right about the missionaries. This guy is tough, but he's golden-hearted."

Lizandro Briñez *was* tough, an ornery little railroad man, and I thought a couple of times that he and Santos were going to go at it. But Santos would stand up and smile a great big smile, then go over and hug him, saying, "*Hermano*, the Lord loves you and your wonderful family, and he wants you to be together forever. Just pray about these things with an open heart, and the Lord will let you know they are true." And the family seemed to move along nicely, reading, praying, coming to church twice. But something was holding them back. All of them called us *hermano* except Lizandro. To him we were just the Mormon boys.

One afternoon, with his wife, his copper-haired eighteen-year-old daughter, and his three sons all in the room, he told us that the daughter was illegitimately pregnant and wondered what Mormon doctrine said about that. The boys all turned to look at their sister with wide eyes, the mother started to cry, and the daughter got up to leave. Briñez told her to stay put; she had cast her bread on the waters, and she should have enough guts to hear the word of the Lord regarding her.

I explained, again, the law of chastity: that sexual relations were appropriate only within the bonds of marriage. Outside of marriage, such relations were improper. And he said, "We all know that—you've already explained." Then he said, "What I want to know is what your religion would do about it now. Your god. My wife and I have already explained to our daughter how we feel and what our Catholic faith appears to teach. But our priest wants us to shut her out, to send her away." At this point his eyes watered up. "We love our daughter, even though she has sinned mightily. What would your Mormon god do? What would your church do to my daughter?"

And Mrs. Briñez said, "Please tell us, *hermanos*."

Santos just looked at me. He could have answered the man just fine, he told me later, but something told him: *Give this one to Elder West.*

I looked at Briñez, and then I looked at his daughter, Miriam, who was curled up in a ball, trying to hide the tears streaming down her face. Her mother was cradling her in her arms like a six-year-old and crying herself.

I looked back at *Señor* Briñez and said as clearly and as forcefully as anything I had ever said in Colombia, "*Hermano*, I thank God for my God. My God would say, 'Little sister, you've made a mistake or two. Big ones. Now turn around and face me, and we'll see if we can solve this one together.' My God would say, 'What's past is passed'" — *lo que haya pasado ha pasado.* "'Don't do it again, turn your life around, and let me make up the difference.' And my church would say the same thing."

Miriam was looking right at me, as were her little brothers. The eight-year-old said, "*Papi,* can Miriam get baptized with us?"

Brother Briñez looked at the two of us, his eyes full to the brim. "That's up to the *hermanos,* Luíz."

So we baptized the whole family, extracting a firm and willing commitment from Miriam that she was done messing around. She would have the baby and then do whatever was best for the next step.

In Armenia the amoebas and tapeworms came back with a vengeance. I lost sixteen pounds in the first three weeks, even though our three squares a day were pretty fair and tasty. Missionaries had been eating at the same place for nearly three years, a family we essentially kept alive with our three-meal deal, worth about fifty U.S. dollars per month. Oviedo Campo, the husband, was completely blind due to a bet he had accepted four years earlier to drink a quart of pure-grain alcohol. He won the bet and a hundred pesos, but now he added very little to the family income by playing his guitar and singing on street corners and in bars. Old Colombian country-and-western stuff, drinking-cuz-you-been-cheatin', gonna-leave-ya songs. Just like old country-and-western in the States, only worse. With fewer pickups.

One night while we were eating dinner, he came home peeled like a banana down one side of his face and body.

Armenia was a city set on a ridge, and as the city expanded, they just bulldozed dirt and garbage into the valleys and run-off channels that flanked the ridge, leveled it all off, and then built houses — hundreds of them piled high and deep — on top. Trouble was, the runoff channels were still the runoff channels, so the poor neighborhoods were being eaten away by underground streams, as were many of the roads. Even though some of the early-1970s municipal-works projects had installed ceramic pipe in the streambeds, the rotting rubbish and decaying pipe led to collapsing neighborhoods in 1980, pits and cavities opening all over the place like falling dominoes.

Oviedo had found one of those pits.

He was crying and cursing not because of his face but because

he'd lost his guitar in the fall. Using his walking cane, he led Elder
Santos and me back to the scene to see if we could find his guitar.
Before long, we spotted the case at the bottom of a thirty-foot crater.
Like a bridge, the guitar was spanning the little stream that flowed
just beneath it. I knew the value of a guitar even when it was a piece
of junk, so I eased myself down into the hole on the far side, where
the slope was more reasonable, and retrieved it.

As we walked away, we noticed that roadblocks were in place
around this hole, but only where a car was likely to approach, not
where a blind man would be hugging the wall.

Just before the end of the year, Santos and I traveled to a zone-lead-
er conference in Cali. Every zone leader in the mission was there,
including the four from Medellín, among them Prieto, Aillón, and
Brad Morrison. Our first morning back in Armenia, I got a call from
one of the president's assistants, who said, "We've just pulled five of
your missionaries out of the zone this morning." And I said, "Transfers?" And he said, "No, girlfriends."

When I whispered to Santos, he said, "Wait a minute, we're the
zone leaders. We're supposed to know everything. Right under our
noses?"

The A.P. said, "Relax, it happened last night while you guys
were still on the bus back to Armenia." The dudes had been caught
coming out of a movie — *Jinete Eléctrico,* or *The Electric Horseman* —
with girls, three of them holding hands with their dates. One of the
local branch presidents had been sitting five rows back with his wife
and kids. He called the mission president right after the family's
nightly prayer.

Within the week, one Colombian had gone home to Bogotá and
one Statesider had gone home to Utah, both ending their missions
dishonorably and scheduled for church disciplinary councils. Those
two had done way more than just go to movies. The other three
were reassigned within slingshot range of the mission office.

I had days — about seven hundred of them — when I just *knew* I
was going to jump some chick if I didn't turn my head, walk away,
and sing a hymn or bite down hard on a broom handle. You're
twenty, twenty-two, twenty-five freakin' years old. You're committed to a religion that prohibits intimate sexual relations outside of
marriage or anything like unto them, meaning hanky-panky and
hooky-pooky and everything else in the bag of satisfaction tricks.
But you're also in a religion that does believe in marriage, does

believe in the value and beauty and honor and, yes, even pleasure of such relations *inside* of marriage — oh, yeah. So you got that carrot hanging out there.

But on a mission . . . on a mission, boy, you Mr. Clean. And winning that one was a daily battle the size of Iwo Jima on Viagra.

But there was also that other carrot hanging out there: if you came home honorably from a mission, you'd really done something. You'd done something big enough and important enough and hard enough that your home congregation would hold you up before all the little kids in Primary and all the teens and say, *Look at this Man, children. This Man is what you can become if you're true and faithful and brave.*

Oh, how I wanted that to be said of me.

On our second day back, we had to go down to the bus station and take a brand-new North American missionary off the *flota* from Cali. Five-hour bus ride, sixteen total hours in the country, probably understanding about every fifth word, scared to death. I remembered my welcomeless arrival in Pereira fifteen months earlier, so we showed up early.

Forty minutes late, the bus pulled in. Out came the pigs, and the chickens, and the guys wearing poncholike *ruanas* and packing machetes and fifths of *aguardiente* and who knew what else, and then the old ladies and the teenagers and finally the lone lonesome lonely totally-freaked-out missionary: Sister Kristine Petry of Mesa, Arizona. She was a redhead, and everyone in the street was staring at her like she'd just stepped off the *Millennium Falcon*.

She came to me, wrapped her arms around me, and started blubbering. I waited for a half-minute and then put my arms around her and patted her back, there there there. And I thought, *Thank the Lord that Annie didn't have to come to South America*, wondering why sister missionaries ever got sent down here.

My second Christmas in Colombia was a lot more fun than the first, with letters and cards arriving on time from the States and Canada and a big party at the branch chapel, people stuffing us full of food. I pulled back into the corner at one point and just sat there alone, amazed to be living in a foreign land, speaking their language, understanding their jokes, receiving hugs and accolades and a third plate of *natilla* or *dulce de leche* from the good Latter-day Saints.

At the same time, my mind couldn't avoid thinking about the

calendar. I would soon have spent every second of an entire year in
Colombia, sometimes feeling toughened, fearless, and competent. I
knew how to move, plan, organize, speak in public; I knew how to
use the busses, guess addresses, negotiate prices—everything was
negotiable—and respond to any and every question ever imagined.
But when we returned to our room at night, I was just a Colorado
mountain boy, scared and tired. Sometimes I wished I could just
sleep for about three weeks straight. I couldn't help ending the year
praying that the best two years of my life would go by a lot faster.

One consolation was that with only four months left, I would
very likely get put out to pasture soon, sent somewhere as just a
co-companion in a district or maybe training a greenie again, some
assignment with nowhere near the pressures of being a zone leader.
The former mission hotdogs in the groups just older than us were
already getting "pasteurized."

And then I got the call.

I was being transferred to Cali to serve as a co-leader of the
largest zone in the mission: eighteen elders, six sisters, and a retired Colombian couple. My chances of place-holding there for just
a month were pretty much nonexistent, since my new companion,
Lucas Cifuentes, was going home in a month. I would clearly have
to remain in place to train his replacement.

Just before I packed my bags at the first of the year, I got a letter
from Hector Anacona up in Medellín.

Dear Hermano Elder West,

*I cannot express the joy we have in our lives now since you pre-
sented the message of the restoration to my family. You have such
a special way of teaching. For me, you are the model missionary
in all Colombia. We were very sad when you told us you were being relocated, for we had hoped you would spend much more time
in this city. This is a great work you are doing, and we pray the
Lord's continual blessings upon you.*

And I thought, *Okay, I can hang on a little longer.*

43

> "Other than to amuse himself, why should
> a man pretend to know where he's going,
> or to understand what he sees?"
> —William Least Heat Moon, *Blue Highways*

EVERYTHING IN CALI was hot when I got there, January or not.

First morning out, Cifuentes pointed out the soccer field right across the street from our *pieza* where Brad Morrison had broken his hand on the guy's face eight months earlier. Just then, two twenty-or-so-year-old girls—really good looking—walked right up to us. As Lucas backed away, they stuffed their hands down my pants— one in front, one in back—and grabbed my attention, so to speak.

With me stuck in the middle, the one on the front end said, "You're new, aren't you?"

Then they pulled out and walked away, looking back laughing as they went. Girl number two called, "Welcome to Cali."

Cifuentes was leaning against a tree, laughing his head off.

As a rule of thumb, females in Cali didn't wear much, even compared to other places in Colombia. The fact that it was always about ninety-five degrees right through the night, with humidity of eighty or eighty-five, didn't help. But it was the social climate of the place as much as anything. I thought to myself, *And this is where they send the missionaries who are having trouble keeping their hands to themselves?*

Skin everywhere. Miniskirts, high-heeled shoes with the little come-chase-me straps winding up the leg, halter tops or really tight T-shirts, no bras.

I sang a lot of hymns in Cali.

And I soon realized that I had, in a way, been sent out to pasture. Only I was still the farmer. This zone had six former zone leaders in it, including big ol' Elder Jolley, and two members of my MTC group, Pfeiffer and Ruff. We added it up one P-day, and between the twenty-six of us we had nearly forty-three years of missionary experience, by far the most experienced zone in the mission. And most of us still wanted to find, teach, and baptize.

Suddenly it felt like the home stretch, and I got nervous. All the pain, the pressure, the daily taunting and threats—I tried to just stuff it all back in my head somewhere and ignore it, just forget myself and go to work. That almost-desperate feeling was there when I woke in the morning and when I fell into bed at night sixteen long hours later.

My first week in Cali, Elder Cifuentes and I baptized two people he and his former companion had been teaching. The second week we baptized nine of our own, a passel by any definition. Ruff, Jolley, and the rest of the zone brought in five others that same service. One of ours was a twenty-nine-year-old girl with no legs since birth who got around on a real strong wooden chair, flipping about on its hind legs. Elder C. and I discussed for some time how to baptize her, as she couldn't walk into the font and her chair was probably unreasonable. In the end he just picked her up and carried her into the font. I said the baptismal prayer and then pushed them both underwater.

Next week, two more baptisms, one of them a young man about the same age I was when I joined the church. His family kicked him out of the house post haste, and having nowhere else to go he would hang out on the corner till late, then sneak back into his own house at night and sleep in the hallway, then get up before dawn and go back out on the street. Finally, a new friend from church found him space in his own room.

Our married missionary couple, Elder and Sister Benitez, were two-year converts from Bucaramanga, in their mid-sixties but looking like they might give up the ghost at any moment, people reaching sixty in Colombia having usually seen a lot of wear and tear. Good, committed, valiant souls but really unschooled in the gospel. We spent several hours a week teaching them the discussions and accompanied them to most of their teaching appointments. One afternoon, when we were crossing the divided avenue that ran through Las Americas, Elder Benitez whipped it out right there in the median and took a nice leisurely leak. His wife said, "Oh my goodness, José, wait till we get to the other side of the road!"

Then we had six sister missionaries, three of them fortyish

spinsters and one a widow with whom I had worked in Palmira, the mother of Elder Fierro. Sister Fierro talked about six hundred words per minute and refused to board a public bus. Having come from money in Bogotá, she walked or took a taxi everywhere, always paying the fare. One of the spinsters, Sister Muñoz, was taking eighteen months out of her career as a nurse. Although she was called to a proselytizing mission, the president had used her in health and welfare assignments all over Colombia, and she handed out gamma shots to missionaries whenever she was in town.

The other two sisters were twenty-oneish North Americans, one who had waited two years back home in Nevada for her missionary and then got her heart broken when he married a girl he had baptized in Illinois and the other a second-year medical student at Johns Hopkins who just woke up one day and said *I wanna go do something really important* and turned in her mission papers, actually stating that she wanted South America.

My own companion, Lucas Cifuentes, was about as un-Colombian as anyone I had met. He was a national high-school basketball star and came from a huge cattle ranch over on the eastern plains. His family was paying for his mission, although only he and his mother had joined the church four years earlier.

Lucas was in his final month and had, in fact, asked the president for an extension, which was sometimes granted for up to eight weeks. So I had no idea what that meant for my status as a zone leader. I could still be pasteurized in a couple of weeks and he could end up training the new zone leader, but I doubted it.

Cifuentes was focused, and he was seemingly oblivious to the calendar, which helped me immeasurably. We did one thing: functioned as missionaries. And we baptized again and again. By the thirteenth day of that first month we had seventeen baptisms. One of them was Maritza Zambrano, a twenty-three-year-old absolute fox who we had to teach staring at nothing lower than the bridge of her nose just so we didn't go nuts. Everything went fine until the day I baptized her. As the two of us entered the font, I realized that she was not wearing underwear beneath her white baptismal gown. When she came up out of the water, everyone in the room could tell. She hugged me close and kissed my cheek, with everyone watching.

"Thank you, Elder," she said, smiling.

All I could think of to say was, "My pleasure."

• • •

Then Amparo Gil, another really well-equipped mid-twenties gal who we had just baptized and who was raising a three-year-old kid that she'd conceived out of wedlock, slipped a note into my Bible when we were doing a follow-up visit. I found it that night.

Dear Elder West,

You must know how special you have made me feel, how full you have made my life. I spend my days thinking of you and my nights dreaming of the great love we could share together. You must know of the desire I have to share myself with you, to hold your warm body close to mine . . .

And so forth.

I showed Cifuentes, and he laughed *hoo-whee* and said, "Elder Johnson got one like that up in Medellín. They're usually just looking for a way to get to the States."

Which is exactly what the next note said, handed to me in person at church that weekend: *Slip out any night while your companion sleeps, and I'll have the window open. You can take me home with you as your bride, a reward for all your valiant service.*

Cifuentes asked, "Who interviewed this gal?" I said, "Elder Ruff," who was now one of our district leaders. When I asked him about her later, he said, "Hey, man, she had a testimony and said she was keeping all the commandments. She's sure stacked, eh?"

On the twentieth, we got baptism number eighteen for the month, tying the zone record. But instead of us breaking the record, all hell started breaking loose. President Bills called us on the twenty-second and said that old Elder Benitez had been rushed to the hospital with a massive heart attack and probably wouldn't make it. Sure enough, he didn't. Six weeks into the couple's mission, Lucas and I accompanied Sister Benitez with all their belongings to the mission office and then waved good-bye.

That Friday Lucas and I were doing baptismal interviews for Elder Ruff's companionship. Ruff had got a whole family: mom, dad, and three daughters, all beautiful. The first girl I interviewed, seventeen years old and loopy as the Fruit Loops toucan, had had so many abortions she couldn't even remember the exact number. I went out to speak with the father, and he told me that over the last year or two his daughter had actually appeared to be going insane, and he knew it was related. I told them both, "One abortion, I make an appointment and you talk with the mission president, see what he thinks. Fifteen of them? I don't even make the call."

The second daughter, a fifteen-year-old, had lost her virginity just two weeks earlier to Jimmy Ivarguen, the lone holdout in a family we had baptized the previous week. She was also quite hooked on cocaine and LSD. She told me all this while crying uncontrollably, saying she was really mixed up in a screwed-up world and didn't know how to get out. The third daughter, Disney (*dees-NAY*), who was hands down the most beautiful girl I ever saw in Colombia, had gotten an abortion just ten days earlier.

I went out to Ruff and said, "Sorry, man, but I think you need to start over with these folks—they're not even close." I assumed Ruff was getting desperate with only ten weeks left on his mission, and he was clutching at straws.

One night we were teaching a great family—fatherless, unfortunately—in *barrio* Alfonso Lopez, enjoying our second visit when a brick came through the front window and smashed into the far wall, missing my head by about three inches. The twelve-year-old boy ran and opened the door to look, and he saw the family dog hanging by its neck from the wrought-iron gate. The animal had been slashed wide open and steam was still rising from his abdominal cavity, and his muzzle was tied shut with a bicycle inner tube. All this had happened while we sat inside twelve feet away discussing the life of the Prince of Peace.

The mother asked us to complete that night's discussion but then inquired very kindly if we might give them a few days to think about it all. We obliged.

The next day we went by Sister Hoyos's house, a family in which we had now baptized thirteen people. She had been crying, and she erupted into a fresh blubber when we appeared at the door. Her niece, Amparo Gil, the gal who had wanted a ride to the States in my suitcase, had just gone and had an abortion. After we baptized her.

Three days before the month ended, Elder Cifuentes got a call from the mission president telling him that he was being extended for one month, not two. Lucas said, "Oh yeah, I forgot about that," and he admitted he wasn't so sure now that he wanted to stay another month. The decision had come down from Salt Lake City. He'd remain with me, and we'd both remain zone leaders.

We ate dinner and then headed over to Alfonso Lopez to try setting a time with a gal we'd been attempting to complete the discussions with for three weeks. The woman who answered the door, a church member living around the corner who had referred us to the gal in the first place, said, "Marlene's sick." We said, "When will she be better? Two, three days?" And Sister Suarez said, "It's gonorrhea. I have no idea how long that takes." Then she said, revealing not a small amount of anger, "Marlene has lain with more guys than she can remember. I've just been trying to get her out of the gutter." She told us that two months earlier, Marlene had received injections for an abortion. The fetus had come out at home right in front of Marlene's eight-year-old daughter, who had run to Sister Suarez's screaming hysterically, "Come help my mommy — she's dying!"

Well, I'd heard enough crap for one month, so I kind of lit into the sister, saying, "Why'd you refer her to us, anyway? What kind of candidate is a slut?" Sister Suarez almost slapped me square upside the head — instead, she just burned a hole through my head with her eyes and said, "Elder, perhaps you should go read the scriptures a little better." Then she slammed the door.

So we just went back to the *pieza* and lay around most of that afternoon, feeling mentally blitzed and spiritually blighted. Lucas eventually slept for three hours straight. I wrote in my journal and then penned a tune I titled "Country Boy," the guitar part sketched in tablature in the margins since I'd sworn off guitars at the eighteen-month mark.

> *My daddy told me, as he rocked me on his knee,*
> *"Here in the country, boy, is the life you ought to lead."*
> *My daddy showed me, when I was just a lad,*
> *In the open sky and the raging moon the good life that we had.*
> *Then Papa told me, when I came to be a man,*
> *"From these mountains to the shining seas," he said,*
> *"Son, this is your land."*
>
> CHORUS
> *Going home to the country, boy.*
> *Home is all I need.*
> *Keep my feet anchored firm and deep*
> *In the land of the brave and free.*
> *Nowhere like the country, boy,*
> *Nowhere else to be.*

But choose your part,
Listen to your heart,
And go where'er that road may lead.

My daddy waved good-bye as I headed off to see
The city lights and the busy, burning, all-night factories.
I gotta make my own way, Daddy, can't you see?
There's so much more to make of the man I want to be.
I spun my wheels around, I climbed toward the top.
But there was nothing there to hold me up,
And my soul began to drop.
I called, Daddy, you still there, living with the breeze?
My burning eyes have been hypnotized,
I think it's time to leave.

CHORUS
Come on home to the country, boy.
Home is all you need.
Keep your feet anchored firm and deep
In the land where a man can breathe.
Livin' free like an eagle,
With the sun across your back.
Lift your eyes to the far horizon,
See all that you can see.

My daddy waved good-bye as I sailed across that sea.
Said, "We'll be waitin', son,
If there's something you should need."
I gotta make my own way, Daddy, can't you see?
There's so much more to living, so much more to be.
But now I'm kind of turned around,
The bullets split the night.
Life is cheap if the price is right.
Either live or die, you're out.
I yelled, Daddy, you still there? The time has come to leave.
There's lots to share but nothing to compare
With that free air that you breathe.

CHORUS
Going home to my country, boy,
Home is all I need.

Far-sighted eyes failed to recognize
The fruit of freedom's seed.
Gotta find the promised land,
The love beneath the greed.
Gotta find the answers —
Just like Daddy,
Just like me.

And then one day I flipped my widget.

Cifuentes and I were walking along at the foot of a large brick wall that fronted the local Catholic church when some guy, college age, leaned down over the wall and smacked me in the head with a textbook. As I stumbled, the book fell from his grip onto the sidewalk at my feet, along with a pack of cigarettes from his shirt pocket. When I looked back up, this knucklehead actually asked me if I would please hand him his book and his cigarettes.

I said, "Yeah, right" — *Pues sí, claro* — and crushed his pack of *gringo* Camel Lights into the concrete with my foot. And then I threw the flat package back at him.

He started to cuss me out, and I went up the wall in about a half-second and started beating the living crap out of the guy while people watched from the front steps of a church. The guy never landed a return punch, just covered his face and tried to get away as I pummeled his head, his face, and his stomach with really good opposing-thrust flat-wristed tae kwon do punches. Then I grabbed the neck of his Michigan State T-shirt and lifted him up with one arm — he was a good five inches taller than me — and ran him back against the church wall with my knee ready to pop his crotch.

Then I proceeded, in almost perfect Spanish, to call him everything I had ever learned that applied to anyone even closely related to him and smacked him against the wall again. Twenty or thirty people were standing there watching the *gringo* with the white shirt and nametag and the Colombian student with blood all over his face and shirt and jeans.

All I could see was the constant fear and the bricks and the bottles and the spit of two years. Those listening probably thought I was either nuts or the guy's brother-in-law, because I cursed him and then yelled in his face, "Everything you've ever called me has been a lie! Every treachery has been made up. I didn't do it!"

Then I just let him drop to the ground and said in English, "What the hell have I ever done to you?"

And walked away.

Lucas was standing at the bottom of the stairs, just looking at me in disbelief. I went down and picked up the kid's book — a college text on American business models — and took it back up to him. He was sitting there crying, and he covered his face when I came back up. I said, "Sorry, man, it's been a long two years," and then I vaulted over the wall and walked off.

44

> "Every mountain has its steepest point, which
> is usually near the summit, in keeping, I suppose,
> with the providence that makes the darkest
> hour just before day."
> —John Burroughs, *Birch Browsings*

THAT AFTERNOON, unable to work, I sat at the kitchen table with the Book of Mormon open and pondered Sister Suarez's words about reading the scriptures better. I knew exactly what she was getting at: the stuff about Christ coming not to heal the whole but the sick, not the righteous but the sinners. The entire meaning of everything I'd been doing for twenty-two and a half months was to tell people they could break free of every vice and every weakness and rise above every lowdown stupid thing they'd ever done. Sometimes I even told myself that unless I taught repentance really well and testified with all my soul, I was gonna carry some of the people's stains upon myself. Not that I hadn't already known plenty of my own stains, including a pretty good one only a couple of hours old.

During the dinner hour I called Elder Ruff and asked him if Cifuentes and I could split with him and his companion that night. I wanted to go see the Giraldos, the family I had interviewed and told to go take a flying leap, more or less.

So that's what we did. And they *were* a great family, the mother and two girls actually crying when we came in, saying they had thought there was no hope for them, no redemption, no chance to ever be clean and start over and get on the road to heaven.

Ruff said to me, "Where do you want to start from, the commandments?" And I said, "Man, I'm going right back to Joseph Smith because I want to tell the story one more time." Not thirty words into the story of the First Vision, I was mentally sitting on the corner of my bed on Paradise Mountain, speaking the words but also looking at myself, a long-haired hippie kid with a hollow cane smelling of marijuana in the closet, thinking *This kid's worth it – I'm gonna lay my soul on the line for him.*

Then I nodded to Ruff, and he told them about the Book of Mormon. *Señor* Giraldo said, "I know, *hermanos*. We're reading as a family, and it makes us feel good." I kept my eyes on Ruff, partly because the three girls were so beautiful that I didn't dare let my focus waver but partly because Ruff was doing so well, twenty-two months and still rolling on train-wreck Spanish but really cutting a swath in their lives by the sincerity of his effort. Then daughter number two, who had swallowed so much acid and snorted so much cocaine that she was getting mushy in the head, took a blue-with-gold-angel *Libro de Mormón* from her father, held it against her chest, and then bore her testimony to *us*: "*Hermanos elderes,* I know this book is the word of God. It is changing my life."

Elder C. and I interviewed them all again on Friday and signed the forms, and then Ruff and his companion, Elder Bohorquez, put the three daughters in a cab and rolled off to an appointment with the mission president. Saturday afternoon they baptized all but the second daughter, President Bills wanting her to demonstrate a couple months of absolute abstinence from both the sex and the substance abuse. She told him, "*Hermano presidente,* I'll do it. You'll see."

Some time in February we heard that the U.S. hostages in Iran had gotten released, and then Elder Jolley's MTC group got their travel papers, going home in eight days. After they left, my group would be the oldest in the mission and the next one to go. I couldn't help but entertain the thought of home from time to time, and it scared me. What was next? What did I want to be? I had told Mianno I wanted to be a forest ranger or something in the woods. My dad had always wanted to be a forest ranger but took a job at age seventeen stringing long lines for AT&T across the Western states, and that was that: Mountain Bell for the rest of his career.

Mianno said, "Forest ranger?" As if I'd said serial killer or latrine salesman or something. We never did see eye to eye on lifestyle stuff. So by the end of our few weeks together, I had modified the professional woodsman thing to geologist, the same subject Cris Wilde was studying. Mianno thought that was pretty weird too, having never seen any geology but brownstone and Bronx Zoo granite, but at least it sounded like a science, a career. He was going to be a football coach, high school first and then maybe college. I said, "You would actually go back and step foot in a high school? And actually contribute to the making of jocks? Every day? Isn't that illegal?"

Anyway, one Thursday night a group of us held a big bye-bye dinner for Jolley and his MTC companions down at the Hotel Intercontinental. Such dinners were not on the mission calendar, nor were they specifically mentioned in the little white handbook, but they were somewhat of a tradition. It was all-you-can-eat Chinese night, and the sixteen of us did our best to clean the place out. I had never seen a place like this before on either side of the ocean, an authentic high-class hotel with chandeliers and waiters in tuxedos and flush toilets and everything.

Then Cifuentes and I got back to it, and we baptized again and again, bringing in friends of friends and families of families, here and there the lone convert. During his last month, his twenty-fifth month, we baptized twenty-eight people of our own making, so to speak. That same month, there were sixty baptisms in the zone and two hundred and fifty-two in the mission. On Cifuentes's penultimate day, two hours before he finished packing his bags and caught a cab for the mission home, we held our fourth baptismal service of the month. He and I had thought we were going to have two final baptisms, Sister Suarez's granddaughters, but the girls' mom decided she was ready as well, so Elder Ruff interviewed her and we had three.

Then Lucas hugged me good-bye and waved for a taxi.

I spent the rest of the day and that night alone, the widow-lady of the house off to see the grandkids in Popayán for a couple of days. About five-thirty I went to the little *panadería* three doors down and bought some peel-and-eat vittles and then went back and sat in my room, where I nursed a bottle of *tamarindo* soda and opened a couple of letters we had picked up on Saturday. One from Armenia, the other from Quebec.

The letter from Armenia was from Diela Oviedo, the gal who had fed her own family by cooking for the missionaries for three years: she and her ten-year-old son Carlos had gotten baptized, and she wanted to let me know how influential Santos and I had been in their conversion. Her blind husband had said, "No way, woman — get real," but he attended the baptism and shook everyone's hand afterward.

Annie's letter said that she was loving her mission, was loving her companion, and had finally seen her fifth convert of the mission enter the waters of baptism that week, a gentle young man named Gilles who played guitar and liked to hitchhike around Canada. She said he reminded her too much of me, a thought she was really trying to avoid because it made her crazy. She never acknowledged that she was finishing her mission in five weeks from the date of the postmark, which was already three weeks ago.

But she did say that she would really like to see me — on Paradise Mountain — after I got home, if that would be all right.

That night was particularly noisy and disconcerting outside our bedroom window — *my* bedroom window. A party was going on two doors down, which meant up and down the street for three blocks. Radios all over the place were blaring continuing updates on the Ronald Reagan assassination attempt the day before. Then a motorcycle and a truck loaded with hay or sorghum or something collided in the intersection thirty feet from my window — nobody was hurt, apparently, but the two drivers stood and yelled at each other in the foulest of terms for ten minutes before they both drove away, the front tire of the motorcycle going *whop whop whop*.

I couldn't sleep, and my mind was going all over the place. The temperature was about ninety-four, humidity about eighty, and our little desk fan did very little. I had figured I would get a call from the mission office as soon as Cifuentes arrived there, when somebody remembered, *Oh yeah, Elder West's got just four weeks left. Let's put him out to pasture somewhere.*

But no call came, and sometime around midnight I finally fell asleep.

Next morning I woke to a knock on the front metal door at 7:12 A.M. — I'd slept in. It was a great big *gringo* elder named Hatch, carrying a pair of suitcases.

I let him in and asked, "So what's the scoop? Am I out of here?"

And he said, "No way, man. You're training me."

"As . . . ?"

"A zone leader."

And I said, "Yeah, I bet." He just looked at me, walked past me, and set down his bags. Then he said, "We live here all alone? Cool."

• • •

I told him about the *doña* being in Popayán with her *nietos*, and then I pressed him again, saying, "You're kidding, right? I'm really supposed to pack my bags and head to Yumbo for a little R and R. Right?"

He pulled the latest one-page mission directory from his shirt pocket and handed it to me. Scanning it, I found no Jolley or Cifuentes.

I said, "Man, where's Morrison and Aillón and Prieto and Mianno, all the old zone leaders?"

"They're on there, but they're no longer zone leaders. President said I was getting the senior zone leader in the mission. The old man of the mud pile."

I thought, *Lucky you.*

I went in and took a shower, and then we went out to find something to eat. I found myself wishing with all my heart and soul for a DeliExpress burrito and a microwave oven and some Minute Maid orange juice. Instead, we went to the *panadería* on the other side of the soccer field, a place with *empanadas* right out of the oven this time of the morning and soda pop out of an actual refrigerator.

I told Hatch that he'd missed a heck of a night, motorcycle wreck and all.

He said, "No, I didn't. I've been on a bus from Medellín since two-thirty yesterday afternoon." Seventeen hours. Then he said, "I hope you're not trunked out, because I've got thirteen months to go, and I want to burn this place up."

That afternoon I got a big, beautiful Mount Rainier postcard from Kurt Jolley in Washington and another letter from Armenia, this one from *barrio* Manzano. I read it that night.

Beloved and remembered Elder West,

We are well. We feel ourselves very blessed to be members of the church and to have the blessed gospel of Jesus in our lives. I wanted to respond to your letter. As I now hold the priesthood of God, it just became my lot to ordain my son Adolfo to the priesthood as well. I hope one day he becomes a great missionary like yourself, a servant of God.

My brother, I will be faithful till death and I will always strive to keep my family strong. I pray our Heavenly Father to give you many blessings, to illuminate you with his holy spirit, and to strengthen you in your great mission as a son of God, for your mission really will never end but continues, someday soon as the father of a family.

I wish you a good and safe trip to your beloved homeland and sweet home. You have helped us find the Kingdom of God, and for that I ever thank you. May we yet meet at his side.

Lizandro Briñez A.
Armenia, Quindío, Colombia

Then the next morning I got a call from the mission office. Elder Juchau read me my flight plans over the phone, twenty-three days away and said, "Got it?" Then he said, "Oh yeah, and the president would like to see you. Can you come in this afternoon?"

I said yes, then hung up and said yippee. To myself.

So Elder Hatch and I caught a taxi to the mission office, the *taxista* going on and on for twenty minutes about how happy he was that *Presidente* Reagan was all right and and about how relieved he was that the crazy kid who shot him — from Colorado — was in custody. On and on, actually crying at one point, breaking down. I thought, *What the heck?* They spat in our faces, called our mothers whores and our nation the evil capitalist exploiting tyrant of the world, but they're all dying to move there, and now they're praying for our president? No sense. No reason. *No comprendo.*

It had been the same in all the newspapers and in every radio broadcast I had heard: everyone in Colombia except maybe the drug lords praying for the damn *gringo Yánqui exploitador imperialista* president's blessed life.

We arrived at the mission office, and Elder White welcomed us wearing one shoe with the big toe on the exposed foot looking like a large pink lollypop. He told us that it was the third time he'd had the entire toenail removed to alleviate an industrial-strength problem with ingrown toenails from too much walking in hard shoes. The president came out and greeted us, then whisked me into his office. It took about four minutes: How was I doing? Could I hang on till the end as a zone leader? After all, he really needed me. Or should he rent me a padded stall at the bus station and just throw food under the door?

I told him I could make it. Elder Hatch was just what I needed. If I could just get him to kick me in the fanny twice a day, I'd be fine.

And we left.

45

"Where would I find a quiet grove to
meditate in, to live in forever?"
—Kerouac, *The Dharma Bums*

WE WENT BACK to Las Americas and La Puente and Alfonso Lopez
and got after it. Halfway through the month, Elder Ruff and his
new companion stopped by at lunchtime and Ruff said he wanted
Elsy Giraldo to be interviewed again. And I said, "You think she's
ready?" He said, "Yeah, I really think she is."

So I interviewed her with Elder Hatch sitting in the little bedroom with us, both because it was often best to have another person present when you were interviewing someone who looked like
Cameron Díaz and Jennifer Lopez combined and because I wanted
Hatch to learn firsthand just how far a person could go and how far
they could come back, when someone would help them. I prayed
with all my soul that she *had* come all the way back.

She had. She would still need another interview with the mission president, but I signed her baptismal recommend form, and we
went out smiling. Ruff said, "Yes!" and the whole family applauded,
the father actually dropping to his knees and saying a little prayer
of thanks right there in the front room, a very Catholic-sounding
Mormon prayer.

On Saturday Hatch and I did four baptisms, Ruff baptized Elsy
and a recent convert's son who had just finished his stint in the national police service raiding drug labs down in Putumayo, and other
companionships added another eleven, Brad Morrison five of them.

For our final month, our entire MTC district was back in Cali.
Elder Morrison had asked for an extension like Cifuentes, and like
Cifuentes he had been granted one month but not two, so he was
going home with my group.

Not one of us had been sent home early, and not one had quit, but every one of us had come close to both. Most of us had been sick with amoebas or tapeworms or black worms for the entire two years, some of us all three. And at least three of us had whomped on Colombian male flesh, unable to take the strain at some point or another. But only Ruff and Morrison had busted their hands on the guys. You gotta keep your wrist flat.

Middle of the month, Elder Morrison and the guys in my MTC district were instructed to show up at DAS, the *Departamento Administrativo de Seguridad*, to get fingerprinted again and turn in our papers. We walked out thirty minutes later as just *gringos* on tourist visas.

And that night it was our turn at the Hotel Intercontinental. Twenty-eight missionaries came, including the six from our MTC group and our companions. It appeared that we'd been a popular district. This time it was Spanish night at the smorgasbord. I remembered thinking when I first entered Colombia that because they spoke the Spanish language, I would obviously spend the next twenty-one months feasting on enchiladas and tostadas, crispy tacos, and big bowls of red-hot chili. I entered the hotel restaurant hoping for the best, but the sign said what it meant: Spanish, not Mexican. But fortunately not Colombian either.

There weren't a lot of items I could identify, in fact.

"*Champiñones*" is what I thought the chef told me over the buzz of the crowd. Mushrooms. Me and mushrooms, we went way back. Yum, yum.

This stuff really did look good. It was in a sort of cream sauce like stroganoff. And it tasted great! But it was really chewy, tougher than any mushroom I'd ever chomped on, including some that were still half-frozen. As I gnawed along, I rolled a few of them around on my plate. These were definitely not mushrooms, more like — ah, yes. He hadn't said "*champiñones*," he had said "*riñones*." Kidneys.

I remembered what I'd learned as a vegetarian meat cutter and chuckled to myself. Then I took another forkful. Not bad, for cat food.

Elder Larsen asked me what it was. "It looks real good," he said.

"*Champiñones*," I told him. "Really tasty."

"Mushrooms, huh? In a cream sauce. Be back in a minute."

The word spread quickly, Larsen saying, "It's just like beef stroganoff." Seven guys, all *gringos*, headed back up to the big table. Meanwhile, I finished my rice and headed back up for some more . . . mushrooms.

In a minute, Elder Larsen said, "That's pretty chewy stuff. Wonder how they cooked 'em."

But we all dug in, and I chuckled as I chewed. Some of these guys didn't have over four or five months in Colombia. They hadn't even had time to figure out what *mondongo* was yet: tripe soup.

One of them said, in English, "Elder West, you sure these are mushrooms?"

Lowering my fork, I said, "Mushrooms? Who said anything about mushrooms?"

Twenty-one mouths stopped chewing all at once. Twenty-seven sets of eyes all turned to stare at me. I felt like E.F. Hutton with a public-address system on the Jersey turnpike.

"I didn't say *champiñones*," I lied. "I said *riñones*."

The Colombians all started laughing, and the new kids all kept staring at me for the translation.

"Kidneys," I shouted, and then I broke into hysterics along with the Colombians. I slid another forkful into my mouth as I mumbled through my smile, "Pretty good, huh? You just boil the piss out of them." Which only worked in English, of course.

That night in our room, laughing along with Elder Hatch, I realized that Annie was at home in Colorado, but I could only imagine what she might be thinking.

Next morning Elder Ruff called me from Elder Pfeiffer's place, where he and Caldwell and Calderón had done a slumber party, and he said he had pretty much thrown in the towel, and Pfeiffer and Calderón had done the same. Elder Caldwell was just sitting around giggling, saying, "No, I'm going to work right up to the end," and then everybody went har-har-har.

Blown out. Blitzed. Totally trunked.

Then he said, "But you're the zone leader, man. Don't let us down." Har-har-har.

So I just put my head down and kept on going. Hatch and I followed up on several leads and even knocked on doors one afternoon, just so I could say I did it one last time. We had nine people committed to baptism and fifteen individuals in our teaching program. I fully believed that some of the nine would actually get baptized before I left. The odds were that only a fourth would, while another fourth would come through a week or two later and half would back out, go away, and forget about us in particular and Mormonism in general. Then in about three years, some elder who was now sixteen with pimples and polishing the chrome on his F-250 truck back in Terre Haute or Grass Valley would knock on their door and say, "*Buenas tardes,* we are personal representatives of the Lord Jesus Christ," and the guy's wife would say, "Elders, please come in." And maybe they would go all the way this time.

Sister Figueroa wrote me from Palmira to say she would be at the airport in Cali if I would please let her know when I was flying. She said she wouldn't miss it for her own funeral. My mom and dad wrote, saying *Man oh man, we can hardly wait to see you, hope this catches you still in Colombia because we probably won't write again.* And civilian Annie wrote, *Dear Elder West, these are your last days, the last days you will ever serve twenty-four hours a day as a full-time representative of the Lord Jesus Christ. Give them everything you've got, don't let up, serve with honor, and I'll see you at the Denver airport.*

I taught my guts out, ignoring the shouts and the rocks and the kids staring at me from nine inches away over the back of the bus seat and smiling a blessed smile when the little ones petted my arms and *hermanos* never to be seen again in this life took my hand and said, "*Grácias a Diós,* Elder *Waist,* that you came to Colombia." Sunday morning I did three baptismal interviews for Elders Larsen and Dávila, Elder Larsen did two for me and Hatch, and we had a fine church service, Bishop Troches asking me if I wouldn't mind bearing my testimony one last time in Colombia. Mild Troches was even more subdued than usual that day because his family had just returned from the United States, where Elder Barrett's dad, a rich dental surgeon, had put them up for a week while the two-year-old got facial surgery to fix her cleft palate. The Barretts had not only put them up for the week but had also taken them to the Los Angeles temple, where the family was sealed for time and all eternity. The Barretts paid for the whole trip.

Then I attended my final church meeting in Colombia, a baptismal service for five new souls who were worth everything it took to find and teach them, including rocks and spit and tapeworms.

Later Hatch and I went to the *pieza* with Elder Casal and Elder Dávila, and I let them divvy up the suit and pair of shoes I wasn't wearing home and four pairs of nice slacks and eleven white shirts and my new tape recorder and filmstrip projector, and then I gave them each a hug, saying, "*Hermanos*, the church in Colombia is now in your hands. Be good to it." And then I packed my bags with what was left, mostly souvenirs, and went out to just sit in the *sala* and chat with the *doña*, who was crying like a baby, saying, "Dammit, I've waved good-bye forever to about thirty of you good boys in the last five years. I'm not going to do this anymore — I'm done."

At the mission home the next morning, Elder White changed all our unused pesos back into U.S. money, the green stuff looking really foreign after two years, and then he handed me a letter that had arrived the day before, return address Palmira.

Esteemed Elder West,

I hope this reaches you before you fly off to your land. I want you to know that Franceddy was baptized and finally my husband, who took as long as he could to stay out of the chapel. Now forty-two members of my extended family have joined the church since you and Elder Mianno came to see us, West. If you ever return to this land, we wait to receive you with open arms, West, because we love you. I continue faithful in the church, reading and praying, for I know it is the true church of Jesus Christ. For this reason I will never quit.

West, we esteem you beyond words. Don't fail to write us. You will always be our special missionary.

Emérita Figueroa
Palmira, Valle, Colombia

The next morning the president and Sister Bills gave us all a big hug and waved good-bye as the mission secretary and finance clerk loaded us into the two mission Suburbans and pulled out for the airport. At the airport I looked all over, but I never found Sister Figueroa and half her genealogy until we were taxiing out to the runway. I spotted them two hundred yards away, waving from the railing that overlooked the tarmac.

So I missed her.

A quick stop in Bogotá, where I'd first gotten spit on twenty-one months earlier, and then up and off to the north. We pulled out over the Caribbean just east of Barranquilla, and I watched the Colombian coastline for as long as I could.

Then I slept.

From Zero to Zion . . .
and Back to Zen

"Where you coming from?"
"Where I've been."
"Where else?"
    —William Least Heat Moon, *Blue Highways*

46

> "The cost of a thing is the amount of life
> which is required to be exchanged for it,
> immediately or in the long run."
> —Henry David Thoreau, *Walden*

WE MET NOT ON Paradise Mountain after all but at the Colorow Inn,
the log-and-knotty-pine restaurant overlooking Interstate 70 halfway between the Great Plains and Mount Evans and, more or less,
halfway between Salt Lake City and Sedalia, Missouri. Neither of us
said as much—I'm not even sure it was a conscious thought when
we set the time and place—but in hindsight it was probably the perfect place to look down the road of our lives, forward and back, and
say, *Okay, where are we now?*

Plus, this way Annie and I didn't have to meet somewhere with
my mom watching. Or anybody else, for that matter. Nobody who
knew where we'd been, what we'd learned, or what we might do
next. Including us, on that last part.

Oh, she'd been at the airport all right. Annie and Cris and Annie's whole family and about half of the Silver Creek Ward. Bishop
Ray Goode held up a sign: *He's Ours, You Can't Have Him!* My mother actually broke security and ran into the Jetway when she saw me
coming, the very last one off the plane. Ruff and Pfeiffer and Barrett
and Morrison all got off real early just to confuse everyone, none of
them actually deplaning in Denver at all. My mother told me later
that this made it that much worse: *All these Mormon missionaries but
where the heck is MY SON?*

She had these bizarre white-lightning streaks in her black hair at
the temples. Natural streaks, the result of a kid in Colombia, South
America, who just had to tell all in the weekly letters. I looked and
looked until I saw Annie standing way back in the crowd, smiling
modestly with tears running down her face. Her mother was doing

the same. When I finally got to her, we shook hands, and I moved on to her mom and then her dad, glancing back a hundred times to see what her face was doing, checking to see what my heart was doing.

But then I had to hug my companions good-bye. People from the Silver Creek Ward were shaking their hands, saying, "Welcome home, Elder—have a good flight" as they headed back to the Jetway, waving as they walked, Elder David Morrison faking a smile through his tears. And I really had to control my own emotions as I actually hurried along with them back to the boarding gate, breathing hard, almost hyperventilating, thinking *Ay Diós mío, se van? Se van?* You're leaving? My head was doing loops, saying *I have no idea what comes next.* Scared to death to be home. Home and alone.

I turned back around and searched the crowd for Annie, not because I wanted a hug or a kiss or a look or anything but because I knew she was the only other person in that entire airport who knew what was going through my head, the only one who had done the same exact thing seventeen days before, thinking *Oh dear Lord, what do I do now?*

I found her, and the tears were still rolling, and I knew she knew, and I knew she had lived so far, and I thought, *Okay, I'm gonna be all right. I'm gonna make it.*

On the way out of the airport, Annie walked right up front with my family, and I reached over and took her hand and never let go clear to the car, although someone shouted, laughing, "Hey, Elder, you're still a missionary."

Which I was until 7:09 that evening, when the stake president extended an honorable release and said to my folks, "Brother and Sister West, we thank you so much for your son's valiant service." They had never been called Brother and Sister West before, but they just said, "Uh, yeah, sure, you're welcome. We're glad he made it."

That's probably about how it went for every one of us, Barrett and Calderón in Los Angeles, Ruff and Pfeiffer in Salt Lake City, and Caldwell in Albuquerque. All except Brad Morrison.

When we had landed in Miami, we actually knelt down in unison and kissed the tiles on the concourse floor. Blond people were everywhere—I hadn't seen so many blonds in two years. In Miami, imagine.

But while we sat and waited for the next plane to take us to Stapleton or, in Elder Caldwell's case, to another connection in Atlanta, Elder Morrison was really quiet, staring out the windows, his eyes far, far away. I sat next to him and said, "What's up?" And he said he wasn't sure where to go. The mission office had issued him plane tickets to both Salt Lake and Minneapolis, so he could take his pick. But it wasn't that easy.

He said, "I don't know if my parents want me to come home."

And I said, "*Qué va, muchacho?* What'd they tell you in the letter?" Every one of us was still speaking in Spanish and English back and forth, especially me and Morrison, neither one of us having had but a few weeks of North American companionship in the last two years.

And he said, "I've never heard from them in two years. *Ni una sola carta.*" Not one single letter.

So I accompanied him over to the rack of phone booths for moral support, and he dug in his pocket for some change, reached for the phone, and then let his hand drop. Finally he picked up the receiver and made the call.

I backed off to a discreet distance and let him talk in private, probably shed a few tears. In about two minutes he hung up and just stood there, whipped. He stared at the phone for another minute. So I went back over and said, "*Qué va, hombre?*"

I could tell he was still sorting out the situation, but really it was pretty simple. His father had answered and immediately handed the phone to his mom, who said, "Oh, so you're back." About like that. And Brad had said, very kind and solicitous, like a son to a mother, "I'd like to come home, see everyone, tell you about my last two years." And his mother said, "For two whole years I've been praying for all the Catholics in Colombia. You just keep on flying to Utah. That's your new home. Those are your people." Then she told him, "Send us your address when you get one. I'm sure one of your Mormon pals will put you up."

And then Morrison made his biggest mistake. Trying to extend a conversation that had apparently already ended, he asked his mom what she thought about all the letters he'd sent, one a week for a hundred and four weeks, just like the little white handbook directed. And she said, "Well, that's what I mean, David. I need your address so I can send you your letters. We have 'em all right here, safe and sound. Never opened a single one."

Two years.

Then she made it very clear. "I'm not even sure what the point of this call is. I have no son. Get us your address, and we'll forward all this stuff."

A mother.

So he rode with us to Denver and then on to Salt Lake, going to bed that night who knew where.

Sitting on a rock above the Colorow parking lot, Annie said, "It's hard, isn't it."

I said, "What, coming home?"

"Yeah. It's one of the hardest transitions I think I've ever gone through, a lot harder than entering the mission field."

And I said, "Oh, yeah," really having no clue what I was doing yet, struggling with English, strangely exhausted after taking a hot shower, trying to remember how to run a car.

But it was so sweet to be back on the mountain. I'd only been there two days when my dad said, "Wanna go somewhere? Let's hit the road." So we packed the little Ford pickup and took off, just the two of us. Two men, two guitars, two sleeping bags. As we drove down through South Park, I craned my neck for thirty miles to keep watching Windy Peak as we arced around it to the west and then south. With a little snow on top, it quietly stood watch over Lost Park and Kenosha Pass.

Then we drove right past the Light Pole of the Many Cursings, west over Monarch Pass and into Montrose. We found a wide spot on a dirt road just west of town and slept in the back of the pickup, our feet sticking right out over the tailgate. Then we headed up through Delta, Grand Junction, over the Cisco bridge, and down the Colorado River to near Moab, Utah, where we camped again. Then I made a suggestion, and my dad said sure and wandered back up to I-70 and then south on Highway 24, right into Capitol Reef National Monument. As I sat on top of a small ridge with my guitar and stared at the sunset, he asked, "Ya wanna go back?" And I said, "I'm fine." And he said, "You haven't said fifty words in three days."

That surprised me, because I'd thought about fifty million.

He said, "What's on your mind?"

I shrugged.

He said, "Jesus," not in quite the way I'd use it, and laughed.

So finally I laughed and said, "It's so weird."

"What's so weird?"

"Being home."

He said, "Not really anything has changed here." But then he told me about coming home from Korea, the culture shock of being back in a country unlike any other in the world. Walk where you want to walk. Drive a car. Buy an ice cream cone or a battery for your clock or a new pillowcase or a loaf of good, clean bread. Drink the water right out of the tap, nothing floating in it.

And I said, "Two-ply toilet paper," and he about slipped down the ridge laughing.

"Yeah, and flush toilets."

He asked me about Annie, and I said, "I don't know. We've barely spoken." Just once on the phone, setting the date at the Colorow Inn. We'd even planned dinner, a real date.

Then he said, "How's your English coming?"

"I can't even think half the words," I answered. "*Sería tanto mas fácil hacerlo en Español. Cómo le parece?*"

So we headed back to Paradise, going right through Glenwood Canyon. That first Sunday back, I gave my homecoming talk in the Silver Creek Ward building, with Bishop Raymond L. Goode presiding. Annie's family was there and mine, my folks' third time in a Mormon building in two years, having attended Annie's homecoming in Fort Collins two weeks earlier. It was a pretty good crowd, and most of them either laughed or cried most of the way through my talk, the laughter mainly because of the unbelievable English. Then afterward, a little barbeque on Paradise Mountain, Annie and I just brushing hands lightly now and then and looking at each other pretty regularly.

About six P.M. we walked out on the little knob to the south of the house, just the two of us, taking hands and looking out over the South Platte River valley and Pikes Peak and Lone Scraggy and then right back into each other's eyes. Annie broke the tension by saying, "And so?"

So we kept our date at the Colorow, and the dang place was actually closed on Monday nights, as if they were off having family home evening or something. Instead, we sat on a log in the woods and talked. And I asked her to marry me. And she said yes and kissed me.

Epilogue

"I walk in the shoes of the men of today.
I fly their planes, I eat their food, but my heart
is in the wilderness with feathers in my hair."
— Louis L'Amour, *Last of the Breed*

ANNIE AND I WERE MARRIED four weeks later in the old Mormon temple in remote Manti, Utah, not a dime to our names. My folks couldn't attend, of course, because they weren't Latter-day Saints with temple recommends. They weren't broken hearted, however. For starters, they thought it was way too quick to get married. And besides, they just weren't the type of folks who gave an enormous hoot about fancy-schmancy stuff like that. They had eloped to New Mexico themselves. Just Mom, Dad, and a borrowed preacher man.

Since we had only a bicycle — hers — Annie's dad lent us his old Plymouth Volare for our honeymoon, and we went down to Capitol Reef, found that big old bush of Mormon Tea, and rolled around in the red dirt for three days straight, and then we headed to Colorado with pine sap in our hair so we could stand around smiling at a pair of receptions: fancy little cakes and punch with doilies on reception-hall tables at her folks' place, barbecued chicken and potato salad out back on the hill at mine. Wanting all along just to get away.

Which we finally did, a little side trip up to the cabin on the ridge to Mount Kolob. When we reached the cabin — it seemed to be awaiting us quietly in the gold air of autumn — I turned and stood for a moment looking back to the south, my whole soul absorbing the air, the beauty, the scent of pine, until Annie took my hand and pulled me inside. At one point later, she said, "I'm sorry about two years ago, but something told me we both really needed to go on missions."

And I said, "Yes, we did. God bless you, girl, for telling me no."

• • •

My mother called us in tears a week later. Something had gone wrong while Ray Goode was test-piloting an experimental biplane, and he nosedived the thing from eighteen hundred feet, dying on impact. Mom said, "That was one of the best men we ever knew."

Rocky Mianno married a girl from Brooklyn, and his English took a nosedive from bad to worse. After several years climbing the coaching ladder of collegiate sports, he made the pros as a quarterback coach and then moved to doing color for ESPN.

Scott Reefer, the missionary who taught me the discussions on Paradise Mountain and baptized me, hung on a few years and then left the church. He could never tell me why. Lucas Cifuentes, who I thought would be a stake president very soon in Colombia, moved to the States, couldn't find work, and then had a heart attack at twenty-five and decided life wasn't working the way he planned — piss on it — and he left the church too.

Orlando Santos, the Colombian tae kwon do fireball, served as a stake president in Bogotá before being granted political refugee status and fleeing with his family to the United States, where they settled in Utah.

Brad Morrison married in the temple and succeeded in forging a passive reconciliation with his folks before they each passed away. His dad told him once, "You sure turned out good, Mormon and everything. How could that be?"

Pedro Alarcón and his family used his little bag of handpicked emeralds to buy passage on a banana freighter leaving one night out of Buenaventura. They arrived in Los Angeles nine days later and were granted refugee asylum. Last I heard, the whole family was employed cleaning a McDonalds at night, very happy.

Cris Wilde finished his degree in geology and worked in the field until the petroleum bust in the early 1980s. After that he spent nearly twenty years in the Peace Corps and USAID, living in nearly fifty countries. He eventually climbed every one of the fifty-four Colorado fourteeners and many of the tallest peaks on five continents. He has covered a lot of miles but never found the girl of his dreams.

Discouraged and worn out, Jack Kerouac drank himself to death at the age of forty-seven, dying in the fall of 1969. In his final years, he became alienated with Buddhism and reaffirmed his faith as a Christian, the faith of his fathers, referring to himself as a "strange solitary crazy Catholic mystic."

• • •

I didn't come home the same as when I left, and neither did Annie. For her part, she discovered an inner strength sufficient to handle everything that got thrown at her: a broken heart, desert survival in the Utah summer, the flesh-brittling cold of the Quebecoise winter, the French language itself, rejection at nearly every door for a year and a half. I would once ask her, having come to know her parents as the kindest, most patient and nonjudgmental folks I had ever met, just what it was that had driven her out of a Mormon home years before. A *good* Mormon home.

And she couldn't answer me. It wasn't a refusal; she just didn't know.

So I'd ask her again years later, needing to know for the sake of our own children. What had gone wrong? Who did what? And she could only say, "I just had to find out for myself. Was I loved? Was I valuable? Could I survive? And was the faith of my parents the faith for me?"

The answers had all come back yes.

I had to ask myself those same kinds of questions a few times that first summer home: Had I done a good work? Had I made a difference? Had I survived it all? I'd look in the mirror and kind of pat myself down mentally. I was all there. Oh, I had to agree with Ebenezer Scrooge at the end of his own tale when he said, "I am not the man I was." I came home with images in my head and lesions on my heart, good and bad, that I would never lose; as Kerouac put it, "new reasons for virtue and new reasons for forgiveness." But I came home in honor among my people, the old and the new — the old being those among whom cosmic circumstance had dropped me in the first place, and the new being those among whom I had chosen to place myself: the Latter-day Saints. I did all I could, everything I could think of, to pour out the old wine and throw away the bottle — actually, I recycled it — and then stand aside to wait for the God my ancestors had never known to fill me up a new one. Which he did, of course.

After all was said and done, I was not the man my true-blue, died-in-the-wool, grandpa-was-a-bishop Mormon-pioneer companions were, either. Nor would I ever be.

I never heard the Mormon Tabernacle Choir as a child or sang carols on doorsteps. I never heard stories about Abraham or Moses or Jesus or Joseph; I didn't know about Moroni or Brigham Young or Nauvoo. I had just wanted to find a path to God that fit my soul and filled my heart. I wanted a vision or a message or handwriting in the clouds or something—and I was willing to risk a lot to find it.

And it worked. I'd trudged a little different trail, but I'd walked it all the way. (Okay, I hitchhiked a good bit of it.) Where it led from here I could not know.

At least I had the girl. The Girl of My Mountain Days and the Woman of My Soul. I would need her desperately over the next few years, and she would always be there. Our journey together would test everything we had ever learned on the road to heaven.

But that's another story altogether.

About the Author

Of twelve million Mormons worldwide, more than seventy percent are first-generation converts, including Coke Newell. A former tree-hugging, Zen-spouting, vegetarian Colorado mountain hippie, the author later worked for more than a decade as an LDS Church media relations officer at world headquarters in Salt Lake City.

His byline or citation on the topic of Mormonism has appeared in more than a thousand North American periodicals, including the *Wall Street Journal, USA Today,* and the *Los Angeles Times.* Newell's award-winning journalism and fiction have appeared in such publications as *Columbia Journalism Review, Grit, Ensign, True West, Irreantum,* and the *Rocky Mountain News.* He lives with his wife and children in rural northern Utah.

Additional Titles Published by Zarahemla Books

Brother Brigham—In this novel by D. Michael Martindale, C.H. Young has sacrificed his dreams to earn a living for his family—until one day he receives an amazing supernatural visitation. As Brother Brigham's appearances and instructions grow increasingly bold, C.H. struggles to hold together his faith, his marriage, and his sanity.

Hooligan: A Mormon Boyhood—Detailing the author's years growing up in Provo, Utah, during the Depression and World War Two, Douglas Thayer's memoir shares literary DNA in common with Frank McCourt's *Angela's Ashes*, Mark Twain's *The Adventures of Huckleberry Finn*, and William Golding's *Lord of the Flies*.

Hunting Gideon—Jessica Draper's Mormon-flavored cyber-crime novel tracks two crack employees of the FBI's National Infrastructure Protection Center. Through her feline avatar, Sue Anne Jones stalks the V-Net along with her partner, ex-cracker Loren Hunter. Embarking on a wild chase through both virtual and actual reality, they scramble to avert the ultimate online disaster. Draper is the author of *Seventh Seal* and its sequels.

Kindred Spirits—In this novel by Christopher Kimball Bigelow, Utah-bred Eliza Spainhower has carved out an independent life for herself in Boston. After she makes a love connection with a local native on the subway, she's forced to reckon in new ways with her Mormon identity and her sometimes-overactive religious imagination.

Long After Dark—In these award-winning stories and a new novella, Todd Robert Petersen takes the reader on expeditions to Utah, Arizona, Brazil, Rwanda, and into the souls of twenty-first-century Mormons caught between their humanity, faith, and church. "It is a wonderful book!" says Richard H. Cracroft, emeritus BYU English professor.

Available at ZarahemlaBooks.com

Also available at Amazon.com and other booksellers

Printed in the United States
134588LV00004B/28/A